S0-BIS-730

The New Consciousness Sourcebook

SPIRITUAL COMMUNITY PUBLICATIONS

Publisher-Parmatma Singh Khalsa

NEW CONSCIOUSNESS SOURCEBOOK:
SPIRITUAL COMMUNITY GUIDE #5

Editor— Parmatma Singh Khalsa.
Editorial Assistants— Lorri Lester, Mary Springer.
Other Staff—GBS Khalsa, Gurubani Kaur Khalsa, Gurubhai
Kaur Khalsa, Heather Hutchinson, Ishvara Kaur Khalsa, Seva
Kaur Khalsa.

Cover & Design— Armando Busick
Production & Design— Kim Gale
Typesetting— Sammie Lee, Clark Coffee Jr., Lewis Pub.

Illustrations—Armando Busick, Glen Eddy, Michael G, Gary
Frutkoff, Kim Gale, Sahaj.

©Copyright 1982 by Spiritual Community, Inc.
Published yearly in the USA by Spiritual Community Publications
as a project of Meeting of the Ways.
Spiritual Community/NAM
Box 1067
Berkeley, CA 94701
(415) 644-3229
ISBN 0-913852-14-7   ISSN 0160-0354

All information, graphics, and material in this book is the
exclusive property of Spiritual Community, Inc. and may not be
used or reproduced in any manner without explicit permission.

NAM MAILING LISTS
These are available for those wishing to do mailings or further
research. See p. 174
From time to time paid positions of all kinds open up on our staff.
Send resume & SASE.

PERMISSIONS
Fear and *How to Defend Yourself Without Even Trying*, by
Dr. Terry Chitwood, Polestar Publications, 1981.
Spiritual Awakening by Darshan Singh, Sawan Kirpal Publi-
cations.

Introduction excerpted from *The Aquarian Conspiracy: Personal
and Social Transformation in the 1980's,* © 1980 by Marilyn
Ferguson, published by J.P. Tarcher, Inc., 9110 Sunset Blvd., Los
Angeles, CA 90069, ($15.00 HB, $7.95 Pbk) used by permission

Short excerpts and quotes used throughout the book are from
the Meeting of the Ways conference: *Enlightened Action for
Nuclear Disarmament.* For information about the forthcoming
book on political and spiritual action in the Nuclear Age write
Stephen Most and Lynn Grasberg, One World Media Book
Project, 124 Linda St., San Francisco, CA 94110.

Contents

Foreword — Parmatma Singh Khalsa 4
Introductions
    Marilyn Ferguson 5
    Daniel Ellsberg 7

New Consciousness Centers
    Title Index 12
    Category Index 17
    Center Descriptions 25
    Articles and Resources

The Hopi Nuclear Prophecy—Thomas Banyacaya, 23; The Essence of Healing—Dr. Mark Kramer, M.D. & Gitela Kushner Kramer, 44; Letting Go of Fear—Dr. Terry Chitwood, 46; Foot Massage, 47; No Nuclear War!—Yogi Bhajan, 66; Local Directories, 90; A Message from God—The Lord, 91; Peace & Nuclear Disarmament Resources, 106; Growing Up In Prison—Bo Lozoff, 126; Spiritual Awakening—Darshan Singh, 146; Peace Affirmations & Meditations, 158.

Community Directory
    United States 175
    Canada 216
    Foreign 217

Classified Listings

Publisher, 221; Magazine/Periodical, 222; Books, 225; Records/Tapes, 229; Films, Video, Tapes & Slides, 232; Communities/Centers, 234; Schools, 235; Workshops/Seminars, 237; Instruction/Individual, 237; Health & Healing, 238; Vegetarianism, 240; Mail Order Book Sellers, 240; Book & Magazine Distributors, 242; Music & Musical Instruments, 242; Services 242; Food & Health Products, 245; Herbs & Seeds, 248; New Age Products, 248; Clothing, Clothware & Cushions, 248; Astrology, Occult & Occult Supplies, 250; Calendars & Photographs, 251; Psychics, 251; Children, 252; Travel & Retreats, 252; Yoga & Meditation, 253; Prison, 254; Young Adults, 254; Handicrafts, 254; Miscellaneous, 254.

Foreword

In 1972, a small devoted group of people envisioned and produced the first *Spiritual Community Guide.* We collected the information on 3 x 5 index cards and did everything ourselves but the printing. There were 22 pages of center descriptions in a 192 page book. The index cards have been replaced by a computer and the current 256 page edition contains 126 pages of center descriptions. But we still do everything ourselves. In the first edition we collected and listed every group we could find. Now we include only those which make arrangements with us to be listed, about 20% of all the groups in existence. Everyday sees the birth of new groups. Many of you, our readers, are now leaders and organizers of such groups and businesses.

The times have changed. Ten years ago only *Spiritual Community Guide* and a few other New Age publications including *The Whole Earth Catalog* and *Mother Earth News* were reporting the shift in consciousness. Now *Newsweek, Time Magazine, The Wall Street Journal* and the TV Evening News regularly cover the New Consciousness. The varied segments of New Age activity -- Spiritual, Health, Ecology, Back to the Land, etc. -- have overlapped and blended and, as reported by Marilyn Ferguson in the *Aquarian Conspiracy,* have spread to all our social institutions. It is this proliferation of consciousness that has led us to switch our name from *Spiritual Community Guide* to *New Consciousness Sourcebook.* A broader title to match a broader outlook.

Originally we had intended to make Holistic Health the feature of this 10th edition. After hearing Daniel Ellsberg and others talk we realized that nuclear war is a terminal disease that has only one cure -- *Prevention* -- and the time for that prevention is now. Of course there are other important problems facing humanity -- hunger, pollution, repression -- but if we cannot prevent nuclear holocaust and eliminate nuclear weapons now, we will not have a chance to solve the other problems. Nothing, outside of cosmic cataclysm, has the power to destroy life on this planet so quickly and completely as *we* do with *our* nuclear weapons. Therefore, we are asking you to take a stand for peace and the elimination of nuclear weaponry from this planet. Whether through prayer, parades, politicking or prison, each one of us can help turn this planet away from the brink of destruction. And with this momentum we can eliminate war, hunger and suffering. We have the technology. We have the consciousness. We need only merge the two. "Now is the time, the time is now." Let us give the world's children and their descendents the chance to see the Golden Age coming at the beginning of the next millenium. "All we are saying is, *Give Peace a Chance.*" We have been happy to serve you over the last ten years and enjoy hearing from you.

All love in the Divine

Parmatma Singh

Parmatma Singh Khalsa -- Publisher

Marilyn Ferguson

A leaderless but powerful network is working to bring about radical change in the United States. Its members have broken with certain key elements of Western thought, and they may even have broken continuity with history.

This network is the Aquarian Conspiracy. It is a conspiracy without a political doctrine. Without a manifesto. With conspirators who seek power only to disperse it, and whose strategies are pragmatic, even scientific, but whose perspective sounds so mystical that they hesitate to discuss it. Activists asking different kinds of questions, challenging the establishment from within.

Broader than reform, deeper than revolution, this benign conspiracy for a new human agenda has triggered the most rapid cultural realignment in history. The great shuddering, irrevocable shift overtaking us is not a new political, religious, or philosophical system. It is a new mind -- the ascendance of a startling world view that gathers into its framework breakthrough science and insights from the earliest recorded thought.

The Aquarian Conspirators range across all levels of income and education, from the humblest to the highest. There are school teachers and office workers, famous scientists, government officials and lawmakers, artists and millionaires, taxi drivers and celebrities, leaders in medicine, education, law, psychology. Some are open in their advocacy, and their names may be familiar. Others are quiet about their involvement, believing they can be more effective if they are not identified with ideas that have all too often been misunderstood.

There are legions of conspirators. They are in corporations, universities and hospitals, on the faculties of public schools, in factories and doctors' offices, in state and federal agencies, on city councils and the White House staff, in state legislatures, in volunteer organizations, in virtually all arenas of policy-making in the country.

Whatever their station or sophistication, the conspirators are linked, made kindred by their inner discoveries and earthquakes. You can break through old limits, past inertia and fear, to levels of fulfillment that once seemed impossible ... to richness of choice, freedom, human closeness. You can be more productive, confident, comfortable with insecurity. Problems can be experienced as challenges, a chance for renewal, rather than stress. Habitual defensiveness and worry can fall away. *It can all be otherwise.*

In the beginning, certainly, most did not set out to change society. In that sense, it is an unlikely kind of conspiracy. But they found that their *lives* had become revolutions. Once a personal change began in earnest, they found themselves rethinking everything, examining old assumptions, looking anew at their work and relationships, health, political power and "experts," goals and values.

They have coalesced into small groups in every town and institution. They have formed what one called "national non-organizations." Some conspirators are keenly aware of the national, even international, scope of the movement and are active in linking others. They are at once antennae and transmitters, both listening and communicating. They amplify the activities of the conspiracy by networking and pamphleteering, articulating the new options through books, lectures, school curricula, even Congressional hearings and the national media.

Others have centered their activity within their speciality, forming groups within existing organizations and institutions, exposing their co-workers to new ideas, often calling on the larger network for support, feedback, back-up information.

And there are millions of others who have never thought of themselves as part of a conspiracy but sense that their experiences and their struggle are part of something bigger, a larger social transformation that is increasingly visible if you know where to look. They are typically unaware of the national networks and their influence in high places; they may have found only one or two kindred spirits in their workplace, neighborhood, or circle of friends. Yet even in small groups -- twos and threes, eights and tens -- they are having their impact.

You will look in vain for affiliations in traditional forms: political parties, idealogical groups, clubs, or fraternal organizations. You find instead little clusters and loose networks. There are tens of thousands of entry points to this conspiracy. Wherever people share experiences, they connect sooner or later with each other and eventually with larger circles. Each day their number grows.

Excerpted from The Aquarian Conspiracy: Personal and Social Transformation in the 1980's, © *1980 by Marilyn Ferguson, published by J.P. Tarcher, Inc.*

Daniel Ellsberg

Certain little-known realities in today's world of American nuclear policy pose important religious questions for us. Let me explore these realities with you by outlining several misconceptions, wide- spread among Americans, about the function and intended targets of nuclear weapons in U.S. national security planning. This subject was my professional concern when I worked in the Pentagon.

Most Americans believe that nuclear weapons are included in our military plans only to deter nuclear attack upon the United States or its NATO allies. Their sole purpose -- as the scientists at the weapons design laboratories will tell us -- is to assure that nuclear weapons will never be used by anyone to initiate nuclear war.

That is Myth #1: The United States will never strike first with nuclear weapons, or even plan or threaten such "first use."

Myth #2 is that U.S. planners would never plan to use weapons of this sort against people -- against cities -- except to retaliate for an attack upon our own cities.

Myth #3 is that the pictures and writings we have seen of the destruction of Hiroshima and Nagasaki adequately convey the destruction which would be inflicted in a modern nuclear war.

The United States, which has pioneered and maintained a lead in virtually every aspect of nuclear technology, developed atomic weapons and plans for their use in the late 40's when we had a nuclear monopoly -- i.e., when *only* the U.S. could initiate nuclear war. And for most of the nuclear era, contrary to what the public was led to fear, we maintained a massive superiority over the Soviets which continued to make it unimaginable that anyone but the United States would "go first." Our government has *never* agreed to a "no first use" constraint on its plans. Successive American presidents have repeatedly rejected offers from the Soviets for a bilateral no-first-use agreement. The Reagan administration has refused to join the Soviets in their unilateral commitment, announced at the 1982 United Nations Special Session on disarmament, never to be the first to use nuclear weapons. Quite the contrary: Each U.S. president, from Truman on, has officially affirmed our intention to initiate nuclear attacks, if necessary, in conflicts not only in Western Europe but in the Middle East or elsewhere. Actual threats of possible *imminent* U.S. first use have been made repeatedly -- usually in secret from the American public -- in conflicts involving Korea, Indochina, China, and Berlin. (For references, see my "Call to Mutiny" in *Protest and Survive*, Monthly Review Press, 1981.)

In the event of nuclear operations *initiated* by the United States against the Soviet Union (presumably arising out of a non-nuclear conflict or a fear of Soviet attack), our plans have always included bombing every Soviet city, in addition to military targets. Every one of the 218 Russian cities with over 100,000 people is targeted for attack, and 80% of the next 800 cities. All of these cities will be destroyed with only a small fraction of our nuclear arsenal, whether we strike first or second.

Cities on both sides would be hit, not by the kind of atomic weapons that destroyed Hiroshima and Nagasaki, but by thermonuclear weapons, H-bombs, which require a Nagasaki-type A-bomb as a *trigger*. Some H-bomb warheads have an explosive power of 20 million tons of TNT, two million times the power of the largest block-busters of World War II, one thousand times the yield of the Nagasaki bomb. Thus, pictures of the destruction of Nagasaki reveal no more than the effects of dropping on a single populated city the *detonator* of one modern hydrogen weapon, of which several tens of thousands now exist on both sides. Nowadays every missile and every bomber, with its multiple warheads, has the lethal capacity -- and thus the moral implications -- of an Auschwitz.

No national leader, of course, has ever wanted to initiate a nuclear war. But each of our presidents has wanted the ability to *threaten,* credibly, to do so, and nearly every one has found occasion secretly to use our weapons in an actual crisis: use them in the precise way that a gun is used when it is pointed at someone's head in a direct confrontation, whether or not the trigger is pulled. It is precisely in hopes of repeating such threats, and of restoring their credibility -- now greatly diminished by Soviet nuclear parity -- by regaining our former first-strike superiority, that the current administration (like its predecessor) proposes to budget several hundred billion dollars to develop, test, produce and deploy many thousands of new nuclear weapons. Yet in a world where opponents are comparably armed, and therefore less likely than before to back down, such threats are no substitute for nuclear war. They are a path to nuclear war.

In this light, long before the final, mutually disastrous breakdown, the very preparations by our society that lead toward this apocalypse involve us all *right now* in a moral catastrophe. Every new test of a nuclear weapon, on either side, is a rehearsal for a holocaust. The taxes we spend on such weapons, the talents and labor and resources we mobilize in order better to threaten or carry out the initiation of nuclear warfare, all express a readiness and intent to massacre: not merely to kill opposing leaders who fail to heed such threats, or their armed followers, but to annihilate their wives and children and elders and sick. We are preparing as well to exterminate their livestock, their birds and fish; to burn all their habitations and buildings; to poison their wells and fields and lakes; to freight their winds with radioactivity carrying death to neighboring lands; to set their forests blazing, with their wild animals; to leave no living things unharmed, save wild grasses and insects, resistant to the radiation from our weapons.

Some questions such plans evoke are, I have said, religious ones. What is the nature and role of humanity, which is now contemplating and readying this project of extermination? How did we get to this? What is our relation and obligation to the rest of life? Is it our destiny to reverse the process of creation?

Indeed, what is the true religion of the men (not women) who made these first-strike plans and who believe they have the right to implement them under certain circumstances (of "enemy intransigence")? And do the rest of us share that same religion? If not, what are we called on to do?

In any Western religious terms, such plans are evil, a sin: which means, or should mean, "what one must not collaborate with or be part of, must not allow, must expose and resist." So Gandhi would question (as might others from Eastern spiritual traditions) whether enlightenment is truly to be sought in ignoring or denying such social realities, while the very silence of one's meditation is being counted as assent.

Every spiritual path is partly defined by some form of ethical consideration, and in particular, restraints on the circumstances and scale of permissible violence. Although, for example, Christianity has not been a pacifist religion except for a small minority since the time of Constantine, for that same period of 1600 years Christian "just war" theory has prescribed limits on legitimate violence even in otherwise justified defensive wars. The heart of this doctrine -- eventually central to international laws of war -- has been *the absolute immunity of non-combatants from deliberate military attack,* with noncombatants defined broadly as people not directly threatening harm to other humans with weapons.

Our war plans, which threaten by their very existence the deliberate annihilation of non-combatants on a scale with no precedent in human barbarism, not only violate Just War principles and international law; they do not fit within the broadest interpretation of *any* traditional system of ethics, whether Christian, Jewish, Buddhist, Hindu, Taoist, Islamic, animist ... There are, indeed, elements within every religious tradition (which in these circumstances demand rethinking!) that foster compliance with state authority; but never to the point of envisioning a collaboration and conscious preparation to launch a form of combat that would murder half a billion to a billion humans, and could end life on earth.

One could understand a religion with such an ethics only as a form of Satanism, a worship of unbridled power that gives national leaders the right to gamble with forces that can undo creation. In historic terms, our current nuclear plans and threats derive directly from the secret adoption by allied leaders (midway in World War II) of Hitler's ethics of power and total war, as expressed in the bombing of Rotterdam and London, and then, a hundredfold, in the firestorms kindled in Hamburg, Cologne, Dresden and Tokyo. Then, as now, the public had to be lied to about the true aiming points and intended effects of the area bombing. To this day, the sustained conversion of highest civilian leaders to a new official ethics, permitting deliberate threat and massacre of non-combatants as an instrument of policy, has had to be kept secret from most American citizens.

Few Americans are pacifists, but even in the cauldron of World War II and the ice-floes of the Cold War, their acceptance and worship of the power of unlimited violence have not kept pace with their leaders'. Our hope of salvation, in whatever sense, rests on that.

These policies, and the leaders who direct them can and must be opposed without relying on violence. Violence would only confirm and reinforce the very values and practices we must oppose. But even in America, with a tradition much stronger than elsewhere of heresy to the ubiquitous religion of state power, that opposition cannot take place without personal risk. Thus, not without personal courage. For that we must draw on our deepest commitments, our sense of who we are and what purposes and values we serve, our deepest and broadest loyalties, and the support of our spiritual beliefs and community.

Yogi Bhajan remarked to me: "What we are up to is a revolt against our own destruction." I hear that as a call to mutiny. I believe we must seek to find and share with each other the political and religious truths and practices that will give us the strength to recall to our fellow Americans that to be loyal to this country does *not, not, not* compel us to be disloyal to the human species and to future life on earth.

Daniel Ellsberg is a former defense consultant, distributor of the "Pentagon Papers," anti-nuclear activist.

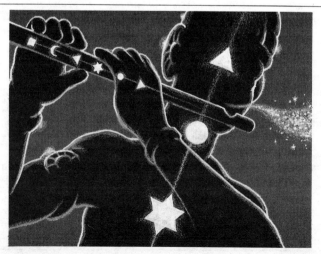

New Consciousness Centers

Title Index

How To Use This Section

The centers in this section are of many kinds and many places. They are those centers which have paid to be listed or have been included because of their importance to the new age community. They are by no means *all* the centers available. Also many of the centers listed are only the national headquarters and have many branch centers. Write them to see if there is a branch in your area. Almost all descriptions are written by the centers themselves. *New Consciousness Sourcebook* does not recommend or endorse any particular center. Contact the centers themselves for fees, schedules and more information.

Check through the *title index* to see which centers are listed, or check the *category index* for the kind of centers you are interested in. Centers are classified by three categories maximum in most cases. Then, to find the descriptions of the centers that interest you look them up alphabetically. All centers listed in this section are also listed in the *Community Directory* by city. Therefore, you can find any center by name, category or location. Let us know any corrections or additions you may find. A complete list of center addresses is available from NAM Mailing Lists. If you would like to have your center listed in the next edition, write us.

A

Academy Of Taoist Healing Arts
Acharya Sushil Jain Ashram
Acutalism
Acutalizations
The Acupressure Workshop
The Acupuncture & Shiatsu Therapy Center
The Acupuncture Education Center
Ahn Tai Chi Studio, Inc.
Ajapa Yoga Foundation
Aletheia Psycho-Physical Foundation
Alpha Logics
The American Buddhist Movement
The American Movement Newsletter
American Holistic Medical Association
The American Holistic Nurses' Association
American-International Reiki Association
American Vegan Society -- Ahimsa
Ananda
Ananda Marga

Anthroposophical Society In America
Aquarian Age Church
Aquarian Fellowship
The Aquarian Minyan
Aquarian Research Foundation
Arcana Workshops
Arica Institute
Association For Research And Enlightenment
The Association For Transpersonal Psychology
Astara
Astro-Musical Research
Atmaniketan Ashram
Aum Temple Of Universal Truth
Auroville
Austin Area Holistic Health Association
The Avadhut

B

Baha'i Faith
Balanced Life Center

Bawa Muhaiyaddeen Fellowship
The Bear Tribe
Berkshire Center For Body/Mind
  Wholeness
Bhagavan Sri Ramana Maharshi Center
Biofeedback Institute
B'nai Or
Brahma Kumaris Raja Yoga Center
Buddhist Association Of The United States
Buddhist Wats (Temples) Of Thailand
Builders Of The Adytum
Burlington College

C
Cafh Foundation
California Institute Of Integral Studies
California Institute Of Transpersonal
  Psychology
California School Of Herbal Studies
Camp Sunburst
Le Centre Du Silence Mime School
Center For Attitudinal Healing
Center For The Healing Arts
Center For Maturing And Evolving
Center For Psychological Revolution
The Center For Self Healing
Center For Shamanic Studies
Center For Spiritual Awareness -- CSA
Center For Vision Improvement
Center For Yoga
Center Of Being
Center Of Health
Chogye International Zen Center
Christ Truth Foundation
Church Of Antioch
Church Of The Healing Way
Church Of Light
The Church Of The Realization
Circle
Clear Mind Center
Columbia Pacific University
Community Center For Wholistic Living
Consciousness Village -- Leonard Orr
Coptic Fellowship International
Consanti Foundation
The Cosmic Circle Of Fellowship
The Creative Living Guidance Center
Cultural Integration Fellowship

D
Dent Info
Devadeep Rajneesh Sannyas Ashram
Dhyanyoga Centers Inc.
Dialogue House
Diamond Sangha
Dimensions Of Evolvement

Djarma Learning Community

E
Earth Community
East-West Cultural Center
The Ecclesia Gnostica
Ecumenical Monks Of St. Benedict
The Edenite Society
Elisabeth A. Ulatovska Workshops
Esalen Institute
Esoteric Philosophy Center
Ewam Choden Tibetan Buddhist Center

F
The Farm
The Fellowship Of The Inner Light
Fellowship Of Religious Humanists
Findhorn
Florida Institute Of Natural Health
The Flower Essence Society
The Focusing Institute
Free For All

G
Genesa
God's Valley
The Graduate Theological Union Library,
  New Religious Movements Research
Grief Management Center
Gurdjieff Foundation Of California

H
Haiku Zendo
Hanuman Foundation
Harbin Hot Springs New Age Community
Hawthorne University
Healing Church Of Karmu
The Healing Circle, ULC
Healing Through Arts, Inc.
Heartwood: California College Of The
  Natural Healing Arts
Heavensong
Hippocrates Health Institute
The Hoffman Quadrinity Process
Hohm
Holistic Health Association
The Holy Shankaracharya Order
Holyearth Foundation
Holy Order Of Mans
Homeopathic Medicine
Human Development Center
The Human Process, Inc.
Huna International
Hypnosis Clearing House, Inc.

I
I Am Nation
I.C.S.A. -- Ananda Ashram

13

Informed Homebirth
Inner Development Center
Inner Growth Seminar
The Inner Light Foundation
Inner Research Institute -- School Of
	T'ai Chi Ch'uan
Insight Meditation Society
Institute For The Development Of The
	Harmonious Human Being
The Institute For Holistic Studies
Institute For Self Development
Institute For The Study Of Conscious
	Evolution
Institute Of Advanced Studies
Institute Of Mentalphysics
Integral Yoga Institute (IYI)
Integrity International
The Intergroup Committee
International Association For World Peace
International Babaji Yoga Sangam
International Buddhist Meditation Center
The International Church Of Ageless
	Wisdom
International Community Of Christ
International Council Of Spiritual Sciences
International Holistic Center, Inc.
The International School Of Massage
	Therapy
Inward Journey
Iskcon -- New Barsana Spiritual Farm

J

Jai Ma Music
Jain Meditation International Centre
Jan's Work
Janus Growth Center
Jemez Bodhi Mandala
The Jersey Society Of Parapsychology, Inc.
The Jeshua Ben Josef School Of The Heart
Jesus Movement
John F. Kennedy University
Jungian-Senoi Institute

K

Kagyu Droden Kunchab
Karma Changjub Ling/Rumtek Monastery
Karma Thegsum Choling
Kerista Consciousness Church
Keshavashram International Meditation
	Center
Khalsa Medical Clinic
Koinonia Foundation
Kripalu Center For Holistic Health
Krishnamurti Foundation Of America
Kriya Yoga Center

L

Labsum Shedrub Ling -- Lamaist Buddhist
	Monastery Of America
Lama Foundation
Lanark Hills Foundation
Land House
Lawrence/Harrison Institute
Legacy International Youth Programs
The Liberal Catholic Church
Life Science Institute
The Light Of The Dove Foundation
The Light of Yoga Society
Lindenself Foundation
Living Tao Foundation
Long Branch Environmental Education
	Center
The Love Project
Lubavitch Youth Organization
Lucis Trust

M

Ma Yoga Shakti Int. Mission
Macrobiotics
Madre Grande
Mahikari-No-Waza
Mandala Society
Mark-Age
Martin Steinberg Center
Matagiri
Matri Satsang (Sri Anandamayi Ma)
The Mazdaznan Elector
Medicine Ways
Meditation Group For The New Age
Meher Baba Center
Meta Tantay Indian Foundation
The Michigan Metaphysical Society
The Ministry Of Healing
Mishakai Center For The Study Of
	Shamanism
Arthur Morgan School
Morning Glory Community
Morningland
Morris Foundation, Inc.
Mount Madonna Center
Movement Of Spiritual Inner Awareness
Movement Puzzles Institute
The Moving Center
Myers Institute For Creative Studies

N

NAM -- New Age Media
Narayananda Universal Yoga (N.U. Yoga)
National Astrological Society (NASO)
National Spiritual Science Center
Network Of Conscious Judaism

The Network Of Light
New Age Awareness Center
New Age School Of Massage
New College Of California
The New Mexico Academy Of Advanced
　Healing Arts
The New Vrindaban Community -- Iskcon
New York Zen Center
Nurses In Transition
Nyingma Institute

O

The Ojai Foundation
Omega Fellowship
Orgonomy-Wilhelm Reich
Oz
Ozark Life Center

P

Pacific Healing Arts Center
PAN -- Planetary Alignment Network
Parapsychology Sources Of Information
　Center
P.E.A.C.E. Network
Philosophical Research Society
Planetary Citizens
Play Mountain Place
Polarity Therapy
Polestar International
The Prison-Ashram Project
The Providence Zen Center
The Psychic Studies Institute
The Pyramid Center Of Bhakti Yoga

R

Rainbow Tribe
Raj-Yoga Math And Retreat
Rajneesh Foundation International
Reiki Natural Health Center
Religious Science Center
Rinzai-Ji
Rocky Mountain Healing Arts Institute
The Roseland Foundation
The Rosicrucian Fellowship
The Rosicrucian Order (AMORC)
Russell House

S

Sakya Tegchen Choling Center
Sat Institute
Sawan Kirpal Ruhani Mission
The Saybrook Institute
Scandinavian Yoga And Meditation School
School Of Spiritual Science
The School Of T'ai Chi Chuan
The Search At Northeon Forest
Seicho-No-Ie

Self Improvement Institute (SII)
Self Realization Fellowship
The Seva Foundation
Several Sources Foundation
Shasta Abbey
Shenandoah Valley Health Ranch
The Shepherd's Bush Centre
Shiatsu Center At Harbin Hot Springs
Shiatsu Massage School Of California
Silva Mind Control
Sino-American Buddhist Association
Sirius
Sivananda Yoga Vedanta Center
Sky Foundation
Society For The Protection Of The Unborn
　Through Nutrition
Soma
Soma Institute
The Soyfoods Center
Spectrum Workshops/CLub Spectrum
Spiritual Advancement Of The Individual
The Spiritual Healing Center
Spiritual Life Institute
Spiritual Science Center
Spiritual Unity Of Nations
The Sproutletter
Sri Aurobindo's Action Center
Sri Centres International
The Sri Chinmoy Centre
Stellar Crystal Communications
Stelle -- City Of Tomorrow
Still Mountain Society
The Stroking Community Network
Subud
Sufi Islamia Ruhaniat Society (SIRS)
The Sufi Order
Sufism Reoriented
The Summit Lighthouse
Summit University
Sunburst -- The Ancient Builders
Suratao
Syda Foundation -- Siddha Meditation

T

Tao Healing Arts Center
Taoist Institute
Teaching Of The Inner Christ
Temenos Institute, Inc.
Temple Of Cosmic Religion
The Temple Of Man
Terra, Inc.
The Theosophical Society
Thomas Institute Of Metaphysics
3HO Drug Program

3HO Foundation -- Yogi Bhajan
The Tibet Society
T.O.P. Training: The Omnision Program
Trager Psychophisical Integration
    And Mentastics
The Tree Of Life
Truth Consciousness
The Twelve Rays Of The Great
    Central Sun

U
Unity Center
The Unity-In-Diversity Council
Unity Woods Yoga Center
Universal Great Brotherhood, Solar Line
Universal Life Church
University Of The Trees

V
Vajradhatu
Valley Light Center
Vedanta Centre -- Ananda Ashrama
Vedanta Societies
Vegetarian Society, Inc.
Vietnamese Buddhist Temple

W
Waking UP In The Nuclear Age
Waldorf Institute
The Washington Buddhist Vihara
Washington Psychic Institute
Well Being Community Center
Wholistic Counseling
Willow Gold
Wilmot Center
Win Systems
The Winged Heart Homestead
Women And Wisdom
Women's Conferences
The Word Foundation, Inc.

Y
Yasodhara Ashram
Yeshe Nying Po -- Orgyen Cho Dzong
Yoga And Growth Center
Yoga Research Society

Z
Zen Center Of Los Angeles
The Zen Center Of Rochester
The Zen Center San Francisco/Tassajara
The Zen Studies Society

ACUPRESSURE/ACUPUNCTURE: The Acupressure Workshop, The Acupuncture Education Center, The Acupuncture & Shiatsu Therapy Center, Tao Healing Arts Center.

ANCIENT TEACHINGS: The Fellowship Of The Inner Light-Inner Light Consciousness Institute, Hohm, The International Church Of Ageless Wisdom, International Community Of Christ, Life Science Institute, The Rosicrucian Order (AMORC), The Summit Lighthouse, Summit University, Suratao, Thomas Institute Of Metaphysics.

ARTS: Anthroposophical Society In America, Astro-Musical Research, Consanti Foundation, Cultural Integration Fellowship, Healing Through Arts, Inc., Heavensong, Jai Ma Music, Le Centre Du Silence Mime School, Martin Steinberg Center, Mount Madonna Center, Movement Puzzles Institute, The Moving Center, Myers Institute For Creative Studies, Sufi Islamia Ruhaniat Society (SIRS).

ASCENDED MASTERS: I Am Nation, Mark-Age, Morningland, PAN -- Planetary Alignment Network, The Summit Lighthouse, Summit University, The Twelve Rays Of The Great Central Sun.

ASTROLOGY: Astro-Musical Research, Inner Development Center, National Astrological Society (NASO).

AUROBINDO, SRI: Atmaniketan Ashram, Auroville, East-West Cultural Center, Matagiri, Sri Aurobindo's Action Center.

AWARENESS TRAINING: Actualism, Actualizations, The Hoffman Quadrinity Process, Inner Growth Seminar, Le Centre Du Silence Mime School, Movement Of Spiritual Inner Awareness (MSIA), School Of Spiritual Science, Silva Mind Control.

BAHA'I: Baha'i Faith.

BIOFEEDBACK: Biofeedback Institute.

BODYWORK: The Acupressure Workshop, The Acupuncture & Shiatsu Therapy Center, Center Of Health, The Creative Living Guidance Center, Florida Institute Of Natural Health, The Institute For Holistic Studies, Morning Glory Community, Movement Puzzles Institute, Ozark Life Center, Pacific Healing Arts Center, Polarity Therapy, Shiatsu Center At Harbin Hot Springs, Shiatsu Massage School Of California, Soma Institute, Tao Healing Arts Center, Trager Psychophisical Integration And Mentastics.

BUDDHISM: OTHER: The American Buddhist Movement, The American Buddhist Newsletter, Buddhist Association Of The United States, Buddhist Wats (Temples) Of Thailand, Insight Meditation Society, International Buddhist Meditation Center, Sino-American Buddhist Association, Vietnamese Buddhist Temple And Forest Retreat Center, The Washington Buddhist Vihara.

BUDDHISM: TIBETAN: Ewam Choden Tibetan Buddhist Center, Kagyu Droden Kunchab, Karma Changjub Ling/Rumtek Monastery, Karma Thegsum Choling, Labsum Shedrub Ling -- Lamaist Buddhist Monastery Of America, Nyingma Institute, Sakya Tegchen Choling Center, The Tibet Society, Vajradhatu, Yeshe Nying Po -- Orgyen Cho Dzong.

BUDDHISM: ZEN: Chogye International Zen Center, Diamond Sangha, Haiku Zendo, Jemez Bodhi Mandala, New York Zen Center, The Providence Zen Center, Rinzai-Ji, Shasta Abbey -- Order Of Buddhist Contemplatives, Zen Center Of Los Angeles, The Zen Center Of Rochester, The Zen Center San Francisco/Tassajara, The Zen Studies Society.

CAYCE, EDGAR: Association For Research And Enlightenment, Inc. (A.R.E.).

CHILDREN: Arthur Morgan School, Camp Sunburst, Legacy International Youth Programs, Play Mountain Place.

CHRISTIANITY: Aum Temple Of Universal Truth, Christ Truth Foundation, Church Of Antioch, Church Of The Healing Way, The Cosmic Circle Of Fellowship, The Ecclesia Gnostica, Ecumenical Monks Of St. Benedict, The Edenite Society, Holy Order Of Mans, International Community Of Christ, Jesus Movement, The Liberal Catholic Church, Spiritual Life Institute, Spiritual Science Center, Teaching Of The Inner Christ, Universal Life Church.

COMMUNITY: Ananda, Aquarian Research Foundation, Atmaniketan Ashram, Auroville, Bhagavan Sri Ramana Maharshi Center, Circle, Consanti Foundation, Consciousness Village -- Leonard Orr, Djarma Learning Community, Ecumenical Monks Of St. Benedict, The Farm, Findhorn, God's Valley, Harbin Hot Springs New Age Community, Hohm, Holy Order Of Mans, I.C.S.A. -- Ananda Ashram, Institute For The Development Of The Harmonious Human Being, Integrity International, Iskcon -- New Barsana Spiritual Farm Community, Jemez Bodhi Mandala, The Jeshua Ben Josef School Of The Heart, Jesus Movement, Kerista Consciousness Church, Keshavashram International Meditation Center, Koinonia Foundation, Kripalu Center For Holistic Health, Lama Foundation, Lanark Hills Foundation, Land House, Lindenself Foundation, Madre Grande, Matagiri, Medicine Ways, Morning Glory Community, The New Vrindaban Community -- Iskcon, Oz, The Pyramid Center Of Bhakti Yoga, Rajneesh Foundation International, The Search At Northeon Forest, The Shepherd's Bush Centre, Sirius, Spiritual Life Institute, Stelle -- City Of Tomorrow, Still Mountain Society, Sunburst -- The Ancient Builders, Syda Foundation -- Siddha Meditation, 3HO Foundation -- Yogi Bhajan, Truth Consciousness, Wilmot Center, Willow Gold, The Winged Heart Homestead, Yasodhara Ashram, The Zen Center San Francisco/Tassajara.

COPTIC: Coptic Fellowship International.

COUNSELING: Center For Attutudinal Healing, Center For The Healing Arts, The Creative Living Guidance Center, Grief Management Center, Human Development Center, Janus Growth Center, Khalsa Medical Clinic, The Light Of The Dove Foundation: World Organization And Healing Ministry, Soma, Wholistic Counseling.

EDUCATION: The American Buddhist Movement, The American Movement Newsletter, American-International Reiki Association, Anthroposophical Society In America, Arthur Morgan School, Burlington College, California Institute Of Integral Studies, Columbia Pacific University, Djarma Learning Community, The Graduate Theological Union Library, New Religious Movements Research Corporation, Hawthorne University, Healing Through Arts, Inc., Heartwood: California College Of The Natural Healing Arts, The Institute For Holistic Studies, Institute For The Study Of Conscious Evolution, John F. Kennedy University, Lawrence/Harrison Institute, Legacy International Youth Programs, Long Branch Environmental Education Center, Mandala Society, New College Of California, The New Mexico Academy Of Advanced Healing Arts, PAN -- Planetary Alignment Network, Philosophical Research Society, Play Mountain Place, The Psychic Studies Institute, The Saybrook Institute, Soma Institute, The Soyfoods Center, Still Mountain Society, Summit University, Temenos Institute, Inc., The Tree Of Life, University Of The Trees, Waldorf Institute.

ENVIRONMENT: The Bear Tribe, Consanti Foundation, Long Branch Environmental Education Center, Oz, PAN -- Planetary Alignment Network, Willow Gold.

ESOTERIC SCHOOL: Astara, Builders Of The Adytum, Church Of Light, The Ecclesia Gnostica, The Edenite Society, Esoteric Philosophy Center, The Human Process, Inc., The International Church Of Ageless Wisdom, Life Science Institute,

Lucis Trust, Philosophical Research Society, Suratao, Thomas Institute Of Metaphysics.

GROWTH CENTER: Alpha Logics, Arica Institute, Berkshire Center For Body/Mind Wholeness, Center For Psychological Revolution, Clear Mind Center, Community Center For Wholistic Living, The Creative Living Guidance Center, Cultural Integration Fellowship, Dimensions Of Evolvement, Esalen Institute, The Human Process, Inc., Institute For Self Development, International Holistic Center, Inc., Inward Journey, Janus Growth Center, Lama Foundation, Madre Grande, Myers Institute For Creative Studies, Omega Fellowship, Oz, Sat Institute, Self Improvement Institute (SII), The Shepherd's Bush Centre, The Tree Of Life, Women And Wisdom, Yoga And Growth Center Of Bergen County.

GURDJIEFF: Gurdjieff Foundation Of California, Institute Of Advanced Studies, Jan's Work, Land House, The Search At Northeon Forest.

HEALTH + HEALING: Academy Of Taoist Healing Arts, The Acupressure Workshop, The Acupuncture & Shiatsu Therapy Center, The Acupuncture Education Center, The American Holistic Nurses' Association (AHNA), Aletheia Psycho-Physical Foundation, American Holistic Medical Association, American-International Reiki Association, Austin Area Holistic Health Association, Balanced Life Center, The Bear Tribe, Berkshire Center For Body/Mind Wholeness, Biofeedback Institute, California School Of Herbal Studies, Center For Attutudinal Healing, Center For The Healing Arts, The Center For Self Healing, Center For Vision Improvement, Center Of Health, Church Of The Healing Way, Community Center For Wholistic Living, Dent Info, Florida Institute Of Natural Health, The Flower Essence Society, Healing Church Of Karmu, The Healing Circle, ULC, Healing Through Arts, Inc., Heartwood: California College Of The Natural Healing Arts, Hippocrates Health Institute, Holistic Health Association Of The Princeton Area, Homeopathic Medicine, I.C.S.A. -- Ananda Ashram, Inner Research Institute -- School Of T'ai Chi Ch'uan, The Institute For Holistic Studies, Institute For Self Development, The International Church Of Ageless Wisdom, The International School Of Massage Therapy, Janus Growth Center, The Jersey Society Of Parapsychology, Inc. (JSP), Khalsa Medical Clinic, Kripalu Center For Holistic Health, Lawrence/Harrison Institute, Life Science Institute, The Light Of The Dove Foundation: World Organization And Healing Ministry, Macrobiotics, Madre Grande, Mandala Society, Medicine Ways, Meta Tantay Indian Foundation, The Ministry Of Healing -- School Of Reflexology, Mishakai Center For The Study Of Shamanism, Morningland, Morris Foundation, Inc., Mount Madonna Center, Movement Puzzles Institute, New Age School Of Massage, The New Mexico Academy Of Advanced Healing Arts, Nurses In Transition, Ozark Life Center, Pacific Healing Arts Center, Polarity Therapy, Polestar International, Reiki Natural Health Center, Rocky Mountain Healing Arts Institute, Russell House, Sat Institute, School Of Spiritual Science, The School Of T'ai Chi Chuan, The Seva Foundation, Shenandoah Valley Health Ranch, Shiatsu Center At Harbin Hot Springs, Shiatsu Massage School Of California, Sky Foundation, Society For The Protection Of The Unborn Through Nutrition, Soma, Soma Institute, The Soyfoods Center, The Spiritual Healing Center, The Sproutletter, Sri Centres International, Still Mountain Society, Tao Healing Arts Center, 3HO Drug Program, 3HO Foundation -- Yogi Bhajan, T.O.P. Training: The Omnision Program, Wholistic Counseling, Yoga And Growth Center Of Bergen County.

HINDU: The Holy Shankaracharya Order, Iskcon -- New Barsana Spiritual Farm Community, Keshavashram International Meditation Center, The New Vrindaban Community -- Iskcon, The Pyramid Center Of Bhakti Yoga, Spiritual Advancement Of The Individual (SAI), Temple Of Cosmic Religion, Vedanta Societies -- The Ramakrishna Order.

HUNA: Huna International.
HYPNOSIS: Hypnosis Clearing House, Inc., Inner Development Center.
ISLAM: Bawa Muhaiyaddeen Fellowship.
JAIN: Acharya Sushil Jain Ashram, Jain Meditation International Centre.
JUDAISM: The Aquarian Minyan, B'nai Or, Lubavitch Youth Organization, Martin Steinberg Center, Network Of Conscious Judaism.
JUNG, CARL: The Ecclesia Gnostica, Jungian-Senoi Institute.
KRISHNAMURTI: Krishnamurti Foundation Of America, Lanark Hills Foundation.
"LIVING MASTERS": Arica Institute, The Avadhut, Bawa Muhaiyaddeen Fellowship, Center Of Being -- Her Holiness Sri Marashama Devi, Consciousness Village -- Leonard Orr, Devadeep Rajneesh Sannyas Ashram, Dhyanyoga Centers Inc., Hohm, The Human Process, Inc., Movement Of Spiritual Inner Awareness (MSIA), Rajneesh Foundation International, Spiritual Advancement Of The Individual (SAI), The Sri Chinmoy Centre, Syda Foundation -- Siddha Meditation, Truth Consciousness.
MACROBIOTICS: Macrobiotics.
MARTIAL ARTS: Academy Of Taoist Healing Arts, Ahn Tai Chi Studio, Inc., Inner Research Institute -- School Of T'ai Chi Ch'uan, Institute For Self Development, Living Tao Foundation, Polestar International, The School Of T'ai Chi Chuan, Taoist Institute.
MASSAGE: Harbin Hot Springs New Age Community, The International School Of Massage Therapy, New Age School Of Massage, Rocky Mountain Healing Arts Institute, Shiatsu Center At Harbin Hot Springs, Shiatsu Massage School Of California, The Stroking Community Network.
MEDITATION: Acharya Sushil Jain Ashram, Ahn Tai Chi Studio, Inc., Ajapa Yoga Foundation, Ananda Marga, Aquarian Age Church & Spiritual Unity Movement Center, Arcana Workshops, Balanced Life Center, Buddhist Association Of The United States, Buddhist Wats (Temples) Of Thailand, Center For Spiritual Awareness -- CSA, Center Of Being -- Her Holiness Sri Marashama Devi, Chogye International Zen Center, Devadeep Rajneesh Sannyas Ashram, Dialogue House, Diamond Sangha, Ewam Choden Tibetan Buddhist Center, Haiku Zendo, The Healing Circle, ULC, The Holy Shankaracharya Order, The Inner Light Foundation, Insight Meditation Society, Institute Of Mentalphysics, Integral Yoga Institute (IYI), The Intergroup Committee, International Babaji Yoga Sangam, International Buddhist Meditation Center, Jain Meditation International Centre, Jemez Bodhi Mandala, Kagyu Droden Kunchab, Karma Thegsum Choling, Labsum Shedrub Ling -- Lamaist Buddhist Monastery Of America, Meditation Group For The New Age (MGNA), The Michigan Metaphysical Society, Narayananda Universal Yoga (N.U. Yoga), Network Of Conscious Judaism, New York Zen Center, Nyingma Institute, Polestar International, The Providence Zen Center, Rinzai-Ji, Sakya Tegchen Choling Center, Sat Institute, Sawan Kirpal Ruhani Mission, Scandinavian Yoga And Meditation School, Seicho-No-Ie, Self Realization Fellowship, Shasta Abbey -- Order Of Buddhist Contemplatives, Sino-American Buddhist Association, Sirius, Sivananda Yoga Vedanta Center, Sky Foundation, Spiritual Advancement Of The Individual (SAI), Sri Aurobindo's Action Center, The Sri Chinmoy Centre, Sufi Islamia Ruhaniat Society (SIRS), The Sufi Order, Syda Foundation -- Siddha Meditation, Taoist Institute, Temple Of Cosmic Religion, 3HO Foundation -- Yogi Bhajan, Universal Great Brotherhood, Solar Line (U.G.B.), University Of The Trees, Vajradhatu, The Washington Buddhist Vihara, Yasodhara Ashram, Yeshe Nying Po -- Orgyen Cho Dzong, Zen Center Of Los Angeles, The Zen Center Of Rochester, The Zen Center San Francisco/Tassajara, The Zen Studies Society.

MEHER BABA: Meher Baba Center, Sufism Reoriented.
METAPHYSICS: Morningland, The Michigan Metaphysical Society, The Word Foundation, Inc.
MISCELLANEOUS: Center For Shamanic Studies, The Church Of The Realization, Dialogue House, Earth Community, Fellowship Of Religious Humanists, Genesa, Kerista Consciousness Church, Mahikari-No-Waza, The Mazdaznan Elector, National Spiritual Science Center, The Network Of Light, The Ojai Foundation, Seicho-No-Ie, Several Sources Foundation, Spectrum Workshops/Club Spectrum, Well Being Community Center, Women's Conferences, The Word Foundation, Inc.
NATIVE AMERICAN: The Bear Tribe, Medicine Ways, Meta Tantay Indian Foundation, Mishakai Center For The Study Of Shamanism.
NATURE SPIRITUALITY: Center For Shamanic Studies, Circle, Findhorn, Mishakai Center For The Study Of Shamanism.
NEW AGE: Aquarian Fellowship, Hanuman Foundation, Heavensong, Holyearth Foundation, Institute For The Study Of Conscious Evolution, The Network Of Light, New Age Awareness Center, The Ojai Foundation, Rainbow Tribe, The Roseland Foundation, Stelle -- City Of Tomorrow, The Twelve Rays Of The Great Central Sun, Willow Gold.
NEW THOUGHT: Christ Truth Foundation, National Spiritual Science Center, Religious Science Center, Teaching Of The Inner Christ, The Temple Of Man, Unity Center, Valley Light Center.
PARAPSYCHOLOGY: Church Of Light, The Jersey Society Of Parapsychology, Inc. (JSP), Parapsychology Sources Of Information Center.
LIFE PASSAGES: Center For Attutudinal Healing, Center For The Healing Arts, Grief Management Center, Hanuman Foundation, Informed Homebirth, Inner Development Center, Institute For The Development Of The Harmonious Human Being, Khalsa Medical Clinic, Society For The Protection Of The Unborn Through Nutrition.
PEACE: Aquarian Fellowship, Aquarian Research Foundation, Brahma Kumaris Raja Yoga Center, Holyearth Foundation, International Association For World Peace, The Light Of The Dove Foundation: World Organization And Healing Ministry, Lindenself Foundation, Lucis Trust, P.E.A.C.E. Network, Planetary Citizens, Waking Up In The Nuclear Age.
PLANETARY TRANSFORMATION: Aquarian Research Foundation, Auroville, Baha'i Faith, Holyearth Foundation, Institute For The Study Of Conscious Evolution, Integrity International, The Intergroup Committee.
PSYCHIC: Aletheia Psycho-Physical Foundation, Aquarian Age Church & Spiritual Unity Movement Center, Community Center For Wholistic Living, The Fellowship Of The Inner Light-Inner Light Consciousness Institute, The Inner Light Foundation, International Council Of Spiritual Sciences, The Psychic Studies Institute, The Roseland Foundation, School Of Spiritual Science, Silva Mind Control, Washington Psychic Institute.
PSYCHOLOGY: The Association For Transpersonal Psychology, Burlington College, California Institute Of Integral Studies, California Institute Of Transpersonal Psychology, The Focusing Institute, Jungian-Senoi Institute, The Saybrook Institute, Temenos Institute, Inc.
RAJNEESH: Devadeep Rajneesh Sannyas Ashram, Rajneesh Foundation International.
RAMANA MAHARSHI: The Avadhut, Bhagavan Sri Ramana Maharshi Center.
REICH, WILHELM: Orgonomy-Wilhelm Reich.
RELATIONSHIPS: Actualizations, Cafh Foundation, Center For Maturing

And Evolving, Center For Psychological Revolution, Clear Mind Center, Elisabeth A. Ulatovska Workskops, The Love Project, Omega Fellowship, The Stroking Community Network.

ROSICRUCIAN: The Rosicrucian Fellowship, The Rosicrucian Order (AMORC), Sant Mat, Sawan Kirpal Ruhani Mission.

SERVICE ORGANIZATION: American Holistic Medical Association, The American Holistic Nurses' Association (AHNA), Ananda Marga, Camp Sunburst, Free For All, Hanuman Foundation, I Am Nation, International Holistic Center, Inc., NAM -- New Age Media, Nurses In Transition, The Prison-Ashram Project, Rainbow Tribe, The Seva Foundation, Spectrum Workshops/Club Spectrum, Spiritual Unity Of Nations, Stellar Crystal Communications, The Unity-In-Diversity Council, Universal Life Church.

SIKH: 3HO Foundation -- Yogi Bhajan.

SOCIAL RESPONSIBILITY: Ananda Marga, The Farm, International Association For World Peace, Legacy International Youth Programs, The Light Of Yoga Society, Morris Foundation, Inc., Planetary Citizens, The Prison-Ashram Project, The Soyfoods Center, Terra, Inc., 3HO Drug Program, 3HO Foundation -- Yogi Bhajan, Waking Up In The Nuclear Age, Wholistic Counseling.

SRI ANANDAMAYIMA: Matri Satsang (Sri Anandamayi Ma).

STEINER, RUDOLF: Anthroposophical Society In America, Waldorf Institute.

SUBUD: Subud.

SUFISM: Institute For The Development Of The Harmonious Human Being, Sufi Islamia Ruhaniat Society (SIRS), The Sufi Order, Sufism Reoriented.

TAOISM: Academy Of Taoist Healing Arts, Ahn Tai Chi Studio, Inc., Living Tao Foundation, Taoist Institute.

THEOSOPHICAL: The Liberal Catholic Church, The Theosophical Society.

THERAPY: The Flower Essence Society, The Focusing Institute, The Hoffman Quadrinity Process, Hypnosis Clearing House, Inc., The Moving Center, Soma, Sri Centres International, The Stroking Community Network, Temenos Institute, Inc., Waking Up In The Nuclear Age, Win Systems.

VEDANTA: Vedanta Centre -- Ananda Ashrama, Vedanta Societies -- The Ramakrishna Order.

VEGETARIANISM: American Vegan Society -- AHIMSA, The Edenite Society, The Farm, Hippocrates Health Institute, The Sproutletter, Vegetarian Society, Inc.

WOMEN: Women And Wisdom, Women's Conferences.

YOGA: Acharya Sushil Jain Ashram, Ajapa Yoga Foundation, Ananda, Balanced Life Center, Brahma Kumaris Raja Yoga Center, Center For Yoga, Dhyanyoga Centers Inc., East-West Cultural Center, The Holy Shankaracharya Order, I.C.S.A. -- Ananda Ashram, Integral Yoga Institute (IYI), International Babaji Yoga Sangam, Kripalu Center For Holistic Health, Kriya Yoga Center, The Light Of Yoga Society, Ma Yoga Shakti Int. Mission, Mount Madonna Center, Narayananda Universal Yoga (N.U. Yoga), Polarity Therapy, The Pyramid Center Of Bhakti Yoga, Raj-Yoga Math And Retreat, Scandinavian Yoga And Meditation School, Self Realization Fellowship, Sivananda Yoga Vedanta Center, Sky Foundation, Sri Centers International, 3HO Drug Program, 3HO Foundation -- Yogi Bhajan, Unity Woods Yoga Center, Universal Great Brotherhood, Solar Line (U.G.B.), Yasodhara Ashram, Yoga And Growth Center Of Bergen County, Yoga Research Society.

YOGANANDA: Ananda, Center For Spiritual Awareness -- CSA, Kriya Yoga Center, Self Realization Fellowship.

The Hopi Nuclear Prophecy
Thomas Banyacaya

When the Hopi found out about the nuclear bombing of Nagasaki and Hiroshima they recalled the Hopi Prophecy that spoke of a small but devastating gourd of ashes. It was said that this gourd, if allowed to fall to the ground would bring devastating destruction, burning everything around it. Living things under the water would also be destroyed from the heat. Many sicknesses would arise which our medicines would not be able to cure. We were told never to go beyond this step, never to allow the manufacture of other such destructive things. We now know that these forseen destructive forces were nuclear weapons. We were told that if we were to continue on this path even greater destruction would follow. Wars can no longer be conducted as a way to reach peace. Peace can only be brought about through spiritual ways, through kindness, understanding, gentleness and love. Only through these spiritual ways can we put aside the wrong action of the past and repair the damage done to our Mother Earth and the peoples of the Earth. It is time for all people to join, actively working to stop the development of war and the use of nuclear forces.

United Nations officials and members of all world governments who are responsible for the safety and well-being of their nations must fulfill their responsibilities and bring to a halt the use of destructive nuclear forces. Warning must be given, for the Hopi Prophecy says that if these destructive actions are not stopped other forces will arise to purify the land. Maybe natural forces, earthquakes, droughts, storms or floods will occur warning us that we must stop these wrong actions and seek peace through spiritual means. What is happening at Big Mountain today is a warning. If these sacred lands are disrupted and the Navajos driven off the land this will signal the longest "walk of death" for the Navajo and Hopi peoples. If this sacred land is abused and ripped apart by mineral exploitation and other destructive activities this in the long run will also signal the "longest walk to death" for all peoples of the world.

Thomas Banyacaya is an interpreter for Hopi high religious leaders.

Return to Return

William A. Gingras

● ACADEMY OF TAOIST HEALING ARTS

Ongoing classes and workshops in all aspects of the Taoist healing and martial arts, including: Ch'i Kung Purification Exercises, The Animal Frolics of Hua T'o, T'ai Chi Ruler, T'ai Chi Ch'uan (Yang, Ch'en and Taoist Styles), Pa Kua Chang, Hsing I Ch'uan, Snake Style, Weaponry and Taoist Meditation. Emphasis on self-understanding and communion with nature. All classes taught by Ken Cohen, well-known Taoist scholar, author and first Westerner authorized to teach the tradition of the sacred mountains of China.

INFORMATION: P.O. Box 234, Nederland, CO 80466.

● ACHARYA SUSHIL JAIN ASHRAM

Acharya Sushil Jain Ashram in Staten Island, New York is a residential learning center dedicated to the practice of the ancient Jain yoga system. Acharya Sushil Kumarji Maharaj, Yoga master and Jain monk, has named this field of study Arhum Yoga. Guruji has Ashrams in Europe, U.S.A. and India.

Activities include classes in meditation, sound vibration, yoga, healing, psychic sciences, vegetarian diet, wholistic health and Jain philosophy.

The Ashram publishes a bi-monthly newsletter. A natural foods distribution company, a candle workshop and production of new age tapes help to support us. The Ashram is planning for a larger rural community within an hour of N.Y.C.

INFORMATION: 722 Tompkins Ave., Staten Island, NY 10305, (212) 447-4948.

● ACTUALISM

Actualism is a teaching that trains man to experience and actualize his untapped potentials for creative self-expression and joyful effortless communication with all forms of life in his world. The School of Actualism, founded by Russell Paul Schofield, teaches tools and techniques of inner light-fire, which bring about the awakening and enlightening of mental, emotional and sensory awareness in a step by step manner. The methods of enlightening awareness, as taught and practiced in Actualism can be applied in all areas of life, including physical welfare, creative media, and interpersonal relationships, to bring about a greater degree of experiencing and expressing of your inner resources of life-light energy. Ralph Metzner is a director of the organization.

INFORMATION: 29928 Lilac Rd., Valley Center, CA 92082, (714) 714-1325.

● ACTUALIZATIONS

Actualizations offers workshops that explore interpersonal communications, relationships and personal effectiveness.

Some questions dealt with are: What works in my life? What doesn't? What do I need for myself? How am I stopping myself from reaching my goals? How do I achieve excellence in all that I do? How can I achieve nurturing relationships?

The workshop environment is very loving and supportive and also totally result oriented. Actualizations means to make real through action. It can help you turn your dreams into reality.

INFORMATION: 3632 Sacramento St., San Francisco, CA 94118, (415) 563-1006.

● THE ACUPRESSURE WORKSHOP

Certified Training Program: The Acupressure Workshop offers a comprehensive, 150 hour program in several types of Acupressure leading to certification as an Acupressure Massage Technician. The program includes training in shiatsu, jin shin, Touch for Health, Do-In, reflexology, anatomy and physiology. Specific areas of learning include the meridians of acupuncture, over 75 points and how they affect the body, The Five Elements Theory, pulse reading, physiognomy, dietary principles, moxabustion, chinese health building exercises, and correlations between physical tension and the emotions.

Enrollment Schedule: Student can enroll at any time. Flexible scheduling: morning, daytime, evening and weekend classes are offered. Ten week summer intensive trainings offered.

Speaker's Bureau: Lecturers and Instructors available for seminars, and presentations for groups of 25 or over on the following topics: Acu-Yoga Self-Treatments; Overeating and Stress; Relieving Headaches; Releasing Back Tension; Releasing Menstrual Tension; Releasing Shoulder and Neck Tension. Call or write for a free school brochure and current schedule.

INFORMATION: 1533 Shattuck Ave., Berkeley, CA 94709, (415) 845-1059.

● THE ACUPUNCTURE & SHIATSU THERAPY CENTER

Shiatsu/Acupressure is a unique and creative one year training program in energetic therapy. Students develop their healing ability progressively through each of 12 levels dealing with the traditional skills of diagnosis and treatment. In a detailed study of the energetic anatomy we trace the development of organs, meridians and pressure points as energy spirals generated from the original forces of Heaven and Earth according to the laws of polarity, a perspective from which deeper insight is gained into the functions of body energy and the applications of its healing power.

Shiatsu/Acupressure is a traditional healing system effective in a broad range of areas including physical, emotional & spiritual problems. It is useful in both the preventive & symptomatic modes. It also easily compliments other approaches to natural health care. Please send $1 for course catalog & application.

INFORMATION: 359 Boylston St., Boston, MA 02116, Dennis Willmont, Director.

● THE ACUPUNCTURE EDUCATION CENTER

The Center is an affiliate of the Dale Institute for Personal and Social Health which offers acupuncture certification courses and apprenticeships, publications by Dr. Dale (books and tapes), acupuncture treatments, and supplies through Acumart.

The Director of the Institute, Dr. Ralph Alan Dale (Ed.D, Ph.D, C.A., F.W.A.S.), is internationally known for his discoveries of the principles and applications of micro-acupuncture systems and for his writing and teaching. Dr. Dale personally conducts the courses sponsored by the Center.

INFORMATION: 13757 N.E. Third Court, Suite 210 A, N. Miami, FL 33161 (November-May), (305) 891-0062 or 891-7333 and Muhlig Road, Parksville (Liberty), NY 12768 (May-November).

● AHN TAI CHI STUDIO, INC.

The Ahn Tai Chi Studio, Inc. established in New York City in 1970, offers a wide variety of Taoist physical and spiritual disciplines. Master Ahn, founder and director, was trained in the Orient and the U.S. for over twenty-five years.

Disciplines taught are Tai Chi Chuan -- Yang Style, as taught by Professor Cheng Man Ching, with emphasis on deep relaxation, rooting and correct alignment. Tai Chi Self Defense involves applying Tai Chi in a combat situation. Push Hands -- mastering Tai Chi principles through joint hand practice with a partner. Chi Kung -- the most powerful Taoist esoteric exercise for increasing energy quickly through breathing and visualization. Taoist Meditation -- sitting meditation to harmonize energy and open blocks. Wu-Chi Breathing -- Taoist breath therapy done in a reclining position, primarily for detoxifying and cleansing.

Weekend workshops offered: Chi is self-healing through various Taoist breathing exercises. Taoist Tantric Sex involves transmuting sexual energy for self-healing, increasing mental power and cultivating spiritual awareness.

Monthly lectures and demonstrations are given for the public. For further information and registration, contact us.

INFORMATION: 81 Spring St., New York, NY 10012, (212) 226-6664.

● AJAPA YOGA FOUNDATION

The Ajapa Yoga Foundation and its two ashrams have been established for the purpose of making Ajapa Yoga and the teachings of Guru Janardan Paramahansa, available in the West. Ajapa Yoga is a simple, practical, and scientific breathing and meditation technique. Ajapa breathing is effortless and natural, and can be done while working, reading, traveling, or relaxing. The effect of Ajapa breathing is to balance the universal forces of attraction and repulsion in man, resulting in improved health, relief from stress, increased vitality, sharpness of memory and clarity of thought. Ajapa breathing leads naturally to improved concentration, which makes meditation highly effective when the two are practiced together. At the Ajapa Yoga

Ashrams, an individual is provided with the ideal environment to learn and practice the Ajapa technique in an intensive manner. Group meditations are held twice daily, vegetarian food is served, useful work is provided, and dialogues, readings, and discussions are often held to analyze in depth this science of Self-Knowledge.

INFORMATION: Shri Janardan Ajapa Yoga Ashram, P.O. Box 1731, Placerville, CA 95667, (916) 626-1585.

● ALETHEIA PSYCHO-PHYSICAL FOUNDATION

The Aletheia Psycho-Physical Foundation was founded in 1958 by Jack Schwarz, who plans to establish in Gold Hill, Oregon, a spiritual, psycho-physical therapeutic complex where human beings can develop to the extent of optimal, spiritual, psychological, and physical health -- wholeness. Such a place will be like a "medicine wheel" with many spokes to provide a multi-dimensional, all-inclusive, diagnostic, therapeutic training center existing and working in a broad framework of holistic methods, alternative methods of healing, preventive methods, and maintenance of optimal health adapted from many other cultural traditions as well as our own already available sources.

INFORMATION: 515 N.E. 8th St., Grants Pass, OR 97526, (503) 479-4855.

● ALPHA LOGICS

Alpha Logics is a school for self directed growth in body, mind and spirit. We are a unique educational center concerned with the whole person. *Whole* means healthy, happy and effectively functional in society; living harmoniously with others and with the environment. It means growing in a balanced, integrated manner to a higher state of being.

Life means growth, and the best growth is self initiated and self directed. Alpha Logics offers a wide range of courses, educational programs, consultations and therapy services, guided experiences and specialized training to help the student transform his life in a way that is personally fulfilling and socially beneficial.

INFORMATION: P.O. Box 920, 229 Cross St., Bristol, CT 06010-0920, (203) 589-2533.

● THE AMERICAN BUDDHIST MOVEMENT

The American Buddhist Movement acts as an American distribution center for information about books, periodicals, study courses, cassettes, newsletters and other material on Buddhism. We have catalogs of publications available, and lists of Buddhist organizations throughout the world.

For those interested in the study of Buddhism, as an academic undertaking or as a way of life, we hope to be able to provide guidance to reference materials and to Buddhist organizations that can assist you. For information, send $1.

INFORMATION: 301 West 45th St., New York, NY 10036, (212) 489-1075.

● THE AMERICAN BUDDHIST NEWSLETTER

This newsletter is a communications medium for all Buddhists in the United States. The Newsletter presents Buddhism in its traditional forms. *The American Buddhist* will help you further your investigation of Buddhism. Study Theravada, Zen, Mahayana, Vajrayana, Nichiren and other forms of Buddhism. Learn how to meditate, study the sutras and develop yourself with the wisdom of the Buddhas. Improve your ability in martial arts by learning what the masters know. 12 monthly issues, $14. Sample issue, $3. Editor, Dr. Kevin R. O'Neil.

INFORMATION: 301 West 45th St., New York, NY 10036, (212) 489-1075.

● AMERICAN HOLISTIC MEDICAL ASSOCIATION

The American Holistic Medical Association was founded in 1978 to unite fully-licensed physicians who also practice holistic medicine. AHMA membership is open to licensed M.D.'s or D.O.'s and to medical students studying for those degrees. AHMA has eight goals, which include educating professionals and the public, advocating insurance coverage of holistic methods, conducting research, and trying to broaden public health policies to incorporate preventive and holistic health principles. All physicians may benefit from a basic understanding of the principles of nutrition, exercise and stress management, and should have a continued awareness of the physical, emotional, mental and spiritual nature of the whole person while practicing in a variety of specialties. The AHMA furnishes the public, upon request, a physician referral listing. A $2 donation is requested to cover handling costs.

INFORMATION: 6932 Little River Tpke., Annandale, VA 22003, (703) 642-5880.

● THE AMERICAN HOLISTIC NURSES' ASSOCIATION (AHNA)

A New Beginning: The American Holistic Nurses' Association (AHNA), founded January 1981 to promote the principles of holistic health care, has as its primary goal education. It conducts an annual national meeting and publishes a newsletter, *Beginnings.* The group's philosophy: "People are beautiful, whole beings when our body, mind, and spirit are in harmony with our environment. That harmony is health, and our role as nurses is to set the example of a health-full life and to teach others the key to health." For information about the organization for RN's, LP/VN's, Students write to Charlotte McGuire, RN MA, President.

INFORMATION: P.O. Box 116, Telluride, CO 81435, (303) 728-4575.

● AMERICAN-INTERNATIONAL REIKI ASSOCIATION

American-International Reiki Association is a not-for-profit membership organization for individuals who have completed a Reiki Natural Healing Course. Reiki, a Japanese word meaning universal life force energy, is a natural energy balancing system for harmonizing and healing the bodies. The association was organized to promote, protect and improve the practice

of Reiki, as well as to establish professional standards. The association is dedicated to educating people about Reiki, health, wholeness and goodwill. It also certifies fully trained Reiki Masters (Teachers) to ensure high-quality Reiki seminars are available to the public.
INFORMATION: P.O. Box 13778, Atlanta, GA 30324, (404) 233-5549.

● AMERICAN VEGAN SOCIETY -- AHIMSA

The American Vegan Society (founded in 1960 and directed by H. Jay Dinshah) teaches veganism (compassionate non-use of animal foods and products) and Ahimsa (dynamic harmlessness), based on Reverence for Life and extending the Golden Rule to others besides humans. Lectures, discussions, annual conventions, total-vegetarian cooking classes, are conducted at Sun Crest, the AVS headquarters. An informative magazine, *Ahimsa,* is published quarterly. Books on veganism and Ahimsa, natural total-vegetarian cookbooks, and a wide range of other literature, are available by mail.
INFORMATION: 501 Old Harding Highway, Malaga, NJ 08328, (609) 694-2887.

● ANANDA

Ananda Cooperative Village is a community where over 300 people live and work, developing spiritual models for marriage, childraising, work, and the arts. For an absorbing introduction to the science of yoga, we recommend *The Path,* by Swami Kriyananda, founder of Ananda. *The Path* contains over 400 previously unpublished stories about the great Master, Paramhansa Yogananda.

Ananda Meditation Retreat invites you to renew yourself in an atmosphere of peace and harmony. The Retreat is open 365 days a year, offering yoga instruction and practice, meditation techniques, and special interest programs.

Cooperative Spiritual Living Program offers you an opportunity to experience life in a new age village serving in an area of your choice: gardening, pottery, vegetarian cooking and more. You'll practice meditation, yoga postures and receive special classes in Raja yoga, and personal counseling.

Yoga Teacher Training Program. A comprehensive five-week or eight-week study of hatha yoga, breathing, diet and health, yogic philosophy and meditation, plus classes in anatomy and physiology and Paramhansa Yogananda's Bible and Gita interpretations. For our free newspaper and a full schedule of programs write Ananda Guest Programs SCG.
INFORMATION: 14618 Tyler Foote, Nevada City, CA 95959, (916) 292-3494.

● ANANDA MARGA

Ananda Marga is a socio-spiritual organization with branches in more than 120 countries around the world. Created in 1954 by P. R. Sarkar, Ananda Marga is founded on the basic principle that all human beings should be given the opportunity to evolve themselves in all spheres of life; physical, intellectual and spiritual. Without the minimum necessities of food, clothing, shelter, education and medical care, higher pursuits are impossible, therefore Ananda Marga's first objective is to provide relief to humanity through extensive social service programs.

Beginning from the principle that all living beings deserve a life of happiness, Mr. Sarkar most recently has propounded a "neo-humanistic" philosophy, which dissolves the barriers that prejudice and narrow sentiments create, and expands human love towards all living creatures. Lastly, Ananda Marga offers free instruction in tantric meditation and yoga as a scientific way to explore our innermost nature and bring equilibrium to the body and mind, so that we as human beings can fulfill our greatest potentials.

INFORMATION: 854 Pearl St., Denver, CO 80203, (303) 832-6465, TLX 450404.

● ANTHROPOSOPHICAL SOCIETY IN AMERICA

Rudolf Steiner (1861-1925) was the Austrian philosopher, scientist and artist who formulated Anthroposophy, and founded the independent Anthroposophical Society in 1912. Anthroposophy postulates the existence of a spiritual world comprehensible to pure thinking, but fully accessible only to the higher faculties of knowledge latent in every man and woman.

Activities derived from Steiner's work include: The Waldorf School Movement, the biodynamic method of farming and gardening; centers for scientific and mathematical research; eurythmy, an art of movement to speech and music; schools for defective and maladjusted children and adults; and a therapeutic movement presently comprising some 100 schools in Europe and America.

INFORMATION: RD 2, Ghent, NY 12075, (518) 672-4601.

● AQUARIAN AGE CHURCH & SPIRITUAL UNITY MOVEMENT CENTER

Emphasizes Ageless Wisdom classes, Meditation, and New Age Festivals; also counseling, journeys to higher consciousness, past life regression. We offer a two year course in Leadership Training, culminating in New Age Ordination for those who qualify.

Our Director, Howard Ray Carey, as time permits, will come to your city to lead a workshop or lectures on Journeys To Higher Consciousness, Meditation, Past Life Experiences, Dreams, etc. No honorarium required, only expenses. In east San Fernando Valley, one mile from Golden State Freeway, #5.

INFORMATION: 9575 Canterbury Ave., Arleta, CA 91331, (213) 892-1832.

● AQUARIAN FELLOWSHIP

The Aquarian Fellowship is dedicated to the concept of wholism. We actively encourage all people to transcend the limited definitions of themselves, their groups, their culture, toward harmony with the Cosmic Society: the brotherhood of all conscious beings in the Universe (under God). We are a coalition of groups and individuals promoting higher consciousness through unconditional love, spiritual wisdom, and philosophical insight so

that we, as a civilization, instead of "fighting it out" might transcend the argument. We publish a newsletter ($1 sample; $5 subscription) and hold Aquarian Celebrations of Joy every Sunday at 7:30 p.m. at 3344 N. Broadway, Chicago, Illinois.
INFORMATION: 1328 W. Newport Ave., Chicago, IL 60657, (312) 528-7254.

● THE AQUARIAN MINYAN

The Aquarian Minyan is a New Age egalitarian Jewish spiritual community that meets weekly as a portable *Shul* in people's homes. Our *Shabbos,* Holyday and Festival celebrations combine traditional prayers and songs with innovative liturgies, dance, storytelling, and other, more specifically personal sharing, to provide an experience of the essence of the observance. The Aquarian Minyan also sponsors workshops, particularly in Jewish mysticism and related topics, invites speakers, and holds retreats. Newcomers and non-Jews are welcome. A newsletter is available.
INFORMATION: P.O. Box 7224, Berkeley, CA 94707, (415) 848-0965.

● AQUARIAN RESEARCH FOUNDATION

Aquarian Research Foundation is forming a community to develop healthier attitudes so that harmony and affection will cover the earth, not nuclear holocaust. We need effective, dedicated people to formulate new methods and assist ongoing projects: Adopt-A-Peaceworker Movement; Big Party to celebrate world's disarmament (October, 1984); Distributing *The Natural Birth Control Book* (including hypnotic control of conception which increases enjoyment, eliminates abstention); publicizing A.R.F. Newsletter and successful alternative communities; distribution of tapes of peace events and negative ion generator kits.

We're tax exempt (501-c-3, scientific and educational) since 1970 and need donations of money and property to start community. No drugs.
INFORMATION: 5620 Morton St., Philadelphia, PA 19144, (215) 849-3237 or 849-1259.

● ARCANA WORKSHOPS

Arcana Workshops is a meditation training center offering the opportunity to participate in the following group endeavors:
Scientific meditation training in weekly workshops and through correspondence courses. Group meditation unites in loving cooperation all who work for the common good. It leads to the cultivation of right human relations and to that deep inner poise which manifests as consistent cheer and courage.
Monthly meditation meetings at the time of each full moon.
Publications for the dissemination of group thinking distilled from group meditation.
Intergroup experiences in cooperative projects, conferences and seminars.
INFORMATION: P.O. Box 506, Manhattan Beach, CA 90266, (213) 379-9990 or 540-8689.

● ARICA INSTITUTE

Arica Institute was founded in 1971 by philosopher and mystic Oscar Ichazo to synthesize his theory and apply his scientific method for reaching enlightenment. Derived from a lifetime of extraordinary study, his theory and method integrates the physical sciences, psychology, and metaphysics, and finally defines the limits of the psyche -- all within one comprehensive system. Books, self-study materials and group courses published by Arica are designed to establish equilibrium on all four planes: physical, emotional, mental, and spiritual. For more information about products and worldwide group program sponsors, contact us.

INFORMATION: 235 Park Ave. South, New York, NY 10003, (212) 673-5130.

● ASSOCIATION FOR RESEARCH AND ENLIGHTENMENT, INC. (A.R.E.)

A.R.E. was founded in 1931 by friends of well-known psychic Edgar Cayce, in order to preserve and share the information in his readings. Cayce, a pioneer in the holistic health field, also gave information on such diverse topics as reincarnation, meditation, psychic and spiritual development, dream study, Atlantis, Egypt, home and family, astrology, Jesus and the Bible. The A.R.E. Library is open to the public and features 14,256 Cayce readings, plus 34,000 volumes in related fields. A.R.E. also offers memberships, seminars across the U.S. and Canada, a catalog of publications, a small group study program, and a year round visitor center.

INFORMATION: A.R.E. Communications, P.O. Box 595, Virginia Beach, VA 23451, (804) 428-3588.

● THE ASSOCIATION FOR TRANSPERSONAL PSYCHOLOGY

ATP is a non-profit membership organization drawn from a variety of fields of interest, working in the transpersonal area. Some members are doing research or working with spiritual disciplines, education, bio-feedback, personality theory, transpersonal and related therapies, to name a few. Other members are practitioners in professional areas, teachers, philosophers or friends who have a common interest in transpersonal psychology. Members receive a quarterly newsletter and the semiannual *Journal of Transpersonal Psychology*. There is an annual conference held in Monterey, California.

INFORMATION: P.O. Box 3049, Stanford, CA 94305, (415) 327-2066.

● ASTARA

Astara, a center of all religions, a school of the Ancient Mysteries, a fraternity of all philosophies, an institute of psychic research, was founded in 1951 by Earlyne and Robert Chaney. Its mystical, esoteric viewpoint serves an international membership in over 90 countries. The name Astara means A Place of Light. The organization's principal activity is publishing over 130 lessons in its Degree series, *Astara's Book of Life* (the mystical story of the individual from before birth through the afterlife), and 40 other lessons. It also operates seminar and conference facilities for nonprofit organizations.

INFORMATION: 800 W. Arrow Hwy., P.O. Box 5003, Upland, CA 91786, (714) 981-4941.

● ASTRO-MUSICAL RESEARCH

One of the most ancient metaphysical ideas is the relationship between music and the planets. Through a computerized synthesis of scientific data on astronomy and the physics of music, the teachings of Pythagoras, Ptolemy and Kepler relating to *The Music of the Spheres* are now available as actual music.

Hearing the Celestial Music of the planets at your time of birth is a powerful aid to meditation and provides a new dimension in astrology chart interpretation. The new field of harmonics in astrology can now be actually experienced in music. Charts are available on cassette. Astro-Musical Research is a member of the National Council for Geocosmic Research.

INFORMATION: P.O. Box 118, New York, NY 10033, (212) 942-0004.

● ATMANIKETAN ASHRAM

The Ashram provides a base for the practice of Sri Aurobindo and the Mother's teachings. This is a work-centered Ashram which involves running the spiritual book and import business, Auromere, which is the main financial support of the Ashram, and growth and maintenance of 2 1/2 acres of land where the Ashram is located. Emphasis is on well rounded *integral* growth in the spirit of the yoga which includes strong physical, emotional, mental and spiritual health.

Visitors are welcome to stay for shorter or longer periods to participate in the collective work. Donations are appreciated and needed but not demanded. A vegetarian kitchen is maintained. Visitors should call before arriving.

In addition, the Ashram owns separate property in Claremont which serves as a lecture and program hall for various functions which are open to the public. The property is the future home of the "Institute of Vedic Culture and Philosophy" which is now in the preparatory stages. Please send your name and address to be added to our mailing list.

INFORMATION: 1291 Weber St., Pomona, CA 91768, (714) 629-8255.

● AUM TEMPLE OF UNIVERSAL TRUTH

Aum Temple is an esoteric Christianity center which teaches living immortality in the body, and a community where those of like mind and heart can live, work and grow Godward together. Anyone wishing to visit the Sanctuary may write for reservations.

INFORMATION: 45837 Deva La., Newberry Springs, CA 92365, (714) 257-3255.

● AUROVILLE

"Earth needs a place where men can live away from all national rivalries, social conventions, self contradictory moralities and contending religions; a place where human beings, freed from all slavery of the past can devote themselves wholly to the discovery and practice of the Divine Consciousness that is seeking to manifest itself. Auroville wants to be this place and offers itself to all who aspire to live the Truth of tomorrow." -- The Mother

Located on the Bay of Bengal, in the state of Tamil Nadu, South India, a few miles north of the Sri Aurobindo Ashram in Pondicherry, 500 spiritual pioneers from 25 nations are living side-by-side with 35,000 Tamil villagers in the developing area called Auroville, the "city of human unity".

Auroville has come into being to provide a field for the working out of the evolutionary vision of Sri Aurobindo and the Mother. Auroville is a continuing process; it is a *collective effort* to deal in the material world with all the conflicts which have prevented man throughout the ages from realizing his full potential as a spiritual being, able to live in harmony with his fellow man.

Auroville is a laboratory. Much research is going on there -- in education, in afforestation, in agriculture, in building, in relations with the Tamil people, in the application of wind and solar energy, in developing a new form of self-government -- all with a common aspiration -- to create a new world based on the Truth-Consciousness, a "Life Divine" on earth.

INFORMATION: Sri Aurobindo's Action Center, P.O. Box 1977, Boulder, CO 80306, (303) 499-3313 and Auroville Cooperative, Aspiration, Kottakuppam, Auroville 605104, India.

● AUSTIN AREA HOLISTIC HEALTH ASSOCIATION

The Austin Area Holistic Health Association is a non-profit, educational organization dedicated to promoting a dynamic state of wellness based on health-care perspectives which fortify the vitality of the whole person.

Our services to the community include: conferences, workshops, retreats, public education classes and materials, referral to holistic services, networking, monthly calendars and quarterly journals. Membership is open to everyone.

Our supportive community offers diversified pathways which lead to the attainment of increased physical, emotional, socio-ethical and psychospiritual health. As we assume responsibility for our own well-being, we and the universe experience more harmony and balance.

INFORMATION: P.O. Box 13281, Austin, TX 78711, (512) 476-8125.

● THE AVADHUT

The Avadhut: the naked One, clothed in space, the Eternally Liberated One, Void Blissful Awareness, space-like Immortality-giving Knowledge, Truth Absolute, the Self.

Bhagavan I. M. Nome has Realized the Truth of His Eternally Liberated Self-nature. He is the Same Living Presence as His Guru, Bhagavan Ramana Maharshi. His Silence, Wisdom and Love defy all description. Truly, He is the Supreme Self, where all words and thoughts turn back. With the non-objective directness of Advaita Vedanta (Ajatavada) and Ch'an Buddhism, Nome shares the simplicity of the Absolute Truth or Reality beyond all dualisms and personal perspectives.

In the spirit of Sri Ramana and the Sage, Sri Nisargadatta Maharj, I. M. Nome communicates, the simple, honest Absolute Truth in an un-

35

compromising manner. Satsang with Nome is direct transmission of the Ultimate and Final Truth. There are no rules, no rituals, no concepts, no forms and no fees. Satsang is open dialogue, dynamic Self Inquiry; free to all. Satsangs are held twice weekly in the Santa Cruz Area, once weekly in the San Francisco Bay Area.

Truth is Free. You are Free. Satsang is Free. Absolutely!

There is no greater joke than this: That Being the Reality ourselves, we seek to gain Reality ... A day will dawn when you will yourself laugh at your effort. That which is on the day of laughter is also now. (Bhagavan Ramana Maharshi)

INFORMATION: P.O. Box 574, Santa Cruz, CA 95061, (408) 338-3923.

B

● BAHA'I FAITH

Baha'i Faith members are followers of the teachings of Baha'u'lah, who, in Persia in 1863, proclaimed that he was the chosen manifestation of God for this age. Baha'u'lah taught the Oneness of mankind, and that spiritual love and unity between men the world over was to be definitely channeled in a New World in which war should be abolished and all nations united in a Great Parliament of Man. Baha'i has a specific plan to realize this aim, and has organized its membership along those principles. Baha'i followers see their faith not so much as a new religion but as a renewal of religion. They affirm the universality and validity of all religions, and uphold the right of everyone to independent search of the truth. With a large membership, Baha'i is found throughout the United States and Canada.

INFORMATION: 112 Linden St., Wilmette, IL 60091, (312) 869-9039.

● BALANCED LIFE CENTER

Balanced Life Center for Yoga, Meditation, Health and Spiritual Counseling, classes, study groups and fellowship through shared creativity in music, the arts and vegetarian potlucks (includes all family members).

Facilities include: massage, sauna, meditation room, research library, organic garden. Selective bookstore offers metaphysical, natural health, self-development information through books, records, cassettes (also vocal and instrumental healing music).

Some space available to accommodate overnight individuals and for small retreats & workshops. Located near Davisburg, one half hour south of Flint, *one hour from* Detroit (north), Ann Arbor, Lansing. Reservations required for all activities.

INFORMATION: Happy Hills Farm, 13120 Rattalee Lake Rd., Davisburg, MI 48019, (313) 634-4571.

● BAWA MUHAIYADDEEN FELLOWSHIP

Only God is real.

Wisdom is the Guide to that Reality, and Love is the Taste. Teachings are valuable only if they bring us to that point of Truth.

More than words we need a model to guide us -- one who lives completely surrendered to God's Qualities. Unless we can experience the Power of God's Qualities in action, words have no real meaning. To find a guide in whom there is no gap between what he is and what he says is very rare. To study with such a one is to live with a pure, pure mirror through which we can see and be transformed into our true selves. His Holiness M. R. Bawa Muhaiyaddeen is such a true and absolutely pure guide.

All who seek the truth are welcome to visit His Holiness in Philadelphia. Students of Bawa Muhaiyaddeen are honored to serve all who come. May God's Peace be upon us all. May He bless our search for His Truth and guide us with clarity and love. Amin.

INFORMATION: 5820 Overbrook Ave., Philadelphia, PA 19131, (215) 879-8631.

● THE BEAR TRIBE

The Bear Tribe is a medicine society composed of Native and non-Native people striving to walk in balance on the Earth Mother. It is formed according to the medicine vision of Sun Bear, Chippewa medicine man. The Tribe has existed since 1970. The Bear Tribe's Self Reliance Center exists to relay the positive aspects of traditional Native American life to today's people. People of any age or race may come to the center and participate in activities designed to allow people to experience their oneness with each other, the Earth Mother and the universe. The activities are also designed to teach people the skills they need to be self-reliant on the land. They publish *Many Smokes Magazine*.

INFORMATION: P.O. Box 9167, Spokane, WA 99209.

● BERKSHIRE CENTER FOR BODY/MIND WHOLENESS

Weekly instruction includes Hatha Yoga, Kinesiology, Polarity, nutrition, massage, creative visualization and various other holistic therapies. We do outreach work with mentally disturbed and retarded adults. We offer lectures and workshops. Our center houses a lending library and a small bookstore. We mail order books, tapes, Bach Flower/Homeopathic essences, astrological readings and crystals. Among the services we provide on a private consultation basis are Biofeedback, Iridology analysis, Astrological and Psychosynthesis counseling and Bach formulas. Carol Mottor/BJ Kielman-Ericson.

INFORMATION: 55 Fenn St., P.O. Box 171, Pittsfield, MA 01202, (413) 442-4418.

● BHAGAVAN SRI RAMANA MAHARSHI CENTER

The Center focuses on the whole-hearted practice of Self-Enquiry and submission and surrender to the Supreme Self as taught by Bhagavan Sri Ramana Maharshi. An urban ashram, Arunachala Ashrama, and an ashram farm in Nova Scotia are maintained in which a rigorous schedule is followed by the residents. Sri Bhagavan's Central teaching of Self-Enquiry is the focal point in the lives of devotees.
INFORMATION: 342 E. 6th St., New York, NY 10003, (212) 477-4060 or 854-0322.

● BIOFEEDBACK INSTITUTE

The Biofeedback Institute of San Francisco offers two week professional training programs towards certification in Biofeedback & Behavioral Medicine. Trainees may take the full program or separate modules. The training faculty is a multidisciplinary group of professionals who specialize in the areas of behavioral medicine & stress management.

The Institute also offers individual training sessions, and publishes books, color videotapes, and offers portable biofeedback devices.

George Fuller-von Bozzay, Ph.D., director, also teaches at Stanford & U.C. Medical Center and is author of *Behavioral Medicine, Stress Management & Biofeedback* and other publications.
INFORMATION: 3428 Sacramento St., San Francisco, CA 94118.

● B'NAI OR

B'nai Or Religious Fellowship founded and guided by its Rebbe, Zalman Schachter-Shalomi, is a non-profit Jewish post-denominational covenant group grounded in the mysticism of the Kabalah and Hasidism geared to facilitate a renewal of one's Jewish growth and identity. B'nai Or is active at the state of the art of transpersonal consciousness and offers weekends, holy day retreats for singles and families as well as classes and workshops. It offers training in meditation, liturgy, chanting and spiritual leadership on a lay and professional level.
INFORMATION: 6723 Emlen St., Philadelphia, PA 19119, (215) 849-5385.

● BRAHMA KUMARIS RAJA YOGA CENTER

Explore the inner workings of the soul in a one-week course on the power of transformation. Raja Yoga is the clearest and most ancient method of attaining mastery over your own life. Unwanted habits are banished forever, stress is replaced with peace, worry transformed into well-being.

Here, people from a wide variety of backgrounds come together to study and practice. This education involves no physical exercise, breath control or chanting but is based upon understanding and recognition of the Supreme Being.

Master the dynamics of karma and learn the natural way of breaking bondages while remaining in the world and fulfilling your responsibilities.

Experience the power of this unique and effortless form of meditation, the silence of the soul in its original perfection.

The Brahma Kumaris World Spiritual University was founded in 1937. There are now over 800 centers worldwide with headquarters in Mt. Abu, India. People on all paths have found this study of great value in bringing the benefits of spirituality into their daily lives. All courses and programs are offered completely free of charge. World Peace Meditation every third Sunday of the month to correspond with 5:30 to 6:30 p.m. in India. Individual introductory courses by appointment.

INFORMATION: 1619 Clement St., San Francisco, CA 94121, (415) 668-3487.

● BUDDHIST ASSOCIATION OF THE UNITED STATES

The center offers teachings from the Ch'an school of Chinese Buddhism, which emphasizes the practice of meditation. Instruction in the meditation of counting the breaths is available. Classes are held on Saturday.

INFORMATION: 3070 Albany Crescent, Bronx, NY 10463, (212) 884-9111.

● BUDDHIST WATS (TEMPLES) OF THAILAND

Wat Buddhawararam of Denver specializes as a training and practice center for *Theravada Vipassana* Insight Meditation under the direction of the Ven. Achaan Sobin Namto, former abbot of Wat Thai of Los Angeles, the first Thai temple in America. Achaan Sobin's presence in Denver now affords Americans an opportunity to explore the workings of the mind through Vipassana insight sitting and walking meditation techniques supported by comprehensive instruction in Theravada Buddhist psychology and philosophy. All programs and instruction are offered free of charge. The center publishes an excellent booklet dealing directly with the insight meditation practice and experience.

The other Thai Temple-Wats offer Americans a chance to become greater acquainted with the Thai people through participation in Buddhist holiday festivities, *Pali* devotional chanting, Pali and Thai language classes, The Thai Immigrant Acculturation Project and regular meditation sittings. All the Temple-Wats have exquisite altars, Buddha images and shrine rooms for your use.

INFORMATION: Wat Buddhawararam, 4801 Julian St., Denver, CO 80221, (303) 433-1826 and Wat Thai, 12909 Cantara St., N. Hollywood, CA 91605, (213) 780-4200.

● BUILDERS OF THE ADYTUM

Builders of the Adytum is an important esoteric school specializing in teaching the theory and practice of the Tarot and the Qabalah. Membership includes a fine correspondence course in these and other esoteric teachings. B.O.T.A. was founded by Paul Foster Case, American mystic and authority on the Tarot. In ancient temples, the Adytum was the house of God, the

inner shrine where dwelt the deity in whose honor the temple was erected.
INFORMATION: 5105 N. Figueroa St., Dept. NC, Los Angeles, CA 90042, (213) 255-7141.

● BURLINGTON COLLEGE

The BA program in Transpersonal Psychology at Burlington College offers you a difference -- both the college and the program offer you an opportunity to revision education and the meaning of learning.

Transpersonal Psychology, as a study of human nature, requires both imagination and discipline. From a solid grounding in traditional schools of psychology, our students move beyond the personal or ego-centered view of human nature and are encouraged to further examine those trans-personal or universal dimensions that encompass the soul or spirit.
INFORMATION: Director of Admissions, 90 Main St., Burlington, VT 05401, (802) 862-9616.

"Hopi means peace, kind and gentle, and Hopi is working towards a peaceful solution of those problems, not with hatred but with real peace and love. I think we can do it. We don't have to change this with hatred and war, with violence. We can do it with song and prayer, meditation, helping one another in a peaceful way."

-- Thomas Banyacya

● CAFH FOUNDATION

Cafh Foundation was founded to provide an environment that nurtures spiritual unfoldment. Within its programs people come together both to awaken their yearning for a more meaningful life and to work toward the integration of that yearning with their daily activities and relationships.

Cafh programs are concerned with spiritual unfoldment. Spiritual unfoldment is a process of discovery and understanding of the inner need of the individual to broaden his vision and way of living. Broadening begins with self-knowledge and an awareness of one's place in the environment. Self-knowledge leads one toward a simplified and meaningful relationship to other people and to life.

Cafh's main purpose is to help individuals walk on a road of love and offering of themselves. This road will not solve the world's problems. It does offer each individual the opportunity to work toward resolving, within himself, the problems that confront humankind as a whole. It is an integral road of transformation and participation with the lives and needs of others.

Activities are held in Boston, New York, Washington, D.C., St. Louis, Los Angeles and San Francisco.

INFORMATION: 2061 Broadway St., New York, NY 10023, (212) 783-4185.

● CALIFORNIA INSTITUTE OF INTEGRAL STUDIES

CIIS is an accredited free-standing graduate school offering three unique and innovative programs leading to the M.A. and Ph.D. degree. Our program is dedicated to the integration of Eastern and Western knowledge and experience for personal, professional, social and global applications. The curriculum utilizes a strong balance of intellect and intuition for advanced study in the following areas:

Clinical & Counseling Psychology provides training in the applications of Eastern and Transpersonal perspectives within Western psychotherapy. Graduates are eligible to sit for M.F.C.C. and Psychology license exams.

East-West Psychology offers in-depth study of consciousness, perception, meditation, personality, and mental health through both the spiritual philosophies of the East, and the scientific objectivity of the West.

Intercultural Philosophy And Religion explores wisdom embodied in the great world traditions, emerging possibilities of a dynamic integrated world view, and methods for personal and social transformation.

Continuing Professional Education and In-Depth Weekend Workshops are offered by Institute faculty and internationally known visitors.

V.A. approved; Scholarships, federal loans, and work study available for

qualified students. Accredited by the Western Association of Schools and Colleges.
INFORMATION: 3494 21st St., P.O. Box CS, San Francisco, CA 94118.

● CALIFORNIA INSTITUTE OF TRANSPERSONAL PSYCHOLOGY

The California Institute of Transpersonal Psychology offers a four-year Ph.D. program in transpersonal psychology. CITP is dedicated to the ideal of balanced growth and development of the intellect, spirit, body and emotions in a community context. Two years of course work, an internship and a dissertation are required. As an educational community committed to applying transpersonal principles throughout the program, students, faculty and staff share in the planning and administration of the school. We encourage applications from those who are already functioning successfully in the world and want to continue their own personal and spiritual development.
INFORMATION: 250 Oak Grove Ave., Menlo Park, CA 94025, (415) 326-1960.

● CALIFORNIA SCHOOL OF HERBAL STUDIES

The California School of Herbal Studies, recognized as one of the nation's leading centers of herbal education, offers a refreshingly unique learning experience. At a time when world chaos seems to reign, we are teaching people the ancient art of the herbalist. Learned in plant skill, the herbalists knew the passing of the seasons, the ebb and flow of the tides, and were masters knowledgeable of the medicines and foods of the earth. In this study of earthly wisdom, a greatness and peace abides in the seeker. It is this earth awareness and balance known by herbalists of old that we wish to share at the California School of Herbal Studies.

Located on an 80 acre ranch in Northern California, we have large herb gardens, a pond, and a schoolhouse. Our faculty consists of some of the United States' and Canada's most highly respected herbalists. We offer a variety of courses including a six month intensive, two month course, week long programs and week-end seminars. Each of our programs focuses on integrating the scientific with the art and soul of herbalism. For inclusion on our mailing list and our brochure send $2.
INFORMATION: P.O. Box 350, Guerneville, CA 95446.

● CAMP SUNBURST

Camp Sunburst is a two-week summer camp dedicated to giving chronically-ill children a rewarding overnight camp experience. Included in the activities will be expressive drama, hand and nature crafts, and wildlife activities set in Willowcreek, the Trinity Valley area of Humboldt County, California.

A staff of recreational counselors, crafts, and drama teachers are on hand to guide the children through their activities; along with psychologists, nurses, and a consulting physician to ensure the individual health needs of each child's mind and body.

Parents are also welcome, with group support sessions available to provide therapeutic guidance.

INFORMATION: Geri Brooks-Ciosek, M.A., Executive, Director, 150 Shoreline St., Mill Valley, CA 94941, (415) 332-7832 (office) or 898-1158 (home).

● LE CENTRE DU SILENCE MIME SCHOOL

Le Centre Du Silence Mime School, Samuel Avital, founder and director, is dedicated to an integration of outward technique of the art with its guiding essence -- the motivator, observateur, or inner being of the student. From this foundation, a conceptual and experiential basis is provided whereby one can begin to create and achieve one's own style and to find one's own uniqueness within the artform. Using the technique as a tool and guide, one moves toward the realization of genuine self-expression in art and in life. In learning to become a total, expressive being, the student finds direction and unites the scattered parts of the self into an emerging wholeness.

INFORMATION: P.O. Box 1015 (NC), Boulder, CO 80306-1015, (303) 494-8729.

● CENTER FOR ATTITUDINAL HEALING

The purposes of The Center for Attitudinal Healing are: (1) To provide educational and support services for children, adults and families with catastrophic illnesses, through which they may learn to let go of fearful attitudes and experience peace of mind. These services are provided free of charge through a facility in the San Francisco Bay Area. (2) To provide educational outreach and a model for others interested in the work of the Center.

INFORMATION: 19 Main St., Tiburon, CA 94920, (415) 435-5022.

● CENTER FOR THE HEALING ARTS

The Center for the Healing Arts offers various support groups: a) for those with life-threatening illnesses, b) for women only, c) for men only, and d) a wellness group. Advanced training is available for therapists interested in working with people with life-threatening illness. The Center also offers a variety of workshops in stress reduction and artistic expression. In addition, the Center holds stimulating evening dialogues and weekend workshops with well-known leaders in the human consciousness field. Recent speakers have included Marilyn Ferguson, Elisabeth Kubler-Ross, Fritjof Capra, Roslyn Bruyere, Robert Bly, Patricia Sun, Carolyn Conger, and Stephen Levine. Free brochure available.

INFORMATION: 11081 Missouri Ave., Los Angeles, CA 90025, (213) 477-3981.

● CENTER FOR MATURING AND EVOLVING

Life itself is a Being of Love needing others to give/receive Love. So the Being segments Itself. "Its," and its parts, essence is Free Will to choose

The Essence of Healing

Dr. Mark Kramer, M.D. &
Gitela Kushner Kramer

In the unfolding of this very beautiful and exciting age we are beginning to see a merging together of health and healing with higher consciousness and spiritual evolution. We are beginning to see that we can no longer view any aspect of our being, whether our physical body, our emotions, our thoughts, or our spiritual nature as separate from any other part of us or from anyone else. For we are in truth whole and one -- every part of our being is connected to and meant to work in harmony with every other part and with each other.

True healing is a healing of our whole being. It is more than a remission of our physical symptoms; it is more than an alleviation of our emotional pain; it is more than the resolution of any particular conflict we may be experiencing. It is a healing process which begins at the very core of our being and permeates outward to every cell of our physical body, to our mental and emotional planes, to every aspect of our lives ... our relationships with our mates, children, parents, and friends, our work and our play. The healing process is a healing or making whole, of all we are, all we think and all we do. It is a stirring awakening to the very essence of our existence, to the truth of who we really are and to our oneness with all life.

We are all meant to live long, long lives of vibrant health, deep inner peace and everlasting harmony. We are meant to have boundless strength and energy for all our years, even our later ones. We are meant to share ourselves and our love openly and deeply in all our relationships, and we are meant to find fulfillment in our life's work. We are meant to love and accept ourselves and believe in our innate beauty. In short, we are meant to rejoice in our lives.

In the hearts of everyone of us there is a song which is always guiding us to radiant health and infinite joy. This song is like a beacon of light which shines forth at all times and shows us our clearest and highest direction. It is a song which leads us back to our natural state of wholeness, balance and integration.

To truly heal ourselves is to learn to listen to, and allow our lives to be guided by our heartsong. For our heartsong is the most powerfully harmonizing and healing force in our being. When we hear it and follow it, we are true to the natural flow of our lives, and we are at one with the very core of our being. We are centered in the moment; balanced and integrated on all levels -- body, mind and spirit. And when we are being true to our heart nature in all areas of our lives and in all our relationships, we are at peace; we are loving ourselves; and we are feeling our deep human connection with every being.

On the other hand, when we forget our heartsong for whatever the reason may be, we are going against the natural flow of our being, and we block the life force energy from nurturing and healing us in the highest way. When we separate from the truth of who we are we create conflict, disharmony and imbalance in our being. At these times we are not present in the moment; we are not at peace with ourselves; we are not integrated in body, mind and spirit, and we are not feeling our connection with others. So many of us have experienced this lack of integration as stress and tension or as a scattered or fragmented feeling ... we seem to be disconnected from the deepest part of ourselves (our heart nature); our minds are racing a mile a minute in thought and our bodies carry on unconsciously. This dis-integration of our energy system may manifest on the physical level in many different ways: as fatigue, shallow or irregular breathing, vertebral disalignment, headache or migraine, nausea, diarrhea or constipation, contracted neck, back or abdominal musculature, high blood pressure, acid stomach or other digestive disturbances,etc. And emotionally we may experience fear, anxiety, anger, blame or guilt.

Regardless of the particular form in which our imbalances may manifest, the overall effect of separating from the truth of who we are, is a partial shutting down of our life force energy and a blocking of our natural healing process.

Dis-ease, physical, emotional and mental is the result of prolonged blockage of this healing life force. The development of dis-ease, as we see it in our culture, is not the natural course of events; quite to the contrary, it represents a disruption of our constantly regenerating life force energy. Therefore, if we are sincerely seeking a meaningful and effective healing process of our being we cannot focus our attention merely on the specific symtoms we are experiencing. What we will want to do most importantly is first to learn how to free our energy system from the blockage which is weakening it, and then to learn how to maintain it in its naturally unobstructed, powerfully healing condition.

The way we do this, *the way to health, harmony, integration and peace,* is the way of the heart. It is the way of compassion and understanding; it is the way of complete acceptance of ourselves and others; it is the way of forgiveness. It is the way of pure and unconditional love. For pure love is the most powerfully healing force in all the universe. Pure love opens up all the energy centers of our being ... physically, emotionally, mentally and spiritually so that the powerfully regenerating life force can flow through unobstructedly. Pure love is the creative, *the* motivating and sustaining force behind all we think, all we do and all we are. Pure love is the all encompassing, all powerful, innate drive of all human life. Without love, there is no life.

Mark Kramer, M.D., a deeply psychic and spiritually oriented psychotherapist, offers (by mail) Guidance for Personal/Spiritual Growth and Higher Consciousness individually channeled on tape. For further information write: Mark Kramer, M.D., P.O. Box 8323, Santa Cruz, CA 95062.

Letting Go of Fear
Dr. Terry Chitwood

Letting go of fear can dramatically change your life. Fear contracts your muscles, stifles your voice, and creates disturbing thoughts. When you realize how you let fear control your life, then you can transform it into more pleasurable emotions.

Relax in spite of fear. Allow your body to move when you are afraid. Movement turns fear into energy. Let the tingling turn into joy as you approach the feared object with open arms. The feared object may be a person, an animal, a part of your environment, or anything that creates fear in you. This technique works even when the feared object is not physically present. Visualize yourself approaching the feared object as if you were going to embrace it, and infuse it with all of the love you can summon. You will no doubt discover that much of your fear is imaginary.

Even in truly dangerous situations, fear does not help your performance but impedes it. Fear may act as a warning signal to assist you in avoiding some danger. But, even then you could use your intuition and avoid the wear and tear on your body.

So realize that fear is synonymous with blocking the energy flow in your body or withdrawing your ki. When approaching your fear with love, you are simultaneously extending ki. Let your power radiate, and your fear will dissolve.

Excerpted from How To Defend Yourself Without Even Trying *by Dr. Terry Chitwood. Available from Polestar Publications, 620 South Minnesota, Sioux Falls, SD 57104.*

FOOT MASSAGE

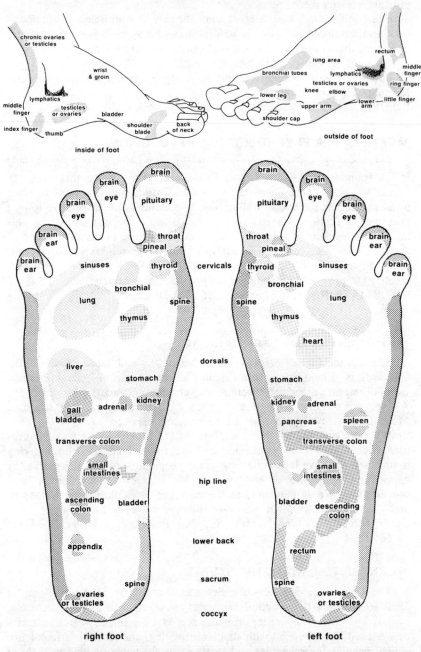

chronic ovaries or testicles

wrist & groin

rectum

lung area

bronchial tubes

lymphatics

middle finger

ring finger

testicles or ovaries

little finger

lymphatics

knee

elbow

middle finger

testicles or ovaries

bladder

lower leg

lower arm

index finger

thumb

shoulder blade

back of neck

upper arm

shoulder cap

inside of foot

outside of foot

brain

brain

eye

pituitary

throat

pineal

thyroid

cervicals

thyroid

pineal

throat

pituitary

brain

eye

brain

brain

eye

brain

ear

sinuses

sinuses

brain

ear

brain

ear

brain

ear

bronchial

bronchial

lung

lung

spine

spine

thymus

thymus

heart

liver

dorsals

stomach

stomach

kidney

kidney

adrenal

adrenal

gall bladder

pancreas

spleen

transverse colon

transverse colon

small intestines

small intestines

hip line

ascending colon

bladder

bladder

descending colon

appendix

lower back

rectum

spine

sacrum

spine

ovaries or testicles

coccyx

ovaries or testicles

right foot

left foot

All the nerves of the body have their endings in the feet. By working the muscles, tendons and crystal deposits, signals are flashed to the corresponding areas of the body, hastening relaxation and rejuventation. Work in spiral motions with vigorous pressure. Use your thumbs, knuckles and fingers.

47

loving Love above its manifestations. Bodies are designed as pain-avoiding, pleasure-seeking mechanisms.

Life Itself is Immortal, eternal and infinite with omniscience, omnipresence and omnipotence. It's the nature of the Being in its instrumentalities. The apparatus is to use these spiritual genetic capacities learning Soul Love. Evolvement is inherited via physical incarnations.

Bodies are self-destructive. Escape death by loving Love. Transcend Mortality Through Immortality.

INFORMATION: 5402 Franklin Ave., Los Angeles, CA 90027.

● CENTER FOR PSYCHOLOGICAL REVOLUTION

This organization is based on a miraculous transformation experienced by its founder, Constance Lerner-Russell, in 1966. Since that time the Center has been doing *living research* with a Core Group. Its work is based on uncovering subjective as well as objective reality in order to move toward principles of economic, sexual, psychological and emotional justice. Its philosophy is based on Groups. Groups are the setting in which theories of change can be tried out and in which actual change can take place. Available: preliminary publications, subscription list, Reading Room. Planned: meetings to provide information and opportunities for public support.

INFORMATION: 1525 Hornblend St., San Diego, CA 92109, (714) 273-4673.

● THE CENTER FOR SELF HEALING

The Center for Self Healing is a therapeutic and Educational Center. Our work is to help people to maintain their health and to facilitate healing, from different degenerative conditions; chronic and acute. For example: All spine problems, arthritis and other joint diseases, multiple sclerosis, Muscular Dystrophy, and other neuro muscular diseases.

We have also had much success with vision problems; cataracts, glaucoma, double vision, astigmatism, near and far sightedness, through new unique and effective techniques that teach people how to heal themselves by eliminating bad habits of body usage. We and teach them correct body movements. We also use and teach breathing, relaxation, special massage and visualizations, through individual therapy, classes and seminars.

INFORMATION: 1718 Taraval St., San Francisco, CA 94116, (415) 665-9574.

● CENTER FOR SHAMANIC STUDIES

The Center for Shamanic Studies was founded by Michael Harner in 1980 to advance the practical reintegration of shamanism and shamanic healing into life. The Center primarily acts as a clearinghouse for information needed in connection with shamanic training, and provides a newsletter which includes the schedules and locations of shamanic training workshops being given by Michael Harner in the United States, Canada, Europe, and elsewhere under the auspices of various institutes and organizations. The newsletter is available without charge.

48

INFORMATION: Executive Director, P.O. Box 673, Belden Station, Norwalk, CT 06852.

● CENTER FOR SPIRITUAL AWARENESS -- CSA

Center for Spiritual Awareness is located about 110 miles northeast of Atlanta, near the Carolina border. Roy Eugene Davis is director of the center. He is a disciple of Paramahansa Yogananda and offers meditation seminars and retreats in the large, new CSA education hall. CSA Press is located here and publishes Mr. Davis' books, as well as titles by other New Age teachers.
INFORMATION: P.O. Box 7, Lakemont, GA 30552, (404) 782-4723.

● CENTER FOR VISION IMPROVEMENT

At our center, emphasis is placed on improving eyesight and preventing visual deterioration. We diagnose the eye condition and utilize the following therapies: Bates eye exercises, hypnosis, nutrition, biofeedback, orthokeratology, and visualization. We have books, in office programs, correspondence classes, workshops, and vision therapy equipment to aid you.
INFORMATION: 616 Ramona St., Palo Alto, CA 94301, (415) 321-9525.

● CENTER FOR YOGA

The Center for Yoga is a non-profit organization that follows no guru or spiritual authority. The Center offers hatha yoga classes Monday thru Saturday. Special workshops and seminars are available including introductory courses and teachers training.
INFORMATION: 230 1/2 Larchmont Blvd., Los Angeles, CA 90004, (213) 464-1276.

● CENTER OF BEING -- HER HOLINESS SRI MARASHAMA DEVI

Her Holiness Sri Marashama Devi, "Mataji," was born Enlightened, and maintained that state until the age of 12 when she consciously decided to forego the state to learn firsthand the life of a spiritual seeker. At the age of 24 she spontaneously regained the Enlightened state and for the next six years spent her time in meditation and integrating the new state into her daily life. During this time Mataji had a few students, one of whom stayed with her, helped her to found Center of Being, and became Enlightened. She began Her public teaching function on January 2, 1980 at the age of 30 and is now fully immersed in Her mission to help others wake up to who they really are.

Under Mataji's guidance all valid spiritual paths are taught; with the paths of Love, Service, Meditation and Grace stressed. Her presence is a healing, purifying and transforming fountain of blessing.

Mataji is American born and resides in Los Angeles. She holds public Darshan three times weekly and a monthly weekend Grace Intensive is held where Mataji transmits Divine Grace and Shaktipat to all participants.
INFORMATION: P.O. Box 3384, Los Angeles, CA 90028, (213) 874-2661.

● CENTER OF HEALTH

The Center Of Health was established to offer to the public a natural, drugless, non-invasive approach to health care. The therapists at the Center work in cooperation with the human organism's natural ability to heal itself.

The major focus of the Center's work is to cleanse the body of accumulated toxins and waste products, rebuild weakened blood cells and body tissues, rebalance the body's energy circulation and help the individual establish a lifestyle conducive to good health.

The following modalities are utilized at the Center to achieve these ends: acupuncture, colonic irrigation, deep muscle massage therapy, homeopathy, dietary and lifestyle consultation.
INFORMATION: 2351 N. Federal Hwy., Boca Raton, FL 33431, (305) 391-8533.

● CHOGYE INTERNATIONAL ZEN CENTER

Looking to *get somewhere*, there seems no end to the search. Sitting still with ourselves and helping others, we see we have already arrived. Not difficult, not easy, only *What is this?* -- ah, tea is ready. Drink it hot.

The Chogye International Zen Center is a multi-faceted practice community under the direction of Zen Master Seung Sahn. We practice *together action* as a way to keep clear and help others.

Student: "*What is love?*" Soen-sa: "*I ask you: What is love?*" Student: (*silent*) Soen-sa: "*This is love.*" Student: (*still silent*) Soen-sa: "*You ask me, I ask you. This is love.*"
INFORMATION: 39 East 31st St., New York, NY 10016, (212) 683-5049.

● CHRIST TRUTH FOUNDATION

The Christ Truth Foundation is a unique and beautiful Revelation of man's Individual Journey Inward in the Living Way of Jesus. It is based upon the *Soul* Teachings of God's Creative Word which reveals man's individual goal as *Soul* Consciousness. It is through the cosmic language of the Soul that man is able to comprehend his Divine Plan for this incarnation.

This is a teaching of the Knowing Ones whereby man becomes conscious of his Real *Self* and recognizes his Infinite Nature free from the restraints of mortal thought. The teaching of the Christ Truth Foundation calls forth man's True Heritage for the New Age. Dr. E. Blair McLean is founder and director.
INFORMATION: 610 S.W. Broadway St., Portland, OR 97205, (503) 222-2060.

● CHURCH OF ANTIOCH

We jumped from Churchianity to a vibrant Christianity by keeping alive the best of the Gnostic Heritage and moving with the new spiritual impact of our time and so are changing religion into experience. Part of the Apostolic Succession, our founding commenced with St. Peter in 38 A.D. and is also integrated into the Initiatory Movement of the Aurum Solis and its restoration of the Mysteria Magica. Our Rule is Jesus' statement of Love.

Church Central, Divinity School, and Chapel are at the address below. The Archbishop-Patriarch is Herman Adrian.

INFORMATION: 257 Castro St., Mountain View, CA 94041, (415) 965-3753.

● CHURCH OF THE HEALING WAY

The Church of the Healing Way, under the guidance of Rev. Elizabeth Johnston, is an interfaith church devoted to utilizing the Christ principles in your life; faith, love, prosperity and healings; meeting Him through prayer. You can call (213) 501-4644, Monday-Friday for Healing Prayers from 9 to 11 a.m.

In the name of Jesus we send forth our prayers for the healing of the afflicted, the disabled, the needy, for all who request help in His name. We are here to share God's love and abundance with each other. Services are at 2:00 p.m. every Sunday.

INFORMATION: 11050 Lorne St., Sun Valley, CA 91352, (213) 995-8591.

● CHURCH OF LIGHT

The Church of Light was incorporated in 1932 to "teach, practice and disseminate The Religion of the Stars," as expounded in the 21-course Brotherhood of Light Lessons, written by C. C. Zain under the auspices of the Brotherhood of Light, a hermetic order dating to 2440 B.C., Egypt. Members are encouraged to better themselves and others through study of the Lessons, research and observation relative to Astrology, Alchemy and Magic. The religion is progressive, incorporating laws of physics as they are discovered and verified. Facts of ESP, Induced Emotion and Directed Thinking are emphasized. Motto: Contribute your utmost to Universal Welfare.

INFORMATION: P.O. Box 76862, Los Angeles, CA 90076, (213) 487-6070.

● THE CHURCH OF THE REALIZATION

We maintain an experiential tradition rather than a doctrinal one, and are dedicated to the search for the *sacred thread* of truth that runs through all cultures and traditions. We respect each person's right and freedom to practice their religion according to their own nature, and seek fellowship with people of all religions. We will assist those in spiritual crisis, when re-quested, helping each one according to their own tradition and need. Please write or call for more information.

INFORMATION: P.O. Box 261, Minneapolis, MN 55440, (612) 227-3505.

● CIRCLE

Founded in 1974 by Selena Fox and Jim Alan, Circle is a non-profit resource center for the Nature Spirituality Movement. Circle Network brings together Medicine People, Wiccans, Eco-Feminists, Hermetic Magi-cians, Neo-Pagans, Shamans, and others in the U.S.A. and other countries

to share knowledge and energy. Circle publishes a quarterly newspaper (*Circle Network News*), an annual sourcebook, recordings, and other items, and hosts a variety of seminars and gatherings throughout North America, including the yearly Pagan Spirit Gathering. Monthly healing circles, herb walks, and magical training take place at Circle Farm. Circle Sanctuary is an in-progress intentional community project. Free brochure on request.
INFORMATION: P.O. Box 9013-N, Madison, WI 53715-0013, (608) 767-2345.

● CLEAR MIND CENTER

The Clear Mind Center (formerly Cornucopia, St. Mary, Kentucky) was founded by Ken Keyes, Jr., author of the *Handbook to Higher Consciousness*. The trainings offered by the Center give effective methods for getting along with other people -- and also yourself. They help you to create a clear mind, a strong body, and a loving spirit. Hundreds of thousands of people are living more satisfying lives today as a result of their tuning into Ken's books and trainings. Over a million copies of Ken Keyes' books are now in print, which include *A Conscious Person's Guide to Relationships, How to Enjoy Your Life In Spite Of It All, Prescriptions For Happiness,* and *How To Make Your Life Work Or Why Aren't You Happy?*

Apprentice programs for those who wish to devote their lives to loving and serving the world by living at the Center and supporting these trainings available. Vision Centers, which feature videotapes of Ken and other trainers at the meetings, are now being formed in various communities.
INFORMATION: Registrar, 790 Commercial Ave., Coos Bay, OR 97420.

● COLUMBIA PACIFIC UNIVERSITY

Columbia Pacific University is the largest non-resident graduate university in the United States with over 2,000 students and 250 faculty. All work is done by correspondence. Students pursue individualized independent study leading to Bachelors, Masters and Doctoral degrees in a variety of fields such as Psychology, Counseling, Business Administration, Wholistic Health Services, etc. Credit is awarded for prior traditional and non-traditional academic work, and for relevant life and work experience. Degree programs cost $2,000 to $3,000 and can be completed in 6 months to 3 years depending on student qualifications and initiative.
INFORMATION: 150 Shoreline Highway, Suite 15NC, Mill Valley, CA 94941, (415) 332-7832.

● COMMUNITY CENTER FOR WHOLISTIC LIVING

This growth center was founded by Rev. Michelle Sycalik, a trance medium who gives life attunements which give an individual's past life experiences pertinent to the present and the future. Her health diagnostic attunements have been verified by research studies. She is the author of *The Future's Blueprint,* a book of prophecies for 1980-2000. In 1982 she channeled the *Wholistic Maps for Health,* a series of booklets on the awakening process, chakras and glands, and other topics.

The purpose of the Community Center for Wholistic Living is to practice and to teach the principles of wholism of the soul, mind, emotions and body, and to guide awakening individuals to realize their oneness with God and their soul's creative purpose.

The Center offers a ministerial program, spiritual counseling, chiropractic adjustment, spiritual astrology, and courses in spiritual psychology, intuitive development, social change, chakras and glands, nutrition, and balancing the body.

The Center offers chapel service every Sunday at 7:30 p.m., including spiritual healing, as well as lectures and workshops on subjects such as cosmic cycles, color psychology, the healing properties of nature, natural health care and alternative communities. Social events include picnics, dances, canoeing, and travel adventures.

INFORMATION: 1477 Chain Bridge Rd. #201, McLean, VA 22101, (703) 556-0650.

● CONSCIOUSNESS VILLAGE -- LEONARD ORR

Consciousness Village, Bhole Baba Herakhan Universal Trust, Campbell Hot Springs, Inspiration University are the home of Leonard Orr who is known as the Founder of Rebirthing and the Money Seminar.

The spiritual purification practices of Babaji -- the eternal yogi -- are taught here as they are learned from the eternal Babaji who currently resides in Herakhan Village in India.

The community has 680 acres which are used mostly for vision quests and the practice of high yoga. There are two hotels available. Conscious breathing, earth, air, water, fire relationships, japa, creative thought are the basis of our curriculum. Regular rebirth and business trainings are given. We are specialists in MLM.

INFORMATION: P.O. Box 234, Sierraville, CA 96126, (916) 994-8984 or 994-3677.

● COPTIC FELLOWSHIP INTERNATIONAL

The coptic Fellowship is dedicated to the spiritual unity of religions, nations, and peoples. Founded by Hamid Bey, they offer simple, time-tested methods for harnessing our unlimited potential to be creative, happy, and productive individuals. Coptic teachings provide many keys to the understanding and application of techniques used in the quest for self-mastery. Their goal is to work in harmony with other groups to achieve a Spiritual Unity of Nations (S.U.N.). Christ-conscious training, home study materials, and children's program (Star Rise) are available.

INFORMATION: 1223 Arbor Vitae Rd., Deerfield, IL 60015, (616) 531-1339.

● COSANTI FOUNDATION

The Cosanti Foundation, (Cosanti from two Italian words meaning "before things") in Scottsdale, Arizona is the educational nonprofit organization established in 1956 by Paolo Soleri. The Cosanti Foundation is the umbrella organization through which Soleri's philosophical, education and construction work is done. The building of Arcosanti as a goal and as a learning process is the main concern of the Foundation. Arcosanti is being built as a prototype town and testing ground for Paolo Soleri's concept of *Arcology* -- the fusion of architecture and ecology. Arcology is the methodology that recognizes the necessity of the radical reorganization of the sprawling urban landscape into dense, integrated, three-dimensional cities. A central tenet of arcology is that the city is the necessary instrument for the evolution of man.

Arcosanti is located 70 miles north of Phoenix near Cordes Junction, Arizona on an 860-acre land preserve owned by the nonprofit Cosanti Foundation.

INFORMATION: 6433 Doubletree Rd., Scottsdale, AZ 85253, (602) 948-6145.

● THE COSMIC CIRCLE OF FELLOWSHIP

The "true conception of the Creators' Handiwork, the concept of the Art of Creation itself" revealed to William Ferguson who saw "Creation in action" and was "shown how all things are created" reveals the Source, the creative process, and the interdimensional Cosmos, bridging the gap between science and religion in fulfillment of biblical prophecies "I shall show you plainly of the Father" and "the mystery of God should be finished."

The New Revelation by the Revelator Himself, a decoding of John's Revelation, received by William Ferguson from Jesus in 1959 is the Holy Writ for the Space Age.

INFORMATION: 7405 Masters Dr., Potomac, MD 20854, (301) 299-7158.

● THE CREATIVE LIVING GUIDANCE CENTER

The Creative Living Guidance Center offers individual sessions as well as on-going group experiences. Sessions involve a combination of the finest techniques from the most popular humanistic therapies, including Gestalt, Psychosynthesis, Bioenergetics, Feldenkrais Movement. Also incorporated are holistic healing techniques of bodywork, role-playing, emotional release, regression, energy healings and sensory awareness. Groups and sessions are led by Sandra Michaelson, M.A. and Peter Michaelson, B.A., experienced professional counselors. The Center also publishes *Simple Times,* the journal of creative living. For a copy of *Simple Times,* send $2.

INFORMATION: P.O. Box 25, Bonita Springs, FL 33923, (813) 992-0834.

● CULTURAL INTEGRATION FELLOWSHIP

Human Transformation through spiritual teachings, the arts, psychological growth and world understanding -- are the themes of our activity.

Toward A Universal Religion lecture series is held each Sunday morning at 11 a.m. Speakers share views on the world's great religions, as well as on contemporary social and spiritual issues.

Community Education classes which are held during the week include tabla, kathak dance, tai chi, bharata natyam dance, language, cooking and art.

Special Events include concerts, recitals, meditations and celebrations.
INFORMATION: 2650 Fulton St., San Francisco, CA 94118, (415) 648-6777.

D

● DENT INFO

At least 98% of us get Oral Disease! If you are anxious about the costs, pain, and benefits of dentistry then consider learning to be your own dentist.

Dent-Info is fighting to reduce the suffering and costs of oral disease. We publish *Natural Dental Wellness* by Soaring Bear -- the only complete and holistic self-care guide. We're also compiling an encyclopedic Herb book and Maya Astrology calendar. Join us in sponsoring research, public education, professional training and the reference center by contributing your time and dollars. Send for brochure.
INFORMATION: 2509 N. Campbell #S262, Tucson, AZ 85719, (602) 432-3081.

● DEVADEEP RAJNEESH SANNYAS ASHRAM

A space where disciples of Bhagwan Shree Rajneesh celebrate his love, while allowing his energy to emerge through dance, groups, and meditation. The Ashram offers individual and group sessions in rebirthing, bioenergetics, tantra -- counseling sessions and massage also available, plus a samadhi (isolation) tank, where individuals may float in a sound/sight-proof chamber going deep within. Books, videotapes and audiotapes are available to be read, seen, and listened to. Sunday a full day of activities occurs as residents and guests get to joyously partake in the following: satsang, dynamic or kundalini meditation, sufi dance, tai chi, divine/spiritual healing, zen.
INFORMATION: 1430 Longfellow St., N.W., Washington, D.C. 20011.

● DHYANYOGA CENTERS INC.

Swargadham Soquel is an ashram devoted to the teachings of Dhyanyogi Madhusudandas, a shaktipat guru who has attracted disciples from all over the world. Born in India, Guruji was drawn to the spiritual path early in life. At thirteen he left home to seek a guru who would show him the way to God. After thirty years of austerities and ceaseless searching, he found a guru who awakened his Kundalini. Guruji is dedicated to awakening that same energy in all who search for self-realization. Kundalini is the internal force that motivates us toward God.

Gurudev teaches Dhyanyoga: Meditation, yogic poses, breath regulation, prayers and healing. At the ashram, Guruji's disciples practice his teachings every day. The atmosphere of peace and cooperation is unique; however the Ashram is not a community; it is a place of worship and devotion where disciples can gather to share in their spiritual practices.

Guruji is now in India, but his most advanced disciple, Asha Devi, is living at Swargadham. Asha is our connection to Gurudev when he is away, and is dearly loved by the disciples who have been blessed by her devoted presence. Visitors welcome for programs.

INFORMATION: 3500 Rodeo Gulch, Soquel, CA 95073, (408) 462-4225.

● DIALOGUE HOUSE

The Ira Progoff *Intensive Journal* method of personal and spiritual growth, including the new development of Process Meditation, is locally available through community sponsored workshops conducted by authorized leaders.

The Dialogue House program, created by Ira Progoff in 1966, provides an ongoing way for individuals, regardless of age and level of education, to draw their lives into focus and enlarge their creative capacities. Nonjudgmental and non-diagnostic, it honors the privacy of each person.

This is a method of clarifying where you are now in your life, determining your resources, and deciding on new directions. Reaching beyond self-analysis, it generates an inner energy with which next steps can be taken. The *Intensive Journal* workbook is the active instrument of the program. Not introspective like a diary, its unique structure makes it a dynamic vehicle for the Journal Feedback techniques that will enable you to make your life-decisions.

The textbooks for the Intensive Journal program are: *At A Journal Workshop* and *The Practice of Process Meditation,* newly published, for the spiritual applications of the *Intensive Journal* Method. Call or write for a schedule of local workshops, books, tapes, and national programs conducted by Dr. Progoff.

INFORMATION: 80 East 11th St., New York, NY 10003, (212) 673-5880 or toll free (800) 221-5844.

● DIAMOND SANGHA

The Sanbo Kyodan Sect seeks to re-establish the way of Dogen Kigen Zenji, founder of the Japanese Soto Zen School, as a religious path for lay people in Japan and in the West. The practice includes zazen (meditation) and frequent personal interviews, usually with Koan study. The Maui Zendo on the Island of Maui is a country retreat, and the Koko An Zendo in Honolulu is an urban center, both offering daily Zen training for residents and for people living nearby. Robert Aitken (Chotan Gyoun-ken Roshi), who has been the authorized master of the Diamond Sangha since December, 1974, conducts four sesshin (retreats) at each center annually.

INFORMATION: 2119 Kaloa Way, Honolulu, HI 96822, (808) 946-0666 and Maui Zendo, R.R. 1, P.O. Box 702, Haiku, HI 96708, (808) 572-8163.

● DIMENSIONS OF EVOLVEMENT

Dimensions of Evolvement is an Ozark Mountain Wilderness Retreat and Growth Center in an area where one can spend time in nature, hiking, meditating, learning or just being.

Classes and workshops are given in kundalini (main emphasis is given to developing the kundalini already moving in each person), the mystical-contemplative life, meditation, nature, herbs and others.

Participants range from beginners to the more highly developed persons who are seeking additional experiences and understandings in their own evolution. The approach is practical, experimental and wholistic. It is based on the belief that persons are responsible for their own destiny.
INFORMATION: S.R. 3, P.O. Box 47, Melbourne, AR 72556, (501) 368-4468.

● DJARMA LEARNING COMMUNITY

Djarma Learning Community, located in the lush privacy of the beautiful Ojai Valley, was founded in 1979 and is dedicated to the pursuit of people learning and living together co-operatively as a family, making decisions as a group, by consensus, and working together in the home and garden. A school is in operation 24 hours a day; children and adults of all ages are both learners and teachers. Resident Fellowship Programs and Workshops are conducted regularly with emphasis on developing individual expression and motivation.
INFORMATION: P.O. Box 263, Ojai, CA 93023, (805) 646-2021.

E

● EARTH COMMUNITY

An I.R.S. approved Holistic Church. We have centers in the Detroit area including a 40 acre wooded estate. Our Detroit home has a pool, sauna, hot tub, greenhouse, and raised bed organic garden.

We struggle with the complexities of organizing and empowering people. Many of us are *est* graduates. We sponsor classes, workshops, parties, and festivals. We are committed to the work of Buckminister Fuller "creating a world that works for everyone." We are into liberated sexuality.

We welcome contact with organizers, fund raisers, entertainers, and potential guests. We try to serve as a New Age Communications Network.
INFORMATION: 19731 Forrer St., Detroit, MI 48235, (313) 494-0543.

● EAST-WEST CULTURAL CENTER

The East-West Cultural Center is working to help integrate the cultural and spiritual values of East and West to create a greater world unity and a more progressive, creative spiritual activity in the fields of education, the living arts, philosophy and religion. The teachings of Sri Aurobindo are the inspiration of the Center. Classes are available in yoga, spiritual enquiry, Sanskrit and Asian Studies and Tai Chi. Lectures, poetry readings and Sufi Universal Worship services are also held at the center.
INFORMATION: 2865 W. 9th St., Los Angeles, CA 90006, (213) 480-8325.

● THE ECCLESIA GNOSTICA

The Ecclesia Gnostica is a church of myth and symbol rather than theology and dogma. Recognizing the seven sacraments of traditional Catholicism, it emphasizes that true *gnosis* is knowledge of the heart and draws meaning from such diverse sources as mystical Christianity, the ancient mystery schools and the writings of the late, great gnostic, Dr. Carl Jung.

The Holy Eucharist, open to all sincere seekers, is celebrated Sundays at 10:30 a.m. Healing services are held Tuesdays at 7:30 p.m. Come join us.
INFORMATION: 3437 Alma St. (The Alma Plaza Shopping Center), Suite 23, Palo Alto, CA 94306, (415) 494-7412.

● ECUMENICAL MONKS OF ST. BENEDICT

The Ecumenical Monks of St. Benedict are an ecumenical Christian monastic community living by the Primitive (contemplative) Observance of the 1500-year-old Rule of St. Benedict. The central inspiration of our lives comes from a deep call to fidelity to the Gospel of Jesus. Our chosen vehicle for living out the Gospel life as fully as possible is community life, as prescribed in the ancient Rule of St. Benedict. This Rule seeks to capture the early church's movement toward asceticism and its idea of the desert experience, leading to a life totally centered in God and being a sign of His Heavenly Kingdom on earth.

Our ecumenicity does not consist of dramatic statements or vast public appeals; rather, by our life together and our fidelity to the Gospel of Jesus and to the Rule of St. Benedict, we seek to be a sign that Christians of different denominational backgrounds can live together as brothers -- a visible sign of reconciliation within the church of Jesus, while praying constantly for the unity of Christians. Each brother maintains ties with his own individual tradition and remains in communion with his church -- a sign that brothers from different backgrounds can be together in unity without forfeiting the richness that led them to become who they are.

We operate as much as possible on the basis of open consensus. We would not be monastic, though, if we did not have an Abbot or father to lead our sharing and to serve the community as counselor, spiritual father, cook, tractor driver, etc. No distinction is made between ordained and nonordained monks.

INFORMATION: Christ of The Hills Monastery, P.O. Box 1049, Blanco, TX 78606, (512) 833-5363.

● THE EDENITE SOCIETY

Essene Christian education as based on the pristine teachings of the Essene Christ. We are a non-profit, non-denominational, self-supporting organization founded in 1976, and dedicated to the ultimate quest of man, self-realization and eventual at-one-ment with (GOD) the Cosmos through a virtuous and humane style of living. The Society is not a religion, but rather presents and suggest *the way* to the good life (through self-help), the better life, by bringing to the fore a modern (not new) explanation and meaning of the ancient mysteries, long veiled through allegorical and symbolic expression. Free book: *Jesus Was A Vegetarian!*

INFORMATION: Imlaystown, NJ 08526.

● ELISABETH A. ULATOVSKA WORKSHOPS

The therapeutic relationship is the focus of our life and work. It is the caring connection which promotes growth and which, when fully developed, connects us via the very roots of our being to our social and natural environment. It leads us to truly "love our neighbor as ourselves."

In individual counseling and workshops we explore specific ways in which we can consciously use it to unfold, to improve the quality of our work and our relationships, and to live in harmony with ourselves and our universe as true planetary citizens.

Elisabeth A. Ulatovska is Dean of Columbia Pacific University's Center for Integrative Psychology and is in practice in Berkeley and Santa Cruz. She teaches in the U.S. and Europe in Dutch, German, and English, and is active with the Planetary Initiative.

INFORMATION: 215 Beach St. #307, Santa Cruz, CA 95060, (408) 427-0243.

● ESALEN INSTITUTE

Esalen, the prototype of the "growth center," focuses on the potentialities and values of human existence within a variety of contexts. It explores new humanistic possibilities in such fields as education, religion, philosophy, and behavioral sciences, sports and art. Its activities encompass seminars and workshops, residential programs, consulting services and research. There are a wide variety of programs geared to particular interests and needs.

INFORMATION: Big Sur, CA 93920, (408) 667-2335.

● THE ESOTERIC PHILOSOPHY CENTER

The Center, founded in 1970, teaches methods of integrating the personality by which persons can gain perspectives and learn to understand themselves, their fellow human beings and their own place in the universe.

Paramount interest is placed on group service and group work. Seven week classes taught at the Center include sound, color and vibration; astrology; tarot and meditation. Students also enjoy lectures, concerts, weekend workshops and full-moon meditations. William David, Executive Director and Founder, travels between sessions giving workshops and past life readings.

INFORMATION: 517 Lovett Blvd., Houston, TX 77006, (713) 526-5998.

● EWAM CHODEN TIBETAN BUDDHIST CENTER

Ewam Choden Tibetan Buddhist Center, under the direction of Lama Kunga Rinpoche, offers classes on the Songs of Milarepa, both classical and colloquial Tibetan language and in Buddhist philosophy. Rinpoche leads a public meditation every Sunday evening at 7:30. Various devotional ceremonies, meditations and Buddhist celebrations are held throughout the month. The center welcomes students with a sincere interest in learning about Tibetan Buddhist religion or culture. Please write or call (evenings) for free newsletter and schedule.

INFORMATION: 254 Cambridge Ave., Kensington, CA 94708, (415) 527-7363.

F

● THE FARM

The Farm is a spiritual community owned and operated by its people. Stephen Gaskin is the founder of the community. Some of the agreements of The Farm include absolute vegetarianism, free medical care (including the practice of spiritual midwifery), free legal services, free food, free spiritual teachings. On the other hand, the price is everything you've got. All members return their energy to the community through their work and also take a vow of poverty according to the *Book of Acts:* "And all who believed held all things in common, and gave to each according to need." To supply medical personnel for relief work, The Farm has developed an intensive medical apprenticeship program for EMT's, midwife practitioners, lab technicians and nursing technicians. To help with the world food crisis, The Farm has developed an extensive soybean technology. Soy milk, soy yogurt, soy ice cream, tempeh, and tofu are some of the products.

INFORMATION: 156-C Drakes Ln., Summertown, TN 38483, (615) 964-3574.

● THE FELLOWSHIP OF THE INNER LIGHT-INNER LIGHT CONSCIOUSNESS INSTITUTE

The Fellowship of the Inner Light is an international organization which relates ancient wisdom teaching and mystery school traditions to modern life in three major areas: Inner Light Consciousness Training, Spiritual Worship, and Holistic Lifestyles. The Fellowship was founded by Rev. Paul Solomon, who guided the growth of the organization through his ability to give deep trance readings. The Solomon readings include discourses on the development of spiritual gifts and psychic abilities; the diagnosis and treatment for a variety of diseases, and profound insights into ancient wisdom teachings. Rev. Solomon remains active in the Fellowship as a lecturer and teacher.

The activities of the Fellowship include: *Inner Light Consciousness Training,* a guided experience in spiritual evolution as a practical and effective way for developing higher sense perception. The I.L.C. experience is offered in local communities when requested.

The *Inner Light Consciousness Teacher Training,* a comprehensive program for developing teachers of the I.L.C. experience.

Synthesis Program, a 30 day live-in mystery school experience and initiation conducted at Hearthfire Lodge, in the panoramic Shenandoah Valley of Virginia.

INFORMATION: 620 14th St., Virginia Beach, VA 23451, (804) 422-0635.

● FELLOWSHIP OF RELIGIOUS HUMANISTS

The Fellowship of Religious Humanists considers itself to be midway between Christian Humanism on the one hand and secular, ethical Humanism on the other. It holds a naturalistic non-theistic view of the universe, but within that general orientation, it poses a religious aspect as well. It is concerned with the worth of man's life here and now, and it is an affirmative stand for the development of man's best thoughts, feelings, and actions. The Fellowship issues a quarterly journal entitled *Religious Humanism.*

INFORMATION: 105 W. North College St., Yellow Springs, OH 45387, (513) 767-1324.

● FINDHORN

The Findhorn Foundation is an international spiritual community of about 200 members living, studying and working together in the north-east of Scotland. Founded in 1962 by Peter and Eileen Caddy and Dorothy McLean, we were first known for communicating with plants and Nature Kingdoms. We have since become a center for spiritual and holistic education as well. Over the years we increased our membership, acquired new buildings and started many new projects. Our programs for visitors and members alike come from the same view of life and attunement to spirit which made our early experiments with plants possible.

We have no formal doctrine or creed. The Foundation is based on the belief that humanity approaches an evolutionary expansion of consciousness which will create new patterns of civilization for all of society. It is our intention to find ways of using this expanded consciousness and sensitivity to all life forms to create a new culture infused with spiritual values.

Communal living is our *common unity*. It forms the living laboratory in which *sacred texts* and spiritual ideals presented in workshops and courses are actually tested out in our daily lives. We can learn to work with love, build self-discipline, understand balanced service to the greater whole, and listen to each other with open hearts through the many experiences which present themselves differently for each of us.

INFORMATION: The Park, Findhorn, Forres, Morayshire, IV 36 OTZ, Scotland, telephone: 030932582.

● FLORIDA INSTITUTE OF NATURAL HEALTH

The Florida Institute of Natural Health is a health, education, and research institute dedicated to increasing the quality of life through training programs in a holistic approach. We recognize that there are many facets which should be included in any approach to improving an individual's experience of life and himself. Consequently, we offer training programs in various methods to improve physical health, emotional well-being, and psychophysical integration. Below is a sampling of programs available.

The Florida School of Massage offers professional licensing programs in a holistic approach to massage therapy. Grounded in scientific principles, the program is presented in a supportive, caring environment and addresses the need to serve the entire individual by improving physical health, aiding psychological clarity, and through balancing body chemistry (i.e. nutrition). The program is licensed by the State of Florida and approved by the AMTA.

We also offer a training program for advanced candidates leading to certification in psychophysical approach to Structural Integration. The program is designed to provide students with the theory and experience necessary for genuine competency in ten session structural bodywork (based on the techniques of Ida Rolf) and other methods of psychophysical integration. We offer an integrated approach which includes concepts and techniques from gestalt, body-centered psychotherapy, right-brain accessing, psychosynthesis, and the use of music and imagery to facilitate personal growth. For additional information on these and other programs please contact us.

INFORMATION: 1115 North Main St., Gainesville, FL 32601, (904) 378-7891.

● THE FLOWER ESSENCE SOCIETY

The Flower Essence Society is a world-wide communications and information network for the many counselors, health practitioners and others who use flower essences as catalysts for inner growth and well-being. In association with *Earth-Spirit,* a non-profit educational and research organization dedicated to human harmony with the spiritual Source of all life on Earth, the Flower Essence Society offers classes, publications and memberships, and is developing research programs incorporating both scientific and intuitive approaches. Richard Katz and Patricia Kaminski are co-directors.

INFORMATION: P.O. Box 459, Nevada City, CA 95959, (916) 265-9163.

● THE FOCUSING INSTITUTE

Focusing offers a new technique of therapy that guides people through the deepest level of awareness inside their bodies. Focusing occurs at the same level at which spiritual experience opens -- intermediate between deep, content-free meditation on the one hand, and the ordinary emotions on the other. This midpoint is of great importance in enabling a person to be whole; not to separate one's spirituality from the development of the person.

In his book, *Focusing* (Bantam, 1981), Eugene T. Gendlin, Ph.D., well-known psychologist and professor at the University of Chicago, explains the step-by-step technique of focusing. Only when one senses the whole of a problem can something new come -- changing the problem itself. There is a built-in test: each step of focusing when done correctly is marked by a physical release. Focusing is being used in psychotherapy and spiritual development, healing and psychosomatic medicine, stress reduction, creative writing, and education. The Focusing Institute sponsors Weekend Trainings in Focusing led by Gendlin and staff. Write for schedule and further information.

INFORMATION: 5637 S. Kenwood, Chicago, IL 60637.

● FREE FOR ALL

Free For All is the non-profit services cooperative, whose members work for each other free in their spare time.

Members offer virtually every skill, including: free dentistry, carpet cleaning, astrology, veterinary services, jewelry manufacture and repair, mending, plumbing, electrical work, haircuts, gardening, vegetarian cooking, rebirthing, photography, manual labor, and hundreds more. Twelve masseurs and masseuses offer everything from acupressure and reflexology to deep muscle work and structural alignment. Five attorneys offer various legal services, etc.

Merchandise supplied by members at cost includes: aloe vera healing products, survival foods and gear, auto parts, food blenders and grinders, juicers, water purifiers, ion generators, and more. Organically grown fruits and vegetables are available free.

Unlike a barter system, in which goods and services are traded, we operate on the basis of *free sharing,* as in a family. There is no "balancing" of services used against services given. (This makes for an important tax advantage.) Built-in controls assure that you won't give more time than you can comfortably afford.

Dues are $25 per year, plus a one-time registration fee of $60. Substantial discounts are available to families, students, and unemployed. Payments can be extended.

INFORMATION: 1623 Granville Ave., Suite 11, Los Angeles, CA 90025, (213) 826-9665.

G

● GENESA

The Genesa concept has its foundation is the discoveries resulting from Dr. Derald G. Langham's work in plant genetics carried out in Venezuela. Genesa is the harmonics of nature applied to the learning process. Through an orderly and repeatable experience in balance, rhythm and symmetry one can achieve an understanding of the form, flow and essence of any life situation, and develop relevant harmonies. Numerous qualities of Genesa make it a valuable method by which people can attain use of their inherent capabilities. The wholistic aspect of this process involves an integration of physically, mentally and emotionally tuning in to whole ideas and experiences. The person-centered aspect allows for individual experiences within a clear and well-defined process. This process, by its very nature, provides the feedback which is necessary for growth and development.
INFORMATION: 4702 San Jacinto Terr., Fallbrook, CA 92028, (714) 728-2822 and P.O. Box 327, Bonsall, CA 92003.

● GOD'S VALLEY

God's Valley was founded in 1966. It has a spiritual orientation but is nondenominational and open to all. Its economic base is sawmilling. The community operates its own schools, bakery, kitchen, craft shops, and canning operation. A yearly meeting is held for the purpose of bringing together new age groups involved in alternative lifestyles, self-sufficiency, health concerns, and spiritual and philosophical quests. God's Valley is not affiliated with any one group but wishes to be a part of a network of communities striving to build a better world.
INFORMATION: Rachel Summerton, R.R. 1, P.O. Box 478, Williams, IN 47470, (812) 388-5571.

● THE GRADUATE THEOLOGICAL UNION LIBRARY, NEW RELIGIOUS MOVEMENTS RESEARCH CORPORATION

The Graduate Theological Union Library, New Religious Movement Research Collection focuses on alternative religions in the U.S. which are new or have grown significantly since 1960. Wide variety of materials on Hinduism, Buddhism, Sufism, Sikhism, Feminist Spirituality, New Age groups, occultism, Neo-Paganism and witchcraft. Donations, suggestions, and questions are welcomed and should be directed to Diane Choquette.
INFORMATION: 2400 Ridge Rd., Berkeley, CA 94709, (415) 841-8222.

● GRIEF MANAGEMENT CENTER

The Grief Recovery Center is for people in pain from loss due to death, divorce, separation and other life transitions. At the Center we conduct "Saying Goodbye And Letting Go" workshops the first Saturday of each month. We also provide support groups and private counseling and therapy, specializing in unresolved grief. Lynn Schwartz, Ph.D., M.F.C.C., founder/director has conducted extensive research on the grief management techniques developed and used at the center.

INFORMATION: 6310 Alvarado Ct., San Diego, CA 92120, (714) 286-1010.

● GURDJIEFF FOUNDATION OF CALIFORNIA

George Ivanovitch Gurdjieff, born in 1877 near the Persian border of Caucasian Russia, appeared in Moscow in 1912, after twenty years of search in Central Asia, bearing a teaching of extraordinary power. Amid the chaos of the Russian Revolution he gathered a nucleus of men and women who followed him through Russia, Eastern Europe and eventually to France, where he based his work until his death in 1949. After his death, his followers carried on his work, and have in the past quarter century established various centers of practical study throughout France, England, the United States and South America. During this time, the name of Gurdjieff has become widely known, due mainly to his own books, *Beelzebub's Tales to His Grandson* and *Meetings With Remarkable Men,* and to the numerous statements by his pupils of their experiences with him. Yet he remains one of the great enigmas of our time. Although his teaching stems from ancient origins, it will probably never be known precisely what sources he drew on for his ideas, his music and sacred dances and his method of life.

The work, as Gurdjieff's teaching has come to be called, has many forms and practices. The central focus is transformation -- within the conditions of contemporary man's ordinary inner and outer life. Gurdjieff apparently never felt compelled to reject what is good in the modern world out of fear of compromising himself. Through the merciless observation of oneself as a creature in fragments, and through a conscious struggle to accept all of these parts as elements of a new man, the individual can enter a process, the end result of which is the "new creation," that the traditions of all times refer to as the real I.

INFORMATION: P.O. Box 549, San Francisco, CA 94101, (415) 921-0218.

"A Protestant, a Catholic and a Jew meet coming out of the doctor's office. The doctor has said, 'Listen, you all have cancer. You're hopeless. You have half a year to live.'

The three ask each other, 'What are we going to do?' The Catholic says, 'My last half a year I'll spend somewhere in meditation and prayer. I'll serve God.' The Protestant says, 'I'll take a trip around the world with my family. I just want to love my family the last half a year.' They ask the Jew, 'What are you going to do?' He says, 'I'm going to another doctor. "

-- Schlomo Carlebach

65

No Nuclear War!

Yogi Bhajan

For the last two years, in every class which I have taught, I say a little prayer, "Let there be peace upon this earth." Have you read the Ten Commandments? There is one commandment which says, "Thou shalt not kill." But now there is a new commandment. "Thou shalt kill all." *All.* The time has come that we must gather together to rebel against our own death. As a Man of God, I must be sensitive to Infinity. How can I call myself a spiritual man and yet be insensitive to the death which is hanging over us? Death is knocking at our door. Death is knocking at our future. We have never talked about it before, but we do want to talk now. We want to tell the people of this country that it is our fundamental right to live and not to die.

I don't fear death. God sent me here. When He wants me, I will go. We all want to die in grace when the time comes. When the switch is off in the heavens, I'm ready to go -- but not when Ronald Reagan throws the switch! Is it fair that because he presses a button, I should die?

As a Sikh, I am a warrior. We Sikhs are known as martial people. We are fighters, but we fight for a cause. And today our cause is that we must declare war on General Death. This nuclear war is not going to be like any human war. It is not going to observe any rule or any law. It will not be a war of knives, or of swords, or of armies, or even a world war in a particular region. It will be like nothing our imagination has grasped.

If a missile with eight warheads strikes Boston, it will destroy everything within a circular area of 750 square miles and turn it into lava. For hundreds of miles there will be deadly radiation. The Hiroshima bomb was a little thing, a ping pong ball. But now nuclear war means total, complete, absolute destruction. Russia can be ruined by our missiles 28 times over, and we can be destroyed by the Russians 14 times over. Altogether the world can be destroyed four times over. It doesn't matter who strikes first. Thirty-six hours after the switches are pressed, the ozone layer of the earth will disappear. After that it will take six months for us to die a slow death. No further bombs will be required. The earth will no longer be a habitable planet. Period.

Now tell me truthfully, how many of you can see your children melting like ice cream before you? That is what nuclear war is like. Those who will evaporate in the atomic blast will be the very fortunate and beloved of God, and those who die later will be most unfortunate. There will be no more United States. Neither will there be any Soviet Union. There will be no more Rome and there will be no more Golden Temple. There will be no more Mecca and there will be no more Gaia. There will be no more you and there will be no more me.

On the dollar bill we write, "In God we trust." What trust? We don't trust in God. We don't trust that God, our Creator, has made us to be "somebody." And so we have got to go out and prove that we are "somebody" at the cost of our own destruction. We say that America must be strong -- so strong that our nuclear waste alone will start killing us after a few years. We are told that if we build up a huge nuclear arsenal we have security. Our only security will be the certainty that, in event of war, we will be evaporated.

As far as the Russians go, we do not believe their "myth of peace" either. We are a free society and we can talk freely, but they are a regimented society. They are the cleverest sellers of "peace." Although they are trying to prove that we are war mongers, they too have been trying to achieve military superiority. Nonetheless, you must understand the Russians. In the Second World War they lost 20 million people. They decided, "Never again on our Fatherland." That is their principle. We call them the Russian Bear. If you threaten a bear, he will come after you, but if you don't threaten him he will not even look at you. Similarly, if the Russians are given an assurance that they will never be attacked, they will not do a thing against us.

Let us face the facts. We were the first ones to make the atomic bomb. We were the first ones to use it on a civilian population in violation of the Geneva accords. We were the first ones to make a hydrogen bomb. We were the first to place eight warheads on a single guided missle. And the law is that if you create a horror you must end it or it will end with you. And so now we are saying, let us take control of our own house and freeze nuclear weapons.

America feels that it is a superpower because it has the power to destroy anyone who will fight with it. Hasn't anyone ever thought that America could become a superpower that gives people life? Twelve million people are unemployed at this time, and their unemployment benefits will run out soon. Despite this, every penny in the budget is going for war machines. All the spending for welfare and medicare has been cut out. There is going to be a human outcry. Blacks are going to riot because 34% of their people are unemployed. The economic situation is so bad and yet we are building the bomb. But then perhaps Reagan is right in cutting expenditures for housing and employment. He knows that after a nuclear war, neither housing nor employment will be required!

There is going to be a psychological turmoil which Americans have to go through and for which they are not ready. When the purpose of life is overshadowed by death, life has no purpose. By building bombs to make America strong, we are actually killing our incentive and initiative to live. Atomic energy is telling us that man is nothing. We feel that there is an energy over us which is everything, and the reaction of that upon our psyche is that we become self-destructive. The effect is that nobody wants to work in America and nobody wants wants to work in Russia. No President can revive the economy because we have neither the resources nor the will to work. In 10 or 20 years we are going to have children who are not going to go to school. They won't. The horror of death is so real. It has been hounding us for the last 20 years and we have not yet recovered.

Our congressmen and senators know how dreadful a nuclear war would be, but unfortunately they are controlled. However, our system is still based on the vote. Let us create a popular opinion that we Americans do not want a nuclear war. Let each congressman feel that if he does not support a nuclear weapons freeze, he will surely be defeated. We are still Americans. We are still free. Register to vote. Register your relatives and friends to vote. Excite and incite the people that they have a right to vote. Then line up and vote!

Spread the word. Write letters to your local newspapers, to your local congressman, to your local senator. Let your children write letters to the President. Write a letter to the President of the U.S.S.R.; he's a human being too. Start a chain campaign. Talk to all you know and make them talk to all they know and we will end up reaching everybody. Spend three minutes each day talking to somebody about nuclear war. We will create an unimaginable wall of people. Whenever you write somebody or call somebody on the phone, just add one or two lines: "Do you want to live in the future? What are you doing about nuclear war?" Or, "If you love me, help me stop the nuclear war." Remember, if war comes, that war will never end. Therefore, at this time, you need an endless effort to live. Proselytize, advocate and educate.

I had the privilege to work with Mahatma Gandhi for a few weeks. That skinny guy was very feeble, but I have never seen a stronger man. He used to say, "Take people with you and fill up all the holes like a beaver. Build the dam of people." And today, I feel the strength of the world is the people. Build people. Let people stand as a wall before the atomic bomb. Russians, Germans, Americans, Indians, Japanese, all people....We are still free. We can still talk. Gandhi was alone. Martin Luther King was alone, but he walked through the United States with thousands of people beside him. Walk with people, or make people walk with you.

You have got to get up. You have got to talk to people in a layman's language. Don't talk statistically or politically. Just talk plain and simple. "We don't want nuclear war, dammit!" And I say to you that if the entire United States of America gets up in rage and says, "We don't want nuclear war," everybody will listen. Wherever you live, call all the religious groups together and talk to them about nuclear war. If you are a doctor or a professional, hand a sign in your reception office that says, "We don't want a nuclear war. It will melt our children like ice cream." Appeal to the grass roots of human consciousness. Make a rubber stamp with a picture of a baby that says, "Nuclear war will kill our children tomorrow," and print it on all of your letters.

And don't forget. There is no power on earth greater than the power of prayer. Let us pray for peace. Let us create a vibration of peace and wash these war mongers away.

These are simple things to do. But simple methods and simple gestures can bring a flood of people on your side. Do whatever you can do if you love the Planet Earth. Trust in God, and start doing something this minute!

Yogi Bhajan (also known as Harbhajan Singh Khalsa Yogiji) is the religious head of the Sikh Dharma in the Western Hemisphere. He is widely known as a master of Kundalini Yoga and White Tantric Yoga and is the founder of the 3HO (Healthy-Happy-Holy) Foundation. He is the Co-President of the World Parliament of Religions and the Co-Chairman of the World Fellowship of Religions. For more information about the teachings of Yogi Bhajan, write: K.R.I. Publications, 800 N. Park Ave. #5, Pomona, CA 91768.

• HAIKU ZENDO

Haiku Zendo provides daily zazen open to the public. Lectures and meditation instruction in the Soto tradition are held Wednesday evenings. Saturday morning after zazen and service there is a breakfast and informal discussion with Kobun Chino or Les Kaye. Kobin guides the various Zen practice communities in Los Altos, Santa Cruz and Ukiah. Several sesshins are held each year.
INFORMATION: 292 College Ave., Mountain View, CA 94040, (415) 948-5020.

• HANUMAN FOUNDATION

The Hanuman Foundation was created by (Baba) Ram Dass in order to carry out a number of projects designed to feed the spiritual scene in the West, to promulgate spiritual-being among members of the society as a whole through education and service, by spiritual training and by publications and recordings and to promote the study, practice and teaching of spiritual knowledge. Since its inception the Foundation has sponsored public gatherings throughout the U.S.A. and Canada. Tapes from these gatherings and retreats of Ram Dass are distributed through the Hanuman Foundation Tape Library through retail outlets and mail order. The Tape Library catalog is updated once or twice a year as new tapes are made available.

The Foundation also functions through the Prison Ashram Project which aids in the formation of Yoga and meditation programs in prisons, half-way houses, mental hospitals and drug abuse programs throughout North America and abroad.

Still another aspect of the Foundation's service is the Alternative Metaphores for Dying project. Its purpose is to bring more consciousness to the process of dying and to create ways in which people can use their own and each other's dying as a valuable experience for spiritual growth.
INFORMATION: P.O. Box 478, Santa Fe, NM 87501.

• HARBIN HOT SPRINGS NEW AGE COMMUNITY

Harbin Hot Springs New Age Community is a 1,100 acre community in Northern California oriented toward New Age ideals. *Residential Community:* Food store, school, gardens, 55 members of all ages, with work/pay option.

Teaching Center: Harbinger Center with varied program of New Age teaching and practical skills with partial work or pay option; Niyama Massage School, issuing certification; East West Center for Macrobiotics; Shiatsu Center.

Cottage Industry Center, including weaving, quiltmaking, handcrafts, etc. We welcome new members and those interested in New Age Education. Write before coming, listing your interests.

INFORMATION: Residency SG, P.O. Box 782, Middletown, CA 95461 (707) 987-3747.

● HAWTHORNE UNIVERSITY

Hawthorne University is a state authorized General Studies graduate degree program (M.A. and Ph.D.) designed for self-directed people working in classic and nontraditional areas of study, including computers, telecommunications, holistic and consciousness studies. Hawthorne provides classes and discussion groups evenings and weekends at various meeting centers in Northern California. Students receive individualized counseling and the opportunity to interact with people pursuing varied interests. Emphasis is on the integration of specialized and general knowledge through dialogue and workshops. Credit is granted for life experience. Assuming you fulfill all requirements, degree may be earned within a year. Tuition: $1200/term. Write or call for catalog.

INFORMATION: 315 East Cotati Ave., Suite F, Cotati, CA 94928, (707) 795-7168; (415) 521-6126 or 239-0887.

● HEALING CHURCH OF KARMU

The Healing Church of Karmu is a non-profit church and a school of healing and therapy. The Church offers a variety of courses in spiritual practice based upon the teachings of Karmu, a black healer working through the tradition of African medicinal healing. He uses shaman techniques, including massage, laying on of hands, and herbs. Karmu also provides individual consultations and healing.

INFORMATION: 526 Green St., Cambridge, MA 02139, (617) 354-6970.

● THE HEALING CIRCLE, ULC

The Healing Circle practices and teaches absentee spiritual healing. Through carefully developed meditation processes members and trainees gain deeper access to intuitive abilities and healing energies. They share this vision and energy with anyone who requests spiritual healing. The requests often come from great distances.

They also use meditation processes to focus on peace, exploring the relationship between personal and world peace. A meditation cassette tape, *Window Of Peace* is also available. To request healing or find out about training, call or write.

INFORMATION: P.O. Box 2819, San Rafael, CA 94901, (415) 435-0383.

● HEALING THROUGH ARTS, INC.

Healing Through Arts, Inc., a non-profit educational organization incorporated in Maine, has been founded to encourage and promote research into the arts and their application to the healing of body, mind and spirit. This knowledge is made available to the public via events, projects and services.

Current projects: *Alcoholism & The Arts:* A Creative Approach to Recovery; *Artswagon,* connecting artists with people of special needs; *A Rainbow Path,* an educational recording with music and visual art designed for healing.

For details about HTA and our projects, send for our introductory newsletter, *The Rose Window.*
INFORMATION: P.O. Box 399, Stonington, ME 04681, (207) 367-5076.

● HEARTWOOD: CALIFORNIA COLLEGE OF THE NATURAL HEALING ARTS

Heartwood: California College of the Natural Healing Arts has earned a reputation for the wise and nurturing environment created for sharing the wisdom of the path of compassionate service in the natural healing arts. The Heartwood curriculum offers a unique blend of career training and personal growth facilitation in our Associate, Bachelor, Masters Degree programs and in our State Approved eleven week certificate programs in Massage Therapy & Natural Health Counseling. Join us at our serene mountain retreat for a joyous and profound experience of professional training and personal transformation. Send $2 for catalog.
INFORMATION: 220 Harmony Ln., Garberville, CA 95440, (707) 923-2021.

● HEAVENSONG

Heavensong is a non-profit, spiritual organization offering a ministry of healing music through celebrations, workshops, retreats, and recordings. Founded in 1978 by Maloah and Maitreya Stillwater, Heavensong is inspired by the teachings of *A Course in Miracles,* and represents an ecumenical philosophy of Oneness, acknowledging all paths to Truth. Maloah and Maitreya are gifted in their ability to create an environment of peace and healing. Their openness to the Presence of Love is expressed through their music, which has been shared with people throughout the world. Their recordings are available at all events and through the mail.
INFORMATION: P.O. Box 605, Corte Madera, CA 94925, (415) 459-7119.

● HIPPOCRATES HEALTH INSTITUTE

Hippocrates Health Institute was founded by Ann Wigmore with the aim of bringing ailing bodies back to a natural state of health by cooperating with Mother Nature through utilizing the essences of organic living foods. While staying at the Institute, one also learns how to detoxify and rejuvenate one's blood stream through the miraculous powers found in chlorophyll wheatgrass extract and the organic live foods program. Activities for resident guests and students include lectures and classes on subjects related to the synthesis of body, mind and spirit, polarity yoga, meditation, reflexology, and organic gardening. A 10 week Health Ministry program is being offered which offers a certification to those completing the course in this field of health science.
INFORMATION: 25 Exeter St., Boston, MA 02116, (617) 267-9525.

● THE HOFFMAN QUADRINITY PROCESS

The Hoffman Quadrinity Process (formerly Fischer/Hoffman) is a comprehensive and intensive 13 week therapy (150-200 hours) using a wide variety of therapeutic techniques to cleanse away the layers of negative patterns, thus allowing us to experience our own positive essence. Childhood programming of insecurities, unworthiness, unloveableness and the whole gamut of self-defeating behaviors are attached on all four levels of being. All aspects of one's current life problems are confronted and explored. The end result is a state of realness as opposed to playing roles, i.e., pretend holiness, dead zombie, forever hostile or helpless victim. The Process begins in May, September and January of each year. The following is what has been said about the Process: "A powerful tool in the service of the development for love for self and others." -- Claudio Naranjo, M.D., Author of *The One Quest;* "... is there anything we can do to change the crippling messages we received early in life? ... Mr. Hoffman has a great deal to offer in relation to this question" -- Virginia Satir, author of *Peoplemaking* and *Conjoint Family Therapy;* "In my experience, only the Quadrinity Process changes a person so deeply and permanently in such a brief time." -- Jack Downing, M.D., Comprehensive Psychiatrist; and "The most comprehensive approach I am aware of in completing unfinished parental issues." -- Will Schutz, Ph.D., Holistic Studies Antioch University West.
INFORMATION: 2295 Palou St., San Francisco, CA 94124, (415) 397-0466.

● HOHM

Hohm is a non-profit religious organization founded in 1975 by Lee Lozowick, an American spiritual Master. Our focus is on the establishment of a truly sacred culture, based on the principles of Lee's teachings, and the ancient wisdom of spiritual traditions throughout the world. We believe in maintaining a sane, balanced lifestyle, glorifying God in all activities.

True service and Love for God is our highest aim as human beings, and to this end we engage the Company of a living Teacher. The first task of spiritual life is to develop ordinary human maturity in relationship to such areas as diet, sexuality and money. Based on this maturity we can consider esoteric devotional practices and service to God.

Our essential practice is that of Remembering. Although our activities include meditation, study, work, and prayer, the binding force of our lives at Hohm is the joyful Remembrance of God's Influence.

Through books and tapes by our Master, lectures, workshops and our bimonthly magazine *Divine Slave Gita* we present our own lessons and experiments to interested friends. Our Ashram in Northern Arizona is open for visitors based on prior correspondence.
INFORMATION: P.O. Box 5839, Prescott Valley, AZ 86312, (602) 778-9189.

● HOLISTIC HEALTH ASSOCIATION OF THE PRINCETON AREA

HHAPA is a non-profit organization of lay people and health-care providers dedicated to promoting optimum wellbeing and preventing disease by

educating the community in the principles of holistic health: aiming for peak physical, mental, emotional and spiritual health. HHAPA provides services that encourage people to assume responsibility for their own health and the quality of their lives. We offer workshops, monthly lectures, informal talks, films, large lending library, Holistic Health Resource Directory of holistically-oriented health-care providers in Central Jersey and the Philadelphia/Bucks County area, Health Evaluations, informational clearing house, assistance in organizing self-help groups, and holistic health networking in New Jersey. Phone or write for brochure.
INFORMATION: 360 Nassau St., Princeton, NJ 08540, (609) 924-8580.

● THE HOLY SHANKARACHARYA ORDER

The Holy Shankaracharya Order is the Hindu Monastic Order founded in India by the great mystic, philosopher and Saint, Adi Shankara (c. 800 A.D.). The Headquarters in the United States is Sri Rajarajeshwari Peetham in the Pocono Mountains of Pennsylvania.

Spiritual Direction and guidance of the Holy Shankaracharya Order brings to aspirants Blessings of the greatest spiritual leaders of India -- the Jagadguru Shankaracharyas. In the United States, all programs of the Order function under the immediate guidance of Her Holiness Mahamandaleshwari Swami Saraswati Devyashram.

The "Ashram Retreat Program" offered by The Holy Shankaracharya U.S.A. encompasses all aspects of Spiritual Life: Meditation, Hatha Yoga, Spiritual Disciplines, Karma Yoga, (Selfless Service) and the Philosophy of Advaita Vedanta and Hinduism.
INFORMATION: R.D. 3, P.O. Box 3430, Stroudsburg, PA 18360, (717) 629-0481.

● HOLYEARTH FOUNDATION

Clarifying the connection between personal and planetary transformation; exploring positive alternatives for our future. Holyearth is -- the Earthstewards Network, a support network for those who see themselves as stewards of our planet -- the *Holyearth Journal,* a quarterly publication -- short-term educational experiences to encourage positive change at personal, social, and global levels. The premise of Holyearth is that if we create and work toward positive alternatives, we can promote attitudes of faith, trust, and effectiveness in the world and thus use the massive energies of change of or times for positive transformation.
INFORMATION: P.O. Box 873, Monte Rio, CA 95462.

● HOLY ORDER OF MANS

The Holy Order of Mans is an ecumenical Christian Order whose members strive to attain the state of contemplation in a world of action, by consciously using the principles embodied in the Scriptures, by being open to the guidance of the Holy Spirit and ultimately, by the Grace of God in the Person of Christ Jesus. The Order seeks to restore an awareness of the mystical dimension in human experience through Christian initiation. Envisioning a "monasticism of the Heart" which will enable men and women to retain the charismatic perspective of God's immediate Presence in the world, without having to cloister their own presence from that world in order to preserve spiritual purity. The Order seeks to embody this monastic dimension by establishing an authentic spiritual community, one that would encompass the primary dimensions of the whole man: spirit, soul, mind and body; a community that embraces not only a single people under vows, but also married couples and families. The Order seeks to re-establish the highest spiritual values in the family itself and sees family life as a way in which the highest potentials of the contemplative life may be realized.

INFORMATION: 20 Steiner St., San Francisco, CA 94117, (415) 431-1917.

● HOMEOPATHIC MEDICINE

The International Foundation for Homeopathy, founded in 1978, offers educational and professional training programs to provide an understanding of health through homeopathy, a method of therapy which stimulates the body's own defense systems. Homeopathy defines health on the physical level as freedom from putting undue attention on the body due to pain; on the emotional level, health is freedom from being bound by one's passions (not an *absence* of emotions, but a dynamic state of feeling a full range of emotions without being trapped by any); on the mental level, health is clarity and selflessness.

INFORMATION: 4 Sherman Ave., Fairfax, CA 94930, (415) 457-8851.

● HUMAN DEVELOPMENT CENTER

Human Development Center is an association of highly trained and experienced counselors. The staff includes a certified psychologist and a clinical social worker. Services provided are individual counseling, couple and family counseling, therapy for children and adolescents, women's problem solving groups, and workshops in a variety of personal growth areas.

INFORMATION: 4572 S.W. 103rd Ave., Beaverton, OR 97123, (503) 643-6036.

● THE HUMAN PROCESS, INC.

The Human Process is the Chicago center for teaching all of the programs of Arica Institute, Inc. Arica is an internationally based mystical school founded by Oscar Ichazo, who has been recognized and fully authorized to teach by several living Masters from different traditions. Oscar has developed an entirely new method for realizing the Unity inside our high-speed technological society -- the Arica Method. Arica programs are available which are as short as a few hours, or as long as three months. One can study a specific subject, or complete the Line of the School. Oscar has produced a radically new theory of consciousness which integrates scientific reasoning with spiritual understanding to accelerate personal growth.

Arica programs are educational and enlightening. People of many religions and spiritual paths find that the Arica work enhances their understanding and experience. Arica is an "open school" -- there are no vows or obligations for participants, and the programs do not interfere with your daily life.

Please call or write for a free catalog or for any questions you may have. Humanity Is One Spirit.

INFORMATION: 6117 North Winthrop, Chicago, IL 60660, (312) 743-0798.

● HUNA INTERNATIONAL

The Order of Huna International was founded in 1973 by Dr. Sage King in Los Angeles, California. It is a non-profit non-sectarian religious order dedicated to the teaching, application and research of the knowledge of the Kahunas of Polynesia. People of many faiths come together in the Order to work in harmony for the benefit of mankind. The objectives of the Order are to teach people the power of mind over matter and to spread the Aloha spirit throughout the world by means of classes, workshops, publications and the formation of spiritual cooperatives. The Order also sponsors the Mindskills Institute in Santa Monica.

INFORMATION: 1535 Sixth St. #202, Santa Monica, CA 90401, (213) 394-8913.

● HYPNOSIS CLEARING HOUSE, INC.

The Hypnosis Clearing House, Inc. was founded in 1977 by Freda Morris, Ph.D., author of *Self-Hypnosis in Two Days* and *Hypnosis with Friends & Lovers.* Dr. Morris, a licensed psychologist, champions the free open uses of hypnosis to further any human endeavor. She has been instrumental in communicating, worldwide, the art of self-hypnosis. And she is a pioneer in the new art of mutual hypnosis. She believes that hypnosis -- a natural function of consciousness -- is the birthright of every human being. Hypnosis Clearing House offers extensive training both in hypnosis as a profession and hypnosis for personal development.

INFORMATION: 1504 Franklin St., Suite 303, Oakland, CA 94612, (415) 451-6440.

I

● I AM NATION

I Am Nation is a government of, for and by the I Am Selves of all people on Earth, regardless of race, religion, gender, age, nationality or spiritual-group affiliations.

I Am Nation has five divisions, which are fully operative through Mark-Age, Inc. (*See:* Mark-Age listing.) They are: MAIN (Mark-Age Inform-Nations), MAM (Mark-Age Meditations network), Healing Haven, University of Life, Centers of Light. Free introductory catalog for books, periodicals, cassette tapes, and self-study and group courses for Self-envolvement.

INFORMATION: Dept. SG, P.O. Box 290368, Ft. Lauderdale, FL 33329, (305) 587-5555.

● I.C.S.A. -- ANANDA ASHRAM

The aims of I.C.S.A. are to experience one's Self as the center of Cosmic Self-Awareness and to recognize the unity of all beings and nations in all aspects of life. I.C.S.A. stands for the ultimate truth and permanent Reality behind all appearances. It does not limit itself with any fixed organization, group, creed, path, system or religion. It respects and honors all teachers and advocates of Supreme Love, Wisdom, Peace and Truth.

The founder of I.C.S.A., Shri Ramamurti Mishra travels extensively, lecturing and assisting other groups and centers. Shri Ramamurti, previously a medical doctor, has devoted his life to the study and teaching of yoga. An eminent Sanskrit scholar, he brings to life the essence of the ancient teachings (scriptures) and their relevance to modern life. Combining his knowledge of the inner life with profound scientific insight, he is a specialist in kundalini and raja yoga.

Ananda Ashram is the main center of Shri Ramamurti and headquarters of I.C.S.A. Ananda Ashram was founded by Shri Ramamurti in 1964. As one of the early ashrams in this country, it has played an important role in the development of Yoga in the West. It has matured over the years into a vital community of approximately 30 full-time residents. Located on 60 beautiful wooded acres in the foothills of the Catskills, one hour from New York City, Ananda Ashram is an ideal setting for programs related to Yoga, meditation, healing and expanding awareness. Open to visitors throughout the year, Ananda Ashram offers retreat facilities and special week-end programs. The best time to visit is summer when Shri Ramamurti is in residence.

INFORMATION: Ananda Ashram, Rt 3, P.O. Box 141, Monroe, NY 10950, (914) 782-5575 and Nada-Brahmananda Ashram, 2872 Folsom St., San Francisco, CA 94110, (415) 285-5537.

● INFORMED HOMEBIRTH

Informed Homebirth is a national organization which has trained childbirth educators in more than 40 states and Canada to help couples get the information they need to create their optimal birth experience. Certified teachers offer six-week classes for pregnant couples; IH offers 5-day intensives in teacher training and midwifery skills as well as a correspondence program. A quarterly newsletter and discounts on books and supplies are offered with annual membership. Referrals are available on birthing alternatives nationally. IH was founded in 1977 by Rahima Baldwin, author of *Special Delivery.*

INFORMATION: P.O. Box 788-S, Boulder, CO 80306, (303) 449-4181.

77

● INNER DEVELOPMENT CENTER

The Inner Development Center offers full service astrological counseling, astrological computer service, natural vision improvement (Bates Method), Emotional Reprogramming through guided Imagery/hypnosis, and death counseling. Astrology and vision classes as well as private sessions can be scheduled conveniently. Astrological counseling and computer calculated charts are available via mail or telephone anywhere. Workshops in imagery, metaphysics, vision training, death awareness. Individuals are encouraged to develop their personal power, self esteem, joy, and abilities to deal with problems in the areas of relationships, health, and finances. Discover your own power tools! Call or write for brochure and price list.
INFORMATION: P.O. Drawer H, Miami, FL 33133, (305) 661-7890.

● INNER GROWTH SEMINAR

Inner Growth Seminar is a 12 week indepth class in self-awareness offering tools for identifying and releasing personal barriers to fulfillment.

Through a climate of unconditional caring in a supportive, non-encounter atmosphere, students are taught how to trace the roots of their present negativity, discovering the impact of negative conditioning of the first 13 years of their life. The Seminar offers instruction in specific and powerful tools for releasing unfulfilling patterns and replacing them with positive attitudes.

One to one relationship with a class assistant provides insightful response to written assignments designed for self understanding. Classes begin January, May, and September.
INFORMATION: P.O. Box 1107, Palo Alto, CA 94302, (415) 328-8552.

● THE INNER LIGHT FOUNDATION

The Inner Light Foundation is a non-profit and non-denominational organization founded and directed by Betty Bethards. A mystic, spiritual healer and meditation teacher, Betty Bethards lectures throughout northern California each month and teaches meditation. The main purpose of the Foundation is in teaching the meditation process, in order to help others awaken their intuitional and spiritual awareness and achieve greater harmony and balance in their lives.
INFORMATION: P.O. Box 761, Novato, CA 94948, (415) 897-5581.

● INNER RESEARCH INSTITUTE -- SCHOOL OF T'AI CHI CH'UAN

The Inner Research Institute is an educational organization founded for the purpose of exploring, investigating and teaching techniques and systems of "inner exercise," most notably T'ai Chi Ch'uan. The Institute accentuates practices which strive for personal development, not external achievement, and believes this can be cultivated by an awakening spiritual consciousness.

Change as it is experienced in T'ai Chi Ch'uan is developed from listening and adjusting to a force so that yielding can be continuous. It is in this continuity of change that the energy of the body is circulated and freely reaches every part, which brings great benefits to the health. In the beginning, this change takes place mainly in the external parts of the body, causing them all to co-ordinate with each other as well as with an outside force. When this process is continued for a length of time, the spine and finally the muscles of the inner organs themselves begin to change with the external. The more this internal movement prevails in the body the quieter the external becomes, until finally the body can go through a great change without apparent movement, thereby dissipating the least amount of energy.

As a health exercise, a foundation for meditation, a form of yoga, T'ai Chi Ch'uan is outstanding. As a martial art it is quite paradoxical; no style of fighting is less effective in its beginning phases, even up to years of practice. On the other hand, probably no style of fighting can equal T'ai Chi Ch'uan at an advanced stage, for it presupposes a complete re-integration of every cell in the body, and the harnessing of the internal force, which is the cultivation of the spirit itself.

INFORMATION: 1133 Mission St., San Francisco, CA 94103, (415) 521-2681.

● INSIGHT MEDITATION SOCIETY

Formal training in Vipassana Meditation in the Theravada Buddhist tradition is given in a strict retreat environment, under the guidance of a qualified meditation teacher. The retreats vary from one weekend to as long as three months. In the practice of Insight Meditation, the mind's conditioned tendencies toward craving, anger, and ignorance are recognized as the causes of suffering. The development of wisdom, which is the ability to see things as they are, free from the mind's projections and expectations, is a path of purification in which these tendencies are uprooted and the mind becomes tranquil and clear. The meditation practice is simple and direct. The systematic examination of the mind-body process through calm and focused awareness. Learning to observe experience from a place of stillness enables one to relate to life without fear of clinging. One begins to accept pleasure and pain, fear and joy, and all aspects of life with equanimity and balance. Life is seen as a constantly changing process. Insight is the deepening experience of the process itself, free of interpretation; calm and compassionate.

INFORMATION: Pleasant St., Barre, MA 01005, (617) 355-4378.

● INSTITUTE FOR THE DEVELOPMENT OF THE HARMONIOUS HUMAN BEING

The Institute for the Development of the Harmonious Human Being is a Sufi community devoted to service to our Endless Creator through the invocation of His Angels on the Planet Earth, following the tradition known as "The Great Work". Operated by a growing volunteer staff of over 40 renunciate pupils, the Institute serves a network of study-circles in which individuals can study data and techniques of voluntary evolution and Angelic invocation in preparation for their candidacy for the Work. In order to introduce new pupils to the Ideas, the Institute publishes a line of teaching books, including the *New American Book of the Dead, The Gabriel Papers, Secret Talks with Mr. G.,* and *The Angels' Songbook,* as well as a series of limited editions intended for use only in study-circles. The Institute also holds an annual summer retreat, the "Pan-Angelic Conference", as well as an ongoing program of workshops and seminars.

In a parallel line of work, the Institute, through the International Society of Terminal Midwives, offers a program of terminal counseling based on the *New American Book of the Dead* and related techniques and exercises, and operates a training and certification program for Terminal Midwives.
INFORMATION: P.O. Box 370, Dept. S, Nevada City, CA 95959.

● THE INSTITUTE FOR HOLISTIC STUDIES

The Institute for Holistic Studies, the most complete and practical holistic health training school in Southern California, offers year-round, State-certified courses for Holistic Massage Specialist (234 hours) and Holistic Health Practitioner (1,064 hours) certification. The program includes studies in polarity, Jin Shin Do, iridology, acupuncture theory, herbology, Ortho-Bionomy, Flower Essences, Personology, deep muscle therapy, nutrition, homeopathy, Reichian Therapy, client counseling, Touch for Health, Shiatsu, holistic massage, and professional ethics.

Our faculty for each 12-week term features nationally recognized instructors. Together we create an educational environment that provides personal growth, health counseling, and occupational competency. Courses begin September, January, April and June. Write for our catalog (send $1) or call for further information.
INFORMATION: 33 W. Canon Perdido, Santa Barbara, CA 93101, (805) 963-5005.

● INSTITUTE FOR SELF DEVELOPMENT

The Institute for Self Development is dedicated to the realization of the Self though the balanced, harmonious development of body, mind and emotions. It offers classes in Hatha Yoga, T'ai Chi Chaun, Karate, Aerobic Dance, therapeutic massage, esoteric philosophy and emotional development. The adjoining Wholistic Health Center provides an integrated health service including internal medicine, chiropractic, nutrition, biofeedback, psychology, acupuncture and amma therapy, a specialized form of oriental massage. The directors are Dr. Robert C. Sohn, acupuncturist, herbalist, author and Master Instructor in T'ai Chi Kung, and Mrs. Tina Sohn, who was trained in oriental healing arts and energy development in her native Korea.
INFORMATION: 50 Maple Pl., Manhasset, NY 11030, (516) 627-0048.

● INSTITUTE FOR THE STUDY OF CONSCIOUS EVOLUTION

The Institute for the Study of Conscious Evolution is a research and education center which recognizes the need for enlightened cooperation and individual/collective responsibility for ourselves and our world. If "everything is related to everything else", as both scientific and mystical traditions are indicating, then our every thought and action have an effect upon the world around us. This awareness cannot help but call us to develop a greater sense of empathy and mutual responsibility for co-creating the future -- thus the term Conscious Evolution. The Institute has a number of projects and publications to develop and further planetary transformation. Program and membership information is available by contacting us.

INFORMATION: 2418 Clement St., San Francisco, CA 94121, (415) 221-9222.

● INSTITUTE OF ADVANCED STUDIES

Fourth Way School. Offers intensive weekends for visitors with sacred gymnastics, meditation, practical work, and talks with elders. Aid by correspondence, manuals, tapes, and tasks. Formal group work based on a year-round semester program.

INFORMATION: 1025 First Ave., North, St. Petersburg, FL 33705, (813) 894-6564.

● INSTITUTE OF MENTALPHYSICS

Mentalphysics is a modern method of Self-Realization. It teaches the Oneness of life, embodied in all substance, energy and thought. It is also a method for physical and intellectual development. The Institute was founded by Rev. Edwin J. Dingle, journalist, geographer and explorer, who traveled extensively throughout the Orient in quest of spiritual knowledge. The Institute operates the Mentalphysics Spiritual Haven at Yucca Valley, on a desert plateau. The Haven boasts motel-like rooms with all the modern conveniences, a large cafeteria and a meditation hall designed by Frank Lloyd Wright. Yoga, breathing exercises and meditation are taught there.

INFORMATION: P.O. Box 640 Yucca Valley, CA 92284, Haven, 59700 Twenty-nine Palms Highway, Star Rt. 2, P.O. Box 435, Yucca Valley, CA 92284, (714) 366-2241 or 366-8471.

● INTEGRAL YOGA INSTITUTE (IYI)

Integral Yoga is a means of achieving an easeful body, a peaceful mind and a useful life. Universal in approach, yet practical in application, it combines the many principles and practices of Yogic science to develop all of the capabilities bestowed on us by nature, and use them for the benefit of humanity. The IYI was founded in 1966 under the guidance of Sri Swami Satchidananda, one of the most revered living Yoga Masters of our time. It offers classes, courses, retreats, workshops and guest programs in: Hatha Yoga (postures, breathing, relaxation), Japa and Raja Yoga (mantram and meditation), Bhakti Yoga (devotion), Jnana Yoga (self-inquiry) and Karma Yoga (selfless service). There are also Ashrams, Health Services and Schools based on the teachings of Integral Yoga.

Dedicated to the cause of Peace, both individual and universal, Sri Swami Satchidananda serves in ecumenical organizations around the globe. In his own words, the goal of Integral Yoga is: "A body of perfect health and strength, mind with all clarity and calmness, intellect as sharp as a razor, heart full of love and mercy, a life dedicated to the common welfare and realization of the True Self."

INFORMATION: Satchidananda Ashram - Yogaville, Route 1, P.O. Box 172, Buckingham, VA 23921.

● INTEGRITY INTERNATIONAL

A mature intentional community provides the home for Integrity International and serves as a point of orientation for associated centers around the globe. Allowing concepts and habits to fall away we find ourselves free to consciously align with the inherent and true processes of life. We operate several businesses locally and further afield are active in healing, nutrition, appropriate technology, education, animal husbandry, the arts, and government. We publish *Integrity International* monthly and offer frequent art of living classes. These resident seminars explore the experience of creative living, encourage interest in the specific design of life, and propose maturity.

INFORMATION: P.O. Box 9, 100 Mile House, B.C. Canada, VOK 2EO.

● THE INTERGROUP COMMITTEE

The Intergroup Committee is a group of workers whose purpose is to help externalize the New World Religion. "Religion is the name given to the invocative appeal of humanity, and the evocative response of the greater Life to that cry." Our aim is to increase the power of mankind's appeal by bringing about a gradual synchronization of the invocative approach of all people of spiritual intent. Three panhuman Holy Days, called the Three Linked Festivals, are held each year to coincide with the full moon in Aries, Taurus and Gemini.

INFORMATION: P.O. Box 5105, Beverly Hills, CA 90210, (213) 379-9990 or 540-8689.

● INTERNATIONAL ASSOCIATION FOR WORLD PEACE

We are dedicated to the aim of harmony and peace for individuals and all nations. All of our programs and activities are geared to human development through thinking peacefully and harmonizing with nature, particularly through "Peace Breathing" -- inhale, thinking "world", exhale, thinking "peace". Peace breathing combined with proper exercise has benefited the young and old, the physically fit and the handicapped in programs throughout Chicago and other areas of the country and world.

INFORMATION: 3315-23 North Clark St., Chicago, IL 60657, (312) 248-7959.

● INTERNATIONAL BABAJI YOGA SANGAM

Babaji's Kriya Yoga is a five-fold path of Yoga consisting of Hatha Yoga (physical postures), Kriya Kundalini Pranayam (breathing), Dhyana Yoga (meditation), Mantras (silent prayer) and Bhakti (devotion).

Yogi Ramaiah, who is the founder of International Babaji Yoga Sangam, is a direct disciple of Kriya Babaji Nagaraj who belongs to the tradition of the Eighteen Tamil Yoga Siddhas whose teachings came from Lord Shiva.

We have over 50 centers throughout the world. Weekly Yoga classes are held in most major cities in the United States. Several times a year, Yogi Ramaiah gives initiation into six Kriya Kundalini Pranayam techniques and six meditation techniques. We have numerous activities and pilgramages during the year including Mt. Shasta (California), Bear Mountain and Richville Muruga Pilgrimage (New York). In addition to these pilgrimages, there are three-day spiritual retreats during which the sacred Bija Mantra initiation takes place. Yogi Ramaiah offers a credit course in Yoga from January-May every year at Arizona Western College at Yuma, Arizona.
INFORMATION: 14011 Mansa Dr., La Mirada, CA 90638, (213) 921-5575.

● INTERNATIONAL BUDDHIST MEDITATION CENTER

Residence at the International Buddhist Meditation Center provides a peaceful environment and group support for sustained, liberation-oriented meditation practice *without* regimentation. Further, it represents an opportunity to interact daily with experienced practitioners of all major Buddhist contemplative traditions, *Vipassana, Zen* and *Tantra.* In addition, daily meditation practice, weekend meditation retreats, classes and workshops are available to non-residents as well as residents. The IBMC has a distinctly American approach, working constantly to adapt Buddhism to Western culture.
INFORMATION: 928 South New Hampshire Ave., Los Angeles, CA 90006, (213) 384-0850.

● THE INTERNATIONAL CHURCH OF AGELESS WISDOM

The International Church of Ageless Wisdom is very unique. It is the only universal, interfaith, ecumenical community known. It teaches the Fatherhood/Motherhood of God and the Brotherhood of mankind. Founded over 55 years ago by Archbishop Primate Beth R. Hand, it is the oldest, largest Metaphysical/Spiritual Church in America teaching the Ancient Wisdoms and Truths taught by great spiritual teachers from ancient as well as modern religions. Studies are contained in the *Esoteric Seminary & College,* in *Pathways to Truth* monographs and in past issues of *Aquarian Lights* magazine.

This Church teaches the truths of reincarnation and karma and recognizes the guidance and inspiration flowing from the spirit world. The Church is Christian in aspect and formulation. The episcopate of the Church is in possession of valid Apostolic Succession along ten historic lines and its Clergy have valid Orders. The Church has a meaningful healing ministry; *Radiant Heart World Healing Ministry* which has successfully served the public. We would be pleased to send more information on the Church. Kindly send three first class stamps with your request. We extend to you and your loved ones greetings for a beautiful day ...
INFORMATION: P.O. Box 101, Wyalusing, PA 18853, (717) 746-1864.

● INTERNATIONAL COMMUNITY OF CHRIST

The International Community of Christ Church of the Second Advent teaches new revelations and supplemental teachings given to the Christian religion. The Community Center in Reno maintains a Chancellery Complex including a Chapel, Espiscopal See, Parochial School, administrative offices, printing and production facilities, and a 1,000 acre consecrated Sanctuary near Reno.

The primary function of the community is the dissemination of the new teachings of the Second Advent Church through its ministerial training program. The Church sponsors and maintains the Sacred College of Jamilian Theology and the Sacred College Jamilian University of the Ordained (state and federally recognized religious institutions). The Sacred College offers a four-year ministerial training program: Seminary, Theological and Divinity Schools, and a canonical internship practicum of pastoral, liturgical training. The Jamilian University of the Ordained is a global university of religious study in a new specialized spiritual science that is separate from secular studies.

The Founder and Head Overseer is Gene Savoy, internationally known educator, theologian, Bible scholar, explorer and author. New revelations and supplemental teachings to the Christian religion are given in The Decoded New Testament; The Essaei Document: Secrets of an Eternal Race; The Lost Gospel of Jesus: Hidden Teachings of Christ; Jamil, The Child Christ; and over a hundred other religious texts.

INFORMATION: Admissions Department, 643 Ralston St., Reno, NV 89503, (702) 786-7827.

● INTERNATIONAL COUNCIL OF SPIRITUAL SCIENCES

The International Council of Spiritual Sciences is an international organization which has been in existence for over 20 years. Its membership is open to Ordained Ministers and Ministry students who practice and study any of the Spiritual Sciences. Annual dues for Ordained Ministers are $10; Ministry students $5. Quarterly meetings. The Council does not issue any credentials. Ministers must be in good standing with their own organization. The Council sponsors a newsletter, Psychic tours, seminars, conferences, psychic phenomena investigation and lectures by top speakers. Membership application available on request.

INFORMATION: 12936 Welby Way, North Hollywood, CA 91606.

● INTERNATIONAL HOLISTIC CENTER, INC.

International Holistic Center, Inc. (IHC) offers holistic networking information through its publications, Holistic HELP Handbook and Arizona Networking News which is published quarterly (Send $1 for sample issue and listing information).

The center also has 90 minute holistic educational cassette tapes with topics i.e., Polarity Exercises, What is Holistic Health?, Indoor Gardening for Survival ...

IHC director and founder, Stanley Steven Kalson, travels worldwide connecting people and ideas for greater harmony. The modalities used by IHC for channeling this message of the New Age are through body, mind and spirit "learn by doing" experiences.

The center offers workshops, lectures and seminars worldwide based upon the holistic principles outlined in the *Holistic HELP Handbook.* Some of these principles include indoor and outdoor gardening for survival, low cost health recipes, Polarity and energy flow techniques, and world networking resources.

Contact the center if you wish to have a teacher for your area. IHC believes that the primary purpose of all individuals is to integrate and develop to the fullest degree, their physical, mental, emotional, and spiritual potential.

Monthly Networking Gatherings are presently being conducted to bring the Light Workers of Phoenix together. We offer help in locating what you need in the Arizona community by suggesting groups or individuals.
INFORMATION: P.O. Box 15103, Phoenix, AZ 85060, (602) 957-3322.

● THE INTERNATIONAL SCHOOL OF MASSAGE THERAPY

The International School of Massage Therapy offers a unique program leading to a State approved Certificate in Holistic Massage. This 153 hour course combines instruction in Eastern and Western techniques; including Shiatsu, European-Swedish Massage, Anatomy, Herbal Therapeutics and Physiology, Internship program; techniques for grounding and centering. Classes create an atmosphere for individuals to experience personal growth and professional preparations.

The 10-week program is offered Fall, Winter and Spring; and there is a 5-week Summer Intensive. There are additional workshops and classes in accupressure, reflexology, lymphatic drainage and deep tissue massage, herbology and others. Full and part-time students are welcomed. CE credit for nurses is available.
INFORMATION: 2872 Folsom St., San Francisco, CA 94110, (415) 285-5040.

● INWARD JOURNEY

The Inward Journey Experience begins at the trailhead as we begin the hike into the wilderness interior in the Vipassana practice of walking meditation. The retreat schedule includes intensive study and training on both beginning and more advanced levels in zazen, t'ai chi chuan, Iyengar and Integral hatha yoga systems and Sufi movement meditations. Western holistic disciplines also taught on these retreats include the tension-release work of Reichean, Feldenkrais and Alexander Bodywork systems. Movement expression incorporates the Effort/Shape Analysis of Bartenieff, Gestalt Synergy and Emotional Release. Pack Animals carry in the supplies and Nutritiously Fresh Vegetarian Campfire Meals are provided.

The Inward Journey Staff consists of a collaborative networking of senior instructors and holistic therapists from various backgrounds and organizations who have studied in their respective disciplines for a number of years. "To turn towards nature is the beginning of discovery. To turn towards self nature is the beginning of wisdom."
INFORMATION: P.O. Box 2592, Santa Barbara, CA 93120, (805) 969-1254 or (415) 845-9498 (Berkeley).

● ISKCON -- NEW BARSANA SPIRITUAL FARM COMMUNITY

This farm community is one of over a hundred farm communities and city centers of the International Society of Krishna Consciousness throughout the world. It is located in the western slope foothills of the Colorado Rockies. Life style is vegetarian. There is daily mantra meditation and reading from ancient Eastern Spiritual/cultural literatures. There is no financial charge for applicants. The only requirement is simply a willingness to follow the life style program and to work cooperatively as a member of the community. Projects include agriculture with oxen, dairy production, and solar home building. This is a new community, established only three years. Good chance to build and grow with community.
INFORMATION: P.O. Box 112, Hotchkiss, CO 81419, (303) 527-4584.

J

● JAI MA MUSIC

Jai Ma Music is a Hawaii based center for the arts, conceived to bring inspiration and transformation to our evolving consciousness through the mediums of music, poetry, and dance.

Our cassette albums feature some of the finest artists of classical, New Age, jazz, and devotional music. Our services include a recording studio for the discriminating artist, complete with a *real time* duplication service and a comprehensive distribution outlet operating throughout the U.S.

In addition, outward bound concert tours are designed to bring an integrated arts experience to the public.
INFORMATION: P.O. Box 359, Pearl City, HI 96782.

● JAIN MEDITATION INTERNATIONAL CENTRE

Gurudev Shree Chitrabhanu is the first master from India's ancient tradition of Jainism to teach in the West. This philosophy is based on reverence for all life, deep awareness of life as it is, the law of karma, and the perfectability of soul. Programs led by Gurudev Chitrabhanu are Friday Talks, advanced classes and periodic weekend retreats. Student-teachers offer a growing range of courses which include: beginning and advanced meditation, Jain philosophy, hatha yoga, pranayama, tai chi and vegetarian cookery. A Jina is one who conquers one's inner enemy. A Jain, therefore, is anyone pursuing the path of self-mastery and the Center is here for those ready and willing to seek it.
INFORMATION: P.O. Box 730, Radio City Station, New York, NY 10101, (212) 765-2232.

● JAN'S WORK

The ultimate, living reality of Real Work. Jan's Work is the contemporary, extreme extension of Mans' actable evolution. It is the modern culmination of Mans' hunger to extend the ordinary development of his nervous-system-I into the realms normally misnamed as "awakening," or "enlightenment." Jan's Work is the secret reality of which all Men unknowingly speak, but it is also an unexpected black-hole in the evolutionary fabric of predictability through which few truly care to fly.

"I do not lead groups of mere seekers, for the path and destination is here. I do not heard bands of religious idiots, for their dreams of salvation is the reality of their destruction. And I do not instruct routine fools in intellectual speculation, for the Secret is known. My Work is the unseen assault on Life's-unfinished-business, for Man's limits are his prison, and I speak only to those who seek escape, not penal reform. There is nothing wrong in ordinary life -- if you're ordinary. But if you are a piece of Life's-unfinished-business, there is but one extraordinary place for you. "aut serere aut mori."

Through the Chan Shal Imi Press we publish all of Jan's public writings, including, *Magnus Machina, And Kyroot Said* and *The Death of Gurdjieff.* For information and a catalog write.

INFORMATION: The Future/Now Federation, P.O. Box 1365, Stone Mountain, GA 30086.

● JANUS GROWTH CENTER

The Janus Center for Counseling and Human Development was founded in 1973 as an alternative counseling center. Located in Baltimore, Maryland, the Janus Center services are designed to awaken and nurture the spiritual processes inherent in both conflict and growth. The Center offers counseling services to individuals, families, and groups. Counseling modalities include gestalt therapy, music, art, movement, psychodrama, and guided imagery.

Special programs are available for drug abusers, youth, and older adults. The Janus Center is certified by the State of Maryland to provide drug abuse treatment services. Psychiatric consultation is also available. The Center is an approved Blue Cross/Blue Shield and Medicare provider. In addition the Janus Center sponsors training seminars for professionals and workshops for the general public. The Center has a special interest in Transpersonal Psychology and healing. Request information by calling or writing the Janus Center for Counseling and Human Development.

INFORMATION: 21 W. 25th St., Baltimore, MD 21218, (301) 366-2123.

● JEMEZ BODHI MANDALA

Jemez Bodhi Mandala is a Rinzai Zen practice center located in the Jemez Mountains 60 miles Northwest of Albuquerque. Bodhi has accomondations for single students,couples, and students/families with children. Our practice is guided by Joshu Sasaki Roshi, a Rinzai Zen Master who has been teaching in North America for 20 years. Besides a daily schedule of zazen/working practice Bodhi sponsors zazen weekends each month for new and continuing students. Each Spring Bodhi holds a two month intensive training period based upon traditional Zen monastic practice. Week long meditation retreats, called dai-sesshin, are held throughout the year to deepen our practice.

Bodhi is also available to individuals or groups who wish to enjoy our hot springs and the scenic beauty of the Jemez Mountains. Guest students join us for morning and evening meditation but are free during the day to follow their own practice. Motel guests have no responsibilities beyond enjoying the quiet atmosphere of the canyon. Retreat groups may rent the center for a day, weekend, week or longer. Rates available upon request.
INFORMATION: Jemez Bodhi Mandala, P.O. Box 8, Jemez Springs, NM 87025, (505) 829-3854.

● THE JERSEY SOCIETY OF PARAPSYCHOLOGY, INC. (JSP)

The Jersey Society of Parapsychology, Inc. has its heart in New Jersey, but its friends are everywhere. JSP was organized to promote the scientific investigation of psychic phenomena in an atmosphere of enlightenment for those interested in awakening their psychic abilities. We offer classes, lectures, a newsletter, and seminars devoted to serious study, metaphysical discussion, healing, and personal growth. Attend our lectures on the fourth Saturday of the month at St. Paul's Church, Main Street (Route 24) Chatham, New Jersey, or join our mailing list.
INFORMATION: P.O. Box 2071, Morristown, NJ 07960, (201) 386-1504.

● THE JESHUA BEN JOSEF SCHOOL OF THE HEART

The Jeshua Ben Josef School of the Heart is a community of Divine Souls dedicated to seeking the truth and living their lives in service to God. We live by the truth that religion in its true sense is simply the relationship that exists between the soul of man and the soul of God. We teach that love worketh all things that man could wish for or conceive of, and more besides.
INFORMATION: P.O. Box 2097, Eugene, OR 97402, (503) 342-8069.

● JESUS MOVEMENT

The Jesus Movement is a phenomenon of the New Age. It is a revival of evangelism with many similarities to early Christianity. Jesus Christ, to the Jesus People, is a living reality -- truly the Son of God, Savior and Judge. Their lives revolve around an intense personal relationship with this Jesus. Their every decision, problem and plan must take Him into account. Like early Christians, their convert's fervor is manifested in apostolic preaching that has made the movement a national phenomenon.

Like the early Christians, and in contrast to conventional Christians, many are willing to forego the rewards of property and social roles, since Jesus is their highest and only value. There are many Jesus communes and farms throughout the country where members have given up personal property and pooled their resources to concentrate on communion with Jesus through Bible reading, prayer and group praising of their Lord.

● JOHN F. KENNEDY UNIVERSITY

John F. Kennedy University's Graduate School of Consciousness Study offers accredited Master's degrees in: Parapsychology, Clinical Holistic Health Education, Transpersonal Counseling Psychology (which meets the requirements for state M.F.C.C. licensing), Consciousness and the Arts, and individualized study plans in Consciousness Studies.

JFKU's unique environment supports personal and vocational transformation. The 1600 students (300 in Consciousness programs) are self-directed adults, rich in life experience. JFKU is the first accredited university in America offering graduate degrees in these areas. JFKU also offers undergraduate majors in parapsychology, mysticism, and holistic health, as well as Master's degrees in Career/Life Development and Clinical Psychology.

INFORMATION: Graduate School of Consciousness Studies, JFKU, P.O. Box 1, 12 Altarinda Rd., Orinda, CA 94563, (415) 254-0200, ext. 47.

● JUNGIAN-SENOI INSTITUTE

We are a community devoted to working with dreams and the individual/wholeness process described by C. G. Jung. Our purpose is to help individuals embody in their everyday lives the "soul thinking", central to working with archetypes and living a meaningful life. We offer innovative training in dreamwork and Jungian psychology, combining discussion of concepts, issues and techniques with tasks to ground the material in daily life. Our dream groups allow us to connect with inner sources for wisdom and personal transformation. We also celebrate the mythic dimension of individual and community life through seasonal gatherings and retreats.

INFORMATION: 1525J Shattuck Ave., Berkeley, CA 94709, (415) 848-0311.

● KAGYU DRODEN KUNCHAB

A Kargyupa center founded by the Venerable Kalu Rinpoche for the teaching and practice of Mahayana and Vajrayana Buddhism. Lama Lodru is Rinpoche's representative in San Francisco.

Practice includes mantra, visualization, and form and formless meditation. Nyung-Ne is observed each full moon. Advanced students do foundation practices.

INFORMATION: 1892 Fell St., San Francisco, CA 94117, (415) 386-9656.

Local New Age Directories

STATE	EPICENTER	PUBLICATION	ADDRESS
AZ	(statewide)	**Arizona Networking News**	P.O. Box 15103, Phoenix, AZ 85060.
CA	Los Angeles	**The LA Light Directory**	4026 Beverly Blvd., Los Angeles, CA 90004
	Los Angeles	**The Whole Person -- A Calendar of Los Angeles Area Events**	207 Norman Pl., 2nd Fl., Santa Monica, CA 90405
	San Francisco	**Common Ground**	9 Mono Ave., Suite B, Fairfax, CA 94930
	San Francisco	**Lifestyle**	2194 Palou Ave., San Francisco, CA 94124
CO	Boulder/Denver	**Nexus**	1535 Upland, Boulder, CO 80306
D.C.	Washington	**Pathways**	P.O. Box 4346, Falls Church, VA 22044
FL	(statewide)	**Rainbow Visions**	P.O. Box 6337, Hollywood, FL 33021
HI	(statewide)	**Common Ground**	217 S. King #308, Honolulu, HI 96813
IL	Chicago	**New Chicago**	2930 N. Lincoln, Chicago, IL 60657
MA	Boston	**Whole Life Times**	132 Adams St., Newton, MA 02158
NY	New York	**Free Spirit**	P.O. Box 279, Riverdale, NY 10471
OH	Cincinnati	**Inner Quest**	3514 Birch St., Cincinnati, OH 45208
OR	Portland	**The Portland Reflection**	P.O. Box 42216, Portland, OR 97242
PA	Philadelphia	**The New Frontier**	670 N. 19th St., Philadelphia, PA 15221
TX	(statewide)	**New Texas**	P.O. Box 18032, Austin, TX 78760
WI	Madison	**Attunement**	114 S. Randall, Madison, WI 53715
	Milwaukee-plus	**New Wisconsin**	2930 N. Lincoln, Chicago, IL 60657

A Message from God
The Lord

The winds of war and the seeds of hate which exist in this world today are a direct result of mankind's disregard and disobedience unto the Word of God. For He has already told mankind as to how he shall and can live in peace with all his breathren on this earth. His message is unto the Books of the Bibles. Remind yourself of His words which are, "Love the Lord thy God with thy whole mind and heart and do likewise unto all men which art thy breathren."

Today the innocent who do follow the Words and the teachings of Christ cry out to the Lord for help. And their plea is such, "Oh Father, in Heaven we beseech Thee to help us and all mankind to follow Thy Word and Thy teachings, so as wars might end, and so peace might prevail on this earth."

And the Lord shall answer them thusly, "Since the time of the murder of Abel by his brother who was called Cain, unto the present devastation in which mankind has embroiled itself in, the Word of the Lord has remained the same. The hearts and the minds of mankind have been hardened against the Lord. Yet He still loves all on earth who are His children. And He desires none of his children to be slain.

The fate of this world is unto the hands of those who exist here. The fate of the souls who depart this earth is unto the hands of the One who created them. Each and everyone who comes unto the Lord shall answer for his actions on this earth."

A message from God as received by Several Sources Foundation. This is an answer to the question: Is there any way we can stop the earth from being destroyed by nuclear war?

"Enough was placed here in the beginning to sustain life for all. We have to protect that which sustains life, and this is why my people have always talked about love, peace, respect -- not only to human beings but with all life, with all the creation."

-- Phillip Deere

91

● KARMA CHANGJUB LING/RUMTEK MONASTERY

His Holiness the Sixteenth Gyalwa Karmapa founded this center/monastery in 1977. It was solely formed to practice the teachings of the Karmapa Lineage in the Karma-Kagyu Sect and is the mother center of Rumtek Monastery in Sikkim, India. Director of the Gompa is His Holiness disciple Drolma Dorje *AH* Rigpe Dorje. Access to the Gompa is by telephone only.

INFORMATION: Karma Changjub Ling/Rumtek Monastery, Los Angeles, CA 90069, (213) 276-4207.

● KARMA THEGSUM CHOLING

The Gyalwa Karmapa tulku has been the head of the Kargyu Order of Buddhism in Tibet since the 12th century. He embodies, represents and guides its accumulated spiritual energy.

The Kargyu Order is the medium of transmission of the meditative teachings known as Mahamudra which have been passed down through the lineages of Naropa, Marpa, Milarepa and Gampopa and successively through the 16 Gyalwa Karmapas up to the present time. In accordance with the wish of His Holiness, a center has been founded in New York City to make available the vast tradition of Mahayana Buddhism as it is taught in the Kargyu lineage of Tibet.

INFORMATION: 412 West End Ave., Apt. 5n, New York, NY 10024, (212) 580-9282.

● KERISTA CONSCIOUSNESS CHURCH

Discover Sister Kerista, the Black Hippie Goddess. She's not a real person. She's a poetic invention, mythological symbol of the religion Kerista, democratic religion fostering Humor, Equality, Liberation, Love.

Kerista is the non-sexist path to world peace and personal liberation. The religion of Kerista blends reason and religion, rationality and mystical ecstasy. Members live communally and practice *spiritual polyfidelity,* (new family structure for people who want to stay single and be non-monogamous). We're also into shared leadership, high verbality, and the search for truth through the elimination of contradictions. Free literature.

INFORMATION: Kerista, 543 Frederick St., San Francisco, CA 94117, (415) 566-6502 or 665-2988.

● KESHAVASHRAM INTERNATIONAL MEDITATION CENTER

Following the ancient Vedic tradition using the science of words or mantras, meditation is taught individually as handed down person to person from the ancient rishis and seers. Emphasizing the path of devotion through adherence to one's own religious beliefs, a special one-to-one relationship is established between the teacher and student with spiritual counseling and personal guidance. The center follows the teachings of Shri Krishna Gopal Vyasji Maharaj of Jaipur, India.

The Center, founded in 1968, opened the first known Hindu Temple in the United States and a research library. Located on 450 acres, guest houses are planned.

INFORMATION: P.O. Box 260, Warrenton, VA 22186, (703) 347-9009.

● KHALSA MEDICAL CLINIC

Gurudarshan Singh Khalsa, M.D. is a family physician who has been studying and teaching yoga and meditation for over 10 years. In addition to the traditional medical approach, (including minor surgery and natural childbirth), Dr. Khalsa uses nutrition, herbs, stress management, homeopathy, kinesiology (muscle testing), Bach flower remedies, and personal and spiritual counseling. Health awareness lectures are offered on Thursday evenings. At present our staff also includes a psychologist-polarity therapist, and nutritionist. Since we believe that each individual is responsible for his/her own health (mental, physical, spiritual), we try to suggest treatments that are most suitable for your life style.
INFORMATION: 27330 Southfield Rd., Lathrup Village, MI 48076, (313) 552-8848.

● KOINONIA FOUNDATION

Koinonia was founded in 1951 as a spiritual and educational center and community, a place for healing and growth. Our 145 acres of woods, meadows, organic gardens, our rooms for study, meditation and artistic self-expression form a fine background for participation in classes, workshops and events, on a non-degree-granting basis. Koinonia is ecumenical, follows no single spiritual teacher or discipline, and is therefore free to present many approaches to spiritual development. As a community we find that the power of the Spirit can be tapped to direct itself towards the healing of the body-mind-spirit and the world.
INFORMATION: 1400 Greenspring Valley Rd., Stevenson, MD 21153, (301) 486-6262.

● KRIPALU CENTER FOR HOLISTIC HEALTH

One of the largest residential preventive health care centers on the East Coast. In keeping with the holistic teachings of yoga, which form the foundation of our work, we emphasize the need to work with you as a whole person -- body, mind, emotions and spirit. Our faculty includes two homeopathic physicians, a licensed clinical psychologist, two registered physical therapists, massage therapists and other professional staff trained in the many aspects of the holistic health field.

All staff members are residents of Kripalu Yoga Retreat and share the common goal of living holisitically. The guidance and teachings of Yogi Amrit Desai provides the zest for life that is the spirit behind the health center. As founder and director of the center Yogi Desai has dedicated more than 29 years of his life to living and teaching the art of leading a vital, healthy, and integrated lifestyle through yoga.
INFORMATION: P.O. Box 120, Summit Station, PA 17979 (717) 754-3051.

● KRISHNAMURTI FOUNDATION OF AMERICA

Since early youth, J. Krishnamurti was trained to become a Messianic spiritual leader. Later, however, he rejected that role and criticized the worth of gurus and teachers for the spiritual path. He asserts that the quest for Truth must ultimately be carried out by the individual alone. The central theme of his counsel is the notion of spiritual freedom -- freedom from authority, from fear, from the past. He recognized the value of the intellectual mind and of thinking, but holds that eventually the mind must transcend the limitations of thought and concepts, and perceive the world at each moment as if for the first time.

Krishnamurti travels extensively, speaking and counseling. His lectures and dialogues with the audience have been published in several volumes, which reflect the style of his thought -- simple, clear and concise. There are Krishnamurti Foundations in England, the United States, India and Canada. All of these Foundations operate elementary or secondary schools.

INFORMATION: P.O. Box 216, Ojai, CA 93023, (805) 646-2726.

● KRIYA YOGA CENTER

Kriya Yoga, the ancient yoga science revived by Babaji Maharaj, is being taught in the United States under the guidance of Swami Hariharananda Giri. Swamiji is the current, realized master of Kriya Yoga in the lineage of gurus that includes Swami Sri Yukteswar and Paramahansa Yogananda, author of *Autobiography of a Yogi*. He is the head of Karar Ashram in the holy city of Puri, India. We teach the authentic Kriya Yoga technique as it has been traditionally taught in India. The practice of Kriya Yoga enables you to go beyond body and mind, to enter the formless state -- to attain self-realization.

INFORMATION: 1201 Fern St., N.W., Washington, D.C. 20012, (202) 723-4077.

L

● LABSUM SHEDRUB LING -- LAMAIST BUDDHIST MONASTERY OF AMERICA

Founded by the Tibetan Buddhist Lama, Ven. Geshe Wangyal. Practice includes prayer, study and translation of Buddhist scriptures, as well as meditation. Seminars and summer programs, taught by an ecumenical faculty of Buddhist priests, college professors, etc. are offered on a regular basis.

INFORMATION: P.O. Box 306A, RD 1, Washington, NJ 07882, (201) 689-6080.

● LAMA FOUNDATION

Lama Foundation, since its founding in 1967, has been a community where all members engage in a variety of spiritual practices and paths: a picture of diversity within the greater Unity. Located in the Sangre de Cristo mountains, north of Taos, New Mexico.

Write for information on: Hermitages, cottage industry products (prayer flags and T-shirts, books and tapes), summer program of seminars and retreats with visiting teachers, work camps, visitor's program, occasional openings for staff members with strong spiritual practice and desire to work and serve.

INFORMATION: P.O. Box 444, San Cristobal, NM 87564.

● LANARK HILLS FOUNDATION

The Foundation's interest is in self-education and in exploring the teachings of J. Krishnamurti. However, the Foundation in no way attempts to be a representative of Krishnamurti and is in no way, shape or form a representative of any particular religious organization.

The foundation maintains a hundred acre farm with buildings in Lanark County, Ontario. For its purposes, the Foundation has the use of the land and buildings as well as the co-operative games business, Family Pastimes. The business provides an economic base and service work for the Foundation.

Daily living on the farm includes construction and care of Foundation buildings, education of the children on the Foundation premises, tending to the large garden, preparation of meals, production and distribution of the co-operative games in addition to hosting and arranging self-education gatherings. Guests and visitors are expected to partake in these activities.

Much of the surrounding woodlands remain undisturbed, inviting quiet relaxation and reflection. The Foundation has a collection of resource material (tapes, books, pamphlets, records, films, etc.) for study and lending and offers for sale Krishnamurti's works.

INFORMATION: R.R. 4, Perth, Ontario, Canada K7H 3C6, (613) 267-4819.

● LAND HOUSE

Land House is a Gurdjieff Group started by the Late W. A. Nyland who was with Gurdjieff since his first visit to America in 1924.

Since Gurdjieff's death in 1949, Mr. Nyland, first as an original trustee of the Gurdjieff Foundation and then by himself, attempted to maintain the clarity of what Gurdjieff himself meant by Work on oneself. He used as the basis for continuing Gurdjieff's work, books written by Gurdjieff, namely *All and Everything* and *Meetings with Remarkable Men.*

In addition to these books, Gurdjieff transmitted an oral teaching to those who studied with him personally. This knowledge makes his ideas practical and relevant in daily life. Land House is affiliated with Chardavogne Barn.

INFORMATION: P.O. Box 801, Monte Rio, CA 95462, (707) 865-2463.

● LAWRENCE/HARRISON INSTITUTE

The Institute is offering the most innovative health care and educational programs available today. Our Certification Training Programs include sections on herbology, nutrition, bodywork and massage, Humanistic Counseling, Success and Life Management. We also offer private consultations in these areas as well as in biofeedback, corrective exercises etc. Membership is available at $35 per year and includes a subscription to our newsletter and many other benefits. Our *Total Health Concept* program is the most complete health evaluation available. For information send a self addressed stamped envelope and $1.

INFORMATION: 1990 Broadway St., Suite 1206, New York, NY 10023, (212) 724-8782.

● LEGACY INTERNATIONAL YOUTH PROGRAMS

For young people at the Legacy Summer Programs, six weeks mean an action-rich adventure in learning about the world, themselves, and others. Intercultural explorations, non-competitive recreation, and learning new skills in a stimulating community setting open unexpected and exciting vistas. Participants discover new ways of thinking that challenge them to see personal, community, and global issues from a different point of view.

The schedule of activities combines today's exciting advances in areas such as computer programming, appropriate technology, and accelerated learning methods, with an intensive program in music, dance, art, crafts, international experiences, and recreation.

Legacy is sponsored by the Institute for Practical Idealism. Other applications for Evolutionary Education, the core of all Institute projects and activities, include: publications, private consultations and training programs in management, communication, human relations, parent-teacher education, public policy and international relations vis-a-vis Practical Idealism.

INFORMATION: 822 South Taylor St., Arlington, VA 22204, (703) 920-1650.

● THE LIBERAL CATHOLIC CHURCH

The Liberal Catholic Church, established in 1916, is independent of the Church of Rome. The L.C.C. makes use of a vernacular liturgy, and attempts to balance ceremonial worship and devotional aspiration with scientific and mystical thought. The L.C.C. seeks to serve all who earnestly desire spiritual enlightenment, and all persons are welcome to participate in the services.

The Orders of the clergy were derived through the Old Catholic Church of Holland, separate from Rome since the 1700's. The clergy are neither enjoined nor forbidden to marry. Their clerical functions are performed as a way of life, and all are self-supporting. L.C.C. philosophy postulates the existence of God, manifesting as creative Trinity, and recognition of the Christ as spiritual teacher to mankind. The opinions or beliefs of an individual are felt to be one's own affair, and each must perceive Truth through his own experiences.

INFORMATION: P.O. Box 598, 1610 Grand Ave., Ojai, CA 93023, (805) 646-2960.

● LIFE SCIENCE INSTITUTE

Life Science Institute unites science with religion in order to reveal the practice and attainment of the Holy Spirit (Kundalini). Due to man's greed, sexual hangups and fear of change, this has been suppressed for millenia. Ours is the first scientific or religious organization to propagate Jesus' Lost Gospels, discovered in Egypt in 1945. LSI is the center of the revival of the original *Gnostic Church of Jesus,* and of the *Brotherhood of the Rosie Cross,* which flourished until three centuries ago, when it was openly patronized by scientists, the king, and the Church of England.

Our inexpensive Graduate Course bestows degrees of Doctor of Divinity or Hermetic Medical Doctor of urine therapy, which heals all illnesses the free, natural way. The Course reveals how Androgeneity rejuvenates the body and opens one's inner vision to another dimension, which is Spiritual Salvation.

LSI is a mail order seminary, publishing over 50 world scriptures, and is the only church offering the Alchemical knowledge taught by Christ. Books include *Jesus' Lost Gospels, Urine Therapy, Rasa Tantra: Blood Marriage-the Sacred Initiation* by Tsampa Yeshe Norbu. Brochure for the Graduate Course is $2.

INFORMATION: P.O. Box 1057, Fort Pierce, FL 33454.

● THE LIGHT OF THE DOVE FOUNDATION: WORLD ORGANIZATION AND HEALING MINISTRY

This Ministry was founded by Sunny Angell for the sole purpose of promoting peace between all nations through informing people of spiritual Light throughout the world, fostering and establishing world peace, and the communication of ideas, possibilities and challenges to the human mind in an effort to understand man and God freely. In order to do this, the Ministry offers psychic consulting services, counseling, healing, yoga therapy, lectures, classes, books, tapes, home study courses, its *World Peace Magazine* sent freely anywhere to individuals, groups, businesses, and political organizations.

INFORMATION: 1120 E. Washington St. #22, Escondido, CA 92025, (714) 747-5085.

● THE LIGHT OF YOGA SOCIETY

The Light of Yoga Society was founded in 1970 by Alice Christensen Rankin under the guidance of her Guru, Shri Swami Rama of Haridwar, India. At all centers a full range of classical Yoga instruction and a wide variety of public service programs and seminars are offered. All of the teaching and programs are under the direct supervision of Alice Christensen Rankin.

The Light of Yoga Society has specially designed Yoga programs for both children and the elderly. The Society has also adapted its courses to serve specialized populations such as prisoners, drug addicts, alcoholics, hospitalized mental patients, learning disabled children and abusive parents, all applying the principles of classical Yoga.

INFORMATION: 2134 Lee Rd., Cleveland Heights, OH 44118, (216) 371-0078.

● LINDENSELF FOUNDATION

"What is Lindenself?" people often ask. The Lindenself Family is a community in relationship that has come together through a process of natural cohesion to give expression to the Love in our hearts for our brothers and sisters. There is no roster with a numbered membership on it, no heavenly hierarchy and no single "way" that we all subscribe to. We are more a family of folks who find that we cannot help but live and work together as fate would allow, learning to express the truth of our Oneness in and through the dance of daily realities. We do not consciously nurture any belief system, but do abide in our faith in Love.

"Who started Lindenself?" There was actually nothing to start! Lindenself rests upon the Ancient foundation of our Oneness, which is its inspiration. No one can begin or end this truth. We simply recognize truth (God) in relationship with One another, thereby realizing God's presence in our daily lives.

Lindenself is thus a grass roots community, a church of relationship, coming together to focus our energies in a synergistic fashion for the purpose of furthering spiritual awakening -- our lives and talents having dovetailed into a family with a story to share ... that of Love. Our worship is the recognition of God in another and our work is to live and share this truth.

INFORMATION: P.O. Box 2321, Chapel Hill, NC 27514, (919) 364-2723.

● LIVING TAO FOUNDATION

Living Tao Foundation, with the guidance and teaching of Al Chungliang Huang, is an international, non-profit network of people. We produce courses, demonstrations, performances and workshops in T'ai Chi, calligraphy, dance and philosophy. Al Huang was born and raised in China and has brought a unique understanding of eastern fine and martial arts into the practice of western living. Our programs are designed to draw a person's sense of ability to live consciously. People of all ages and nations are most welcome.

INFORMATION: P.O. Box 5060, Station 'A', Champaign, IL 61820.

● LONG BRANCH ENVIRONMENTAL EDUCATION CENTER

Long Branch is a secluded mountain educational and retreat center in Western North Carolina between the Great Smokies and the Blue Ridge Mountains. The connection between ecological awareness and spiritual growth seems of paramount importance to us.

Watershed consciousness and strong conservation instincts lead us towards a sense of earth stewardship and community responsibility. Earth-healing takes the form of intensive gardening, permaculture (ecological agriculture including tree crops, small fruits, and aquaculture), and maintaining our 120 acres of wilderness as an ecological sanctuary. Our community education outreach includes low-cost solar design, composting toilet design, meditation retreats, and alternative natural birthing.

Please write or call for more information. Peace through perennials.

INFORMATION: Route 2, P.O. Box 132, Leicester, NC 28748, Big Sandy Mush Creek, (704) 683-3662.

● THE LOVE PROJECT

The Love Project is a way of life available to persons who want to be more loving and who seek alternatives to passive, apathetic, negative, hostile, critical and violent living. It is six simple principles which make of Love, not an ideal to reach for, but specific attitudes and actions to be and to do. The Love Project is a way for Seekers to link energies in a universal chain of caring -- a chain forged with the strength of the uniqueness of each individual. It is person-to-person love.

The Love Project is structureless and organizationless. Sponsors of The Love Project are kept in touch with each other through *The Seeker Magazine.*

INFORMATION: Arleen Lorrance (OSO) & Diane K. Pike, P.O. Box 7601, San Diego, CA 92107, (714) 225-0133.

● LUBAVITCH YOUTH ORGANIZATION

The Lubavitch Youth Organization, a Hassidic movement with branches throughout the United States, seeks to bring young Jews back to traditional Jewish roots. It is connected with the Lubavitch community in Brooklyn, New York.

INFORMATION: 305 Kingston Ave., Brooklyn, NY 11213, (212) 778-4270.

● LUCIS TRUST

The Lucis Trust was founded by Alice and Foster Bailey in 1922. It is a nonprofit, nonpolitical, tax-exempt world service corporation. Its activities include the Arcane School, the Lucis Publishing Companies, World Goodwill, Triangles, and the Lucis Trust Lending Library. The Arcane School is a correspondence school presenting courses of study and meditation in esoteric philosophy. Triangles serves to establish a global network of light and goodwill through the power of thought and invocation. The purpose of World Goodwill is to help establish right human relationships and to stimulate the potency of goodwill in the hearts of all people. The Lucis publishing Companies publish and distribute Alice Bailey's books of esoteric teachings. The Lending Library has approximately 2,000 books on metaphysical and related subjects.

INFORMATION: 866 United Nations Plaza, Suite 566-7, New York, NY 10017, (212) 421-1577.

● MA YOGA SHAKTI INT. MISSION

Reject the Old. Reject the Gold. The founder-inspirer of Yogashakti Mission is Her Holiness Maha Mandaleshwar Ma Yogashakti Saraswati, teaching the *Ancient Wisdom of Yoga*. She has been in the United States since 1977 and spends alternately one month at each of her two Ashrams. Five Yoga Retreats are regularly organized a year at the New York and Florida Ashrams. The Mission has three Ashrams in the U.S.A. and four in India (Bombay, Calcutta, Delhi & Gondia). Her Ashrams are Centers of Peace and Wisdom.

INFORMATION: MYSIM, 114-23 Lefferts Blvd., S. Ozone Park, NY 11420, (212) 322-5856, (212) 641-0402 or (305) 725-4024.

● MACROBIOTICS

Macrobiotics is a philosophy and practice of diet, health and happiness developed by George Ohsawa in the spirit of Zen and ancient Oriental wisdom. The theory is simple: there is One Principle, Yin-Yang. Yin and Yang are two antagonistic but complementary forces of the universe, the two dialectic absolute extremes that define everything else. The following physical phenomena are consequences of these two fundamentals: cold-hot, light-heavy, water-fire, positive-negative, acidic-alkaline, female-male, tropical-frigid, sweet-sour. The ideal of a Macrobiotic Way of Life is to balance these forces as they affect our lives. As far as diet is concerned, this means that it is advisable to eat foods that are reasonably near the midpoint between extreme Yin and extreme Yang. Ohsawa recommends a diet principally based on cereals, and in particular, brown rice. However, he also stressed that the general principle is to live in harmony with our environment and the general laws of nature.

INFORMATION: George Ohsawa Macrobiotic Foundation, 902 14th St., Oroville, CA 95965, (916) 533 7702.

● MADRE GRANDE

Nestled in a high mountain desert, 45 minutes from San Diego, is a valley rich with natural resources, oak trees, large stone outcroppings, springs, seasonal lakes, abundant protected wildlife, herbs and flowers. This valley is the fulfillment of a dream -- the dream of 10 dedicated spiritual seekers who came together in 1975 and generated the purchase of 264 acres and dedicated the Land to certain specific purposes.

Madre Grande is dedicated to being a holistic healing center, a school for spiritual unfoldment, and a permanent site for celebrations. The Monastery is part of an independent, religious, healing and teaching order. Its only dogma is to encourage each one to discover the Divine Light within and to follow a spiritual path to positive perfection.

INFORMATION: Star Route 118, Dulzura, CA 92017, (714) 468-3810.

● MAHIKARI-NO-WAZA

Mahikari means True Light. It is an energy that is used for spiritual awakening and healing. This Light, this ability, can be acquired by doing a three-day lecture course. At the end of this course one receives a Divine pendant called omitama. The Light that one radiates, this energy from the hand, is also called Mahikari. The organization originated in Japan in 1959. There are now about three or four hundred thousand people who belong to it in the world.

A man called Okada had a revelation from God that the world is in for rough changes. By the end of the century we have to prepare to become purified quickly. This blessing was given to mankind so that they could be awakened to God quickly. We have entered a New Age since the early 1960's. He calls it the Age of Baptism by Fire. It is replacing the water age. Healing by water, miracles by water, spirituality by water is a thing of the past. There is a special type of energy called hi-no-ki which is increasing daily in the universe. That is why there are many unusual phenomena. Spirituality is now on the upswing and materialism is on the down.

INFORMATION: 6470 Foothill Ave., Tujunga, CA 91042, (213) 353-0071 and 2489 19th Ave., San Francisco, CA 94116, (415) 661-2505.

● MANDALA SOCIETY

The major purpose of the Mandala Society is to support and promote Transformation 2000, The National Center for the Exploration of the Human Potential, holistic health and holistic education. Founded in 1975 by David Harris, Mandala presents an annual conference program which includes as presenters those individuals who are leaders in the rapidly expanding fields of holistic health and holistic education.

INFORMATION: P.O. Box 1233, Del Mar, CA 92014, (714) 481-7751.

● MARK-AGE

Mark-Age, Inc. is a nonprofit spiritual-educational organization founded in February 1960 by Nada/Yolanda/Pauline Sharpe and El Morya/Mark/Charles B. Gentzel. She is a prophet or channel for the New Age and the Second Coming. Primary purpose of Mark-Age is to externalize on Earth the Hierarchal Board (spiritual government of our solar system, composed of ascended master and angelic forces in the etheric or Christ and the celestial realms) in preparation for the Second Coming in its dual meaning: (a) second coming of each one's I Am Self, expressed through the mortal personality; (b) Second Coming of the Messiah, Prince of Earth, last incarnated on Earth as Jesus of Nazareth.

Mark-Age has been commissioned by the Hierarchal Board to implant a prototype for spiritual government on Earth, the I Am Nation. (See: I Am Nation listing.) This has five divisions to educate and to lift all mankind, all life forms and the planet into the fourth dimension. Mark-Age provides hardcover and softcover textbooks; a bimonthly periodical to coordinate all life groups on Earth; weekly joint-meditation cassette broadcasts; medical research for holistic healing methods. Free introductory catalog.

INFORMATION: Dept. SG, P.O. Box 290368, Ft. Lauderdale, FL 33329, (305) 587-5555.

● MARTIN STEINBERG CENTER

The Torah wears new garments in each generation.

The Martin Steinberg Center is a center for Jewish artists in the performing, visual, and literary arts. Jewish traditions are expressed in new and creative ways. Programs include coffee houses, workshops, films, art festivals, and holiday celebrations. We publish *Jewish Arts Newsletter* which lists our activities, Jewish spiritual and cultural events, and artisitic resource information. Artists and those interested in the arts are invited to join our community. No one is turned away for lack of funds.

INFORMATION: 15 East 84th St., New York, NY 10028, (212) 879-4500.

● MATAGIRI

Matagiri is a resident center for the evolutionary vision and integral yoga of Sri Aurobindo and Mother. It provides information on Sri Aurobindo's transformational yoga, the Sri Aurobindo Ashram and the city of Auroville being constructed in South India. It sells the works of Sri Aurobindo and Mother, including *Mother's Agenda,* a remarkable record of conversations with Mother covering 19 years of her exploration and experimentation in the transformation of her body. A catalog is available. Matagiri also publishes *Collaboration,* a quarterly devoted to Sri Aurobindo's vision of a new humanity, with passages from his writings and those of others, news of Auroville and Sri Aurobindo centers around the world. It also maintains an extensive library of Sri Aurobindo's and related works, tapes, periodicals, photos.

Visitors are welcome but should telephone or write in advance. As Matagiri is not a retreat, a typical day is devoted to work done in a spirit of consecration and detachment.

INFORMATION: Mt. Tremper, NY 12457, (914) 679-8322.

● MATRI SATSANG (SRI ANANDAMAYI MA)

The devotees of Sri Anandamayi MA are a widely-varied group of individuals united by Mother's presence in their lives. There exists no national organization nor any desire for one. For Sri MA there is no far or near, also no inner circle or unknown circle. MA is for everyone.

Matri Satsang provides photographs of and information cassettes and books about Sri Anandamayi MA. (Send stamp for free catalog). We appreciate hearing from anyone with stories, slides, or cassettes to share. An archive of MA-related materials is being collected to help make supraphysical darsan of MA more accessible.

INFORMATION: 2103 Holcomb Rd., Yuba City, CA 95991.

● THE MAZDAZNAN ELECTOR

Mazdaznan is a science of life encompassing everything appertaining to life. It is based on the original teaching of Zarathustra or Zoroaster, going back 6,000 years before Christ. It predates the faith of the Parsees, which most scholars attribute to Zarathustra. Dr. Otoman Zar-Adusht Hanish was sent as a messenger to teach the simple Mazdaznan teaching to the world about 1844 by the Temple Community of El Karhman high in the Himalayan Range. Mazdaznan, "The Master Thought," is based on the three phases of man: the spiritual, the intellectual and the physical, or spirit, mind and body. The key to developing all three phases equally is accomplished through the breath. By breathing consciously and rhythmically by the unique Mazdaznan system of breath culture we can attain the perfection in the physical that we already have and are in the spirit. The present leader is Dr. Henry L. Sorge.

INFORMATION: 1159 S. Norton Ave., Los Angeles, CA 90019, (213) 734-4359.

● MEDICINE WAYS

Medicine Ways is located in Sonoma County, northern California. We are a collective of people dedicated to exploring cross-cultural indigenous healing systems and mythologies. In our programs and projects we are joining community and planetary needs with pragmatic and economically feasible services and activities. Studying with poets, artists, scientists and medicine people from various traditions, we are working to acquire and share skills that enable us to create conscious intentional communities.

We are part of the Earth Community Network and support non-competitive, co-operative sharing among organizations and communities. Medicine Ways staff is skilled in the areas of wilderness, healing and ceremonial practices.

INFORMATION: P.O. Box 443, Valley Ford, CA 94972, (707) 795-4789.

● MEDITATION GROUP FOR THE NEW AGE (MGNA)

The Meditation group for the New Age (MGNA) helps many through a five year course in techniques and aspects of meditation. In increasing depth, clear understandings of the great guidelines of the New Age are developed. Attention is ever focused upon service to humanity -- and ever upon the good of the larger whole.

MGNA has centers in many countries; its meditation course is available in various languages. Booklets are mailed free upon request on a bi-monthly schedule.

INFORMATION: P.O. Box 566, Ojai, CA 93023, (805) 646-6300.

● MEHER BABA CENTER

Meher Baba asserts that he is the same Ancient One known before as Krishna and Christ, come again to redeem man from his bondage of ignorance and guide him to realize his true Self which is God. Meher Baba is acknowledged by his many followers all over the world to be the Avatar, or God Incarnate, of the present Age.

In accordance with his teachings, his followers, often called Baba Lovers, believe that the most direct path to Self-realization is love and complete surrender to him. Meher Baba has always allowed his followers to express their love for him in their own way, whether it be through meetings and groups, through reading and meditating on the master, or through silently loving him (i.e. God) in the midst of one's daily life and activities. Several information centers around the country distribute information on his life and work. He himself has also written numerous books.

INFORMATION: P.O. Box 487, Myrtle Beach, SC 29577, (803) 272-6213 or 272-5295.

● META TANTAY INDIAN FOUNDATION

Rolling Thunder, a Cherokee Indian Intertribal Medicine Man known both here and abroad, is Founder and Director of the Meta Tantay Indian Foundation, dedicated to traditional life and protection of the Earth Mother.

Daybreak at Meta Tantay finds a circle of people around a fire in sunrise ceremony greeting Father Sun, Mother Earth, and the new day.

The people come to the land (262 acres) to participate in the traditional Indian way, to learn the natural way of life, and to experience the spiritual way of the Great Spirit. The expression of this philosophy is manifested in a six day work week for all. The work includes building dome-shaped lodges called wiki-ups, gardening, tending to the animals, cooking, and caring for each other.

After the duties are fulfilled, many crafts, such as beadwork, wood carving, leather work, knitting and jewelry making bring joy to all.

In the evenings a campfire warms the hearts and bodies of all as they relax after a day of work. There is much conversation, song music, and the opportunity to be with Rolling Thunder and beloved clan mother, Spotted Fawn, and learn the indian way through their story telling and guidance.

INFORMATION: P.O. Box 707, Carlin, NV 89822, (702) 754-9928.

● THE MICHIGAN METAPHYSICAL SOCIETY

The Society is dedicated to research and education in the processes of human consciousness. The Esoteric Sciences are taught, including: Healing and Vibrations, Tarot, Numerology, Meditation, Bio-Feedback, Hypnosis, Astrology, Scientific Hand Reading, Expanded Awareness, Practical Metaphysics, Zone Reflexology, Phrenology, Prophecy, Reincarnation, Graphology.

INFORMATION: 3018 W. Twelve Mile Rd., Berkeley, MI 48072, (313) 399-8299.

● THE MINISTRY OF HEALING -- SCHOOL OF REFLEXOLOGY

The Ministry of Healing/School of Reflexology is directed by Rev. Hilde Maria Frey.

Reflexology in conjunction with applications of an herb tincture called

Swedenbitter, (17 different herbs) is a most marvelous tool of healing. I myself got rid of a severe sciatic nerve pain in seven days. A last century Swedish physician composed this formula. This knowledge should be spread in the most unselfish way. People from all over come to my house to learn about this *Reflexherbology* as I call it. I respect other people's religious beliefs, but I counsel those who seek it.
INFORMATION: 3828 Kramer St., Harrisburg, PA 17109, (717) 545-7155.

● MISHAKAI CENTER FOR THE STUDY OF SHAMANISM

Mishakai offers Shamanism workshops to individuals interested in learning techniques which have been employed for millenia to heal oneself, the community and environment. Shamanistic subjects of study and exploration include: Healing ceremonies and rituals, chanting, dancing, pilgrimage, dreaming, and transpersonal experience. Instruction is provided by the Mishakai Staff and Associate Instructors which is composed of Native American Shamans and Spiritual Leaders, as well as experts in the aforesaid subjects of Shamanism.

The workshops are half either at the Center which is located near Covelo, California, or at other locations of natural beauty and high life force energy in various areas of North America. The number of workshop participants is limited to 15 in order to enhance personal instruction and group rapport. Several work scholarships and student discounts are available per workshop. For workshop descriptions and brochure write.
INFORMATION: P.O. Box 388, Covelo, CA 95428.

● ARTHUR MORGAN SCHOOL

This school was developed in 1962 by Ernest and Elizabeth Morgan to further the educational ideas of Arthur Morgan, father of TVA, proponent of cooperatives and president of Antioch college. The school is located on 100 acres in the Black Mountains of North Carolina. The school is a way of life for 35 boys and girls in grades 7 to 9. They, plus 14 staff people, are involved in working, studying, caring, coping and generally learning not only by doing but by living according to Ghandi's credo, "A school should be built by the children, should seek to be self-supporting, and should never be finished."
INFORMATION: Rt. 5, P.O. Box 335, Burnsville, NC 28714, (704) 675-4262 or 675-4555.

● MORNING GLORY COMMUNITY

Morning Glory Community is 40 acres -- 40 minutes from St. Louis. We share our beautiful land for different groups sponsoring activities, seminars, classes. We are vegetarians working towards raising our consciousness. We offer classes in polarity and Esalen-style massage. Inquiries and visits are welcomed.
INFORMATION: 2700 Oaker Dr., Arnold, MO 63010, (314) 296-7846.

Peace & Nuclear Disarmament Resources

The organizations and resources listed should be able to refer you to a range of disarmament and peace groups and activities in your area.

Abalone Alliance, 2940 16th St. #310, San Francisco, CA 94103, (415) 861-0592. West Coast referrals.

Action for Nuclear Disarmament, 56 Beacon St., Watertown, MA 02172.

Ads for Peace, P.O. Box 191, Staten Island, NY 10314. Promotes outreach and peace education through ads in local newspapers.

Alliance for Survival, 1503 N. Hobart Blvd., Los Angeles, CA 90027, (213) 462-6243.

American Citizens Together, P.O. Box 3046, Taos, NM 87571, (505) 758-1347. Southwest referrals.

American Friends Service Committee, 1501 Cherry St., Philadelphia, PA 19102, (215) 241-7000. Quaker-based; research, public information, and training programs.

American Library Association, Attn: Office for Library Outreach Services, 50 E. Huron St., Chicago, IL 60611. Publishes *Peace Research and Activist Groups -- A North American Directory*. Lists libraries, periodicals, etc.

Armistice/Live Without Trident, P.O. Box 12007, Seattle, WA 98102, (206) 324-1489. Grass-roots action/education.

Artists for Survival, c/o Mitchell Kamen, 144 Moody St., Waltham, MA 02154, (617) 891-4235.

Arts Alive!/Poets against the End of the World, 490 Riverside Dr., 19th Flr., New York, NY 10027, (212) 460-8980.

Bay State Conversion Project, 120 Bellevue Rd., Watertown, MA 02172. Organizes and lobbies for conversion of aerospace plants in Massachusetts.

The Blue Ribbon Watch, P.O. Box 10884, Marina del Rey, CA 90291, Wear a Blue Ribbon for World Nuclear Disarmament. Wear it over your Heart -- Every Day. It reminds you and others about the Danger and the Hope.

Brushfire Graphics/Food, Not Bombs, 1430 Massachusetts Ave., Rm. 306-35, Cambridge, MA 02138, (617) 492-0878.

Business Alert to Nuclear War, P.O. Box 7, Belmont, MA 02178, (617) 253-1578.

Catholic Workers League, 36 E. First St., New York, NY 10003, (212) 254-1640.

Center for Defense Information, Capital Gallery, West Wing #303, 600 Maryland Ave., S.W., Washington, D.C. 20024, (202) 484-9490. Research, media resource.

Center for Law and Pacifism, P.O. Box 1584, Colorado Springs, CO 80901. Provides information on legal ways to refuse to support war with your taxes.

Children's Campaign for Nuclear Disarmament, P.O. Box 550, RD. 1, Plainfield, VT 05667, (802) 454-7119.

Citizen Action for Lasting Security (CALS), P.O. Box 12763, Salem, OR 97309, (503) 371-8002. Is compiling a *Whole Freeze Catalog*.

Citizens Against Nuclear Power, P.O. Box 6625, Chicago, IL 60680, (312) 786-9041. Midwest referrals.

Citizens' Guide For Preventing Nuclear War, listing films, publications, and organizations, $3, from 1-800 528-6600 ext. 60.

Clergy & Laity Concerned, 198 Broadway #302, New York, NY 10038, (212) 964-6730. Multi-issue ecumenical group.

Coalition Against Registration & the Draft, 201 Massachusetts Ave., N.E., Washington, D.C. 20002, (202) 547-4340.

Coalition for a New Foreign & Military Policy, 120 Maryland Ave., N.E., Washington, D.C. 20002, (202) 546-8400. Research, bulletins, legislative updates.

Committee for Nuclear Disarmament, 11 Goodwin St., London N4, England.

Communicators for Nuclear Disarmament, 44 Hunt St., Watertown, MA 02172. A coalition of radio, film and graphic artists and writers who offer their services to other disarmament groups for peace work.

Council For A Liveable World, 100 Maryland Ave., N.E., Washington, D.C. 20002, (202) 543-4100. Lobbying, education, research; Arms Control Hotline, (202) 543-0006.

Council on Economic Priorities, 84 Fifth Ave., New York, NY 10011. Supports the Conversion Information Center and in-depth studies on military economic issues.

Council for a Nuclear Weapons Freeze, 2161 Massachusetts Ave., Cambridge, MA 02140. An umbrella organization with an extensive list of affiliates nationwide.

Disarmament Resource Center, 942 Market St., Rm. 708, San Francisco, CA 94102. Publishes a calendar of disarmament events in Northern California and is publishing a regional resource library.

Ecumenical Peace Institute, P.O. Box 9334, Berkeley, CA 94709. Coordinates peace fasting activities.

Educators for Social Responsibility, P.O. Box 1041, Brookline, MA 02147, (617) 277-1686.

European Nuclear Disarmament, 6 Endsleigh St., London WC1HO-DX, England.

Fellowship of Reconciliation, P.O. Box 271, Nyack, NY 10960, (914) 358-4601. International interfaith pacifist organization.

Friends of the Earth, 124 Spear St., San Francisco, CA 94105.

Fund for Peace, 345 East 46th St., New York, NY 10017. The fund advocates a no first use of nuclear weapons policy.

Ground Zero, 806 15th St., N.W., Suite 421, Washington, D.C. 20005, (202) 638-7401.

High-Tech Professionals For Peace, 2161 Massachusetts Ave., Cambridge, MA 02140.

Housemans Booksellers and Publishers, 5 Caledonian Rd., King's Cross, London N1, Great Britain. Publishes the *World Peace Diary* which contains over 1600 peace groups and periodicals worldwide. Your best single source of peace group information. Also available from Fellowship Publications, P.O. Box 271, Nyack, NY 10960.

Institute for Defense & Disarmament Studies, 251 Harvard St., Brookline, MA 92146, (617) 734-4216. Randall Forsberg's disarmament "think tank"; information. Publishes *North American Peace Directory*, a computerized list of over 2000 groups. Probably your best directory for U.S. groups and your best reference group for miscellaneous questions ($6).

Interfaith Center to Reverse the Arms Race, 132 North Euclid, Pasadena, CA 91101. The center advocates a bilateral freeze and maintains a resource center that includes a film and print library.

Interhelp, 84 Anderson St., San Francisco, CA 94110, (415) 641-8522.

International Physicians for the Prevention of Nuclear War, 635 Huntington Ave., Boston, MA 02115, (617) 738-9404.

Jobs With Peace, 2990 22nd St., San Francisco, CA 94110, (415) 821-1064.

Jonah House, 1933 Park Ave., Baltimore, MD 21217, (301) 669-6265. Nonviolent resistance.

June 12 Coalition, 853 Broadway, Suite 2109, New York, NY 10003, (212) 460-8980.

Larry Langdon Publications, 34735 Perkins Creek Rd., Cottage Grove, OR 97424. *Creating Peace, A Positive Handbook*. A lot of information on Peace and nuclear disarmament from a positive New Age viewpoint.

Lawrence Livermore Lab Conversion Project, 944 Market St., San Francisco, CA 94102. The project is developing alternate-use plans for the U.S. nuclear weapons laboratories at Livermore and elsewhere.

Lawyers Alliance for Nuclear Arms Control, 14 Beacon St., Suite 719, Boston, MA 02108, (617) 227-0118.

Meeting of the Ways, P.O. Box 1080s, San Rafael, CA 94915. New Age Spiritual Centers for nuclear disarmament.

Mid-Peninsula Conversion Project, 867 W. Dana, Suite 203, Mountain View, CA 94041, (415) 968-8798.

Mobilization for Survival, 48 St. Marks Pl., New York, NY 10003, (212) 460-8545.

National Center for a World Peace Tax Fund, 2111 Florida Ave., N.W., Washington, D.C. 20008, (202) 483-3751. Supports a bill to permit people to request military part of their taxes to go for peace instead.

National Peace Academy Campaign, 110 Maryland Ave., N.E., Suite 409, Washington, D.C. 20002. Works on legislation to set up a national peace academy.

National Peace Coalition, P.O. Box 5789, Fresno, CA 93755. A coalition of grassroots activists that works with other peace groups toward a bilateral freeze.

The Nuclear Film Guide. By David Brown. Lists more than 100 films on nuclear issues. $5.50 from *Nuclear Film Guide*, 2114 Golden Gate Ave., San Francisco, CA 94118.

Nuclear Information and Resource Service, 1346 Connecticut Ave., N.W., Washington, D.C. 20036. NIRS is a clearinghouse for materials and information on nuclear power and disarmament. Call toll free for urgent information requests (800-424-2477, 1-5 p.m. EST) or write for its publication list.

Nuclear Network, 1346 Connecticut Ave., N.W., Washington, D.C. 20036, (202) 835-0777. Is compiling a *Nuclear Whole Earth Catalog*.

Nuclear Weapons Freeze Campaign, 4144 Lindell, Rm. 201, St. Louis, MO 63108, (314) 533-1169. National clearinghouse.

Nukewatch, 315 West Gorham St., Madison, WI 53705. A public education project of the Progressive Foundation, it serves as a catalyst for local action and as a nationwide information clearinghouse on nuclear issues.

Parenting in Nuclear Age, c/o Bananas, 6501 Telegraph Ave., Oakland, CA 94609. Sponsored by Bananas, a parent resource center, it has handouts and speakers available for parent education.

P.E.A.C.E. Network, c/o Truth Research Foundation, P.O. Box 7705, Stockton, CA 95207. Provides a vehicle for conscious linking to co-create a cohesive World Spirit. (Prayer, meditation, networking, and action!)

Planetary Peace Alliance, P.O. Box 18886, San Francisco, CA 94118. *Peace News To Share* provides listings of new groups, events, and materials. It seems to provide the best peace networking information around. $8 suggested contribution for 1 year (6 issues).

Physicians for Social Responsibility, P.O. Box 114, Watertown, MA 02172, (617) 924-3468.

Riverside Church Disarmament Program, 490 Riverside Dr., New York, NY 10027. A national program to educate the religious community on peace issues and to organize conferences and workshops.

SANE, 711 G. St., S.E., Washington, D.C. 20003, (202) 546-7100. Research, lobbying, education, rallies.

Promoting Enduring Peace, 112 Beach Ave., Woodmont, CT 06460. Provides peace tours to Russia!

Solidarity Peace Fund, Diocesan Pastoral Center, P.O. Box 5644, Amarillo, TX 79107. Support for Pantex weapons plant workers seeking peaceable employment.

Union of Concerned Comics, P.O. Box 1200, Berkeley, CA 94704.

Union of Concerned Scientists, 1384 Massachusetts Ave., Cambridge, MA 02238, (617) 547-5552.

Waging Peace: A Handbook for the Struggle to Abolish Nuclear Weapons. Edited by Jim Walls, *Harper & Row*, 1982. $4.95. A guidebook for action that includes U.S. and Canadian resource listings.

War Resisters League (WRL), 339 Lafayette St., New York, NY 10012, (212) 228-0450. Tax resistance information.

Wilmington College Peace Resource Center, Pyle Center, P.O. Box 1183, Wilmington, OH 45177. The center has a collection of printed, graphic and audiovisual resources, including comprehensive holdings of print and film on the Hiroshima and Nagasaki bombings.

Women's Action for Nuclear Disarmament, 691 Massachusetts Ave., Arlington, MA 02174. WAND is a political action committee dedicated to ending the nuclear arms race. Founded by Dr. Helen Caldicott, it now has affiliate groups nationwide.

Women's International League for Peace and Freedom, 120 Maryland Ave., N.E., Washington, D.C. 20002, (202) 546-8644. Education, lobbying, grass-roots action; has initiated national Stop The Arms Race (STAR) movement.

Women's Strike for Peace, 145 South 13th St., Philadelphia, PA 19107. WSP is a 21 year old organization campaigning to end the arms race through political action and public education.

World Goodwill, 866 United Nations Plaza, Suite 566-7, New York, NY 10017. Publishes *World Goodwill* magazine which provides a listing of international peace groups.

"*There's a very fine line between inner and outer work.
We would like, I'm sure, to have all of our actions come
out of enlightenment, come out of calmness and quietness
and spaciousness and appreciation of what is, but we've
taken form. We're in bodies and by that very nature, we
are lost, involved in action. We can't not act, so what we
do is act as consciously as we can, as compassionately as
we can from moment to moment.*

*The art of using the experiences of life as a vehicle to
awaken is to use them to bring you closer to that calm
center and that quietness. This includes the work you
would do to alleviate the suffering that is inherent in the
use of nuclear weapons.*

*You don't complete your inner work before you do outer
work. Nor do you say, 'Well, the hell with the inner work:
I'll go do the outer work because it's so important and
pressing.' That's not conscious either. The conscious thing
is the simultaneous doing of both.*"

-- Ram Dass

● MORNINGLAND

Established first in 1973, Morningland was set into motion by the Spiritual Hierarchy as a necessary vehicle through which people could develop their spiritual potentials. "Oneness" is the core of Morningland's teachings, given by the founder and spiritual Master Donato, who walked in the footsteps of the Ascended Masters as he received the telepathic directions under which Morningland was born.

The universal tools, the divine sciences of astrology, aura, numerology, palmistry, tarot, yoga and telepsychology, have been evolved by Donato to channel through these metaphysical teachings so we can learn to see clearly our own mirror reflections in our brothers and sisters.

As a healing center Morningland is the home of the Queen of Peace, Sri Donato, who is the living presence of the Master. All healings in Morningland are performed by the Holy Father through the Master, Donato the Christ and his living presence our modern day saint, Sri Donato. Miraculous healings happen daily. It is possible to have a private audience with the Queen of Peace, Sri Donato, on request.

INFORMATION: 2600 E. 7th., Long Beach, CA 90804, (213) 433-9906.

● MORRIS FOUNDATION, INC.

Our program is to provide a growthful environment for alcoholics where the process of creating a new life is allowed to flourish. Treatment is designed to facilitate resocialization, not by merely acquiring new labels, but by initiating an exploration into self. The discovery experience that comes out of increased awareness is a desired result at the Morris Foundation. Some Areas covered are AA, stress management, exercise, nutrition, individual/group counseling.

A holistic approach to sobriety is offered. Your life is important to us. Please call or write.

INFORMATION: 26 North Elm St., Waterbury, CT 06702, (203) 755-1143.

● MOUNT MADONNA CENTER

Mount Madonna Center for the Creative Arts and Sciences is an educational institution set on 337 acres of forest and meadowland overlooking Monterey Bay. Inspired by Baba Hari Dass and managed by students whose talents and interests are unified by the practice of yoga, the Center is dedicated to fostering individual creativity. We offer seminars in 1. *Yoga* -- several four day retreats throughout the year, weekend meditation intensives, hatha yoga, and two three-week long Ashtanga Yoga Teachers Training courses (July and December). 2. *Healing Arts* -- Ayurveda (an ancient holistic healing science from India), herb workshops, massage, and various other healing techniques. 3. *Fine Arts* -- dance, music, art, drama.

In addition to the above we have personal retreat, seclusion, and work study programs for those who wish to take some time out of their regular routines and spend it in the mountains in a positive environment.

For those who have carpentry, electrical, plumbing, or architectural

skills, and are interested in joining the on-site work crew for a period of time, we are currently accepting applications.
INFORMATION: P.O. Box 51-BB, Watsonville, CA 95077, (408) 847-0406.

● MOVEMENT OF SPIRITUAL INNER AWARENESS (MSIA)

The Movement of Spiritual Inner Awareness has centers of learning located at various points across the nation where people come together to awaken higher states of consciousness within themselves. Seminars are given by Dr. John-Roger Hinkins, spiritual director of MSIA (Pronounced "Messiah"). John-Roger teaches that there is a Universal Energy flowing through all life, and it extends from the Heart of God as a pure connection to all planes of existence. When beings come into the guidance of this Consciousness, then they can experience great spiritual growth. This is the ultimate aim of the Movement.
INFORMATION: P.O. Box 3935, Los Angeles, CA 90051, (213) 733-4055.

● MOVEMENT PUZZLES INSTITUTE

The institute sponsors training in Leistiko Somatics, a kind of movement therapy/body work developed by Norma Leistiko. The training is 1000 hours and includes traditional studies in anatomy and physiology as well as the more innovative kinesiology, creative dance, body image awareness, and visualization drawings. Enrollment is limited to 12 students, and all of the work is done in partners. Upon completion of the course, the student will have a concrete, step by step method to teach another person kinaesthetic and body image awareness. The institute also sponsors Feldenkrais method taught by Norma Leistiko, both Awareness through Movement (group lessons) and Functional integration (individual lessons).
INFORMATION: 2575 Washington St. #1, San Francisco, CA 94115, (415) 922-8809.

● THE MOVING CENTER

The Moving Center is the name, context, spirit and location of Gabrielle Roth's life work. She's an artist, author, teacher and healer whose current work is on the leading edge of experimental dance/theater, holistic philosophy and creative self-exploration. Her understanding of the human psyche and the dynamic of healing its wounds have catalyzed the lives of people the world over. Although grounded in the living language of the dance, Gabrielle uses all the arts to connect people to their power and spontaneity, to release them from layers of conditioning and belief that imprison the human spirit. Contact Center for details on events and trainings.
INFORMATION: P.O. Box 2034, Red Bank, NJ 07701, (201) 530-0250 or (212) 772-0946.

● MYERS INSTITUTE FOR CREATIVE STUDIES

In all the programs at the Myers Institute for Creative Studies, the underlying philosophical theme is that the most meaningful and fulfilling creative process you can choose in your life is to search for the knowledge which leads to making life itself a work of art.

We feature ideas rather than entertainment, exploration rather than closure, questions rather than dogma. In brief, we attempt to nurture and support creative thinking, creative solutions and creative living on a day-by-day basis. This is done through private meetings, courses, lectures, workshops, cassette tapes and Friday night events.

We are a non-profit, tax-exempt educational organization located near Children's Hospital. Please call or write for dates and details on our programs, to be included on our mailing list, or to receive a brochure of Rochelle Myers' cassette tapes.

INFORMATION: 3827 California St., San Francisco, CA 94118, (415) 668-1555.

● NAM -- NEW AGE MEDIA

NAM is devoted to gathering, channeling, storing and disseminating information vital to the New Consciousness re-appearing on this planet. It receives information from alternative media and individual correspondence, filters this information, keeps what it can deal with effectively and passes on what it can't directly use to other groups. Information is made available to the public through such projects as: this book, *New Consciousness Sourcebook, A Pilgrims Guide to Planet Earth,* and other Spiritual Community publications, NAM Mailing Lists, participation in New Age expositions and gatherings and other direct informational services. Through better organization and use of computers NAM eventually hopes to offer more services geared to each individual's needs. For more information on existing services, send a stamped self-addressed envelope.

INFORMATION: NAM, Box 1067, Berkeley, CA 94701, (415) 644-3229.

● NARAYANANDA UNIVERSAL YOGA (N.U. YOGA)

Sri Swami Narayananda, a realized sage from India, is the spiritual leader of ashrams and centers in many countries. He is available to all sincere Truth seekers. The Swami gives personal guidance and has written many authoritative books on yoga philosophy, psychology and kundalini shakti. The ashramites live a simple, pure and holy life with regular meditations, yoga, asanas & pranayama and they earn their own income. Visitors are welcome and spiritual retreats encouraged.

INFORMATION: Route 2, P.O. Box 24, Winter, WI 54896, (715) 266-4963 and N.U. Yoga Center, 1418 North Kedzie Ave., Chicago, IL 60651, (312) 278-2737.

● NATIONAL ASTROLOGICAL SOCIETY (NASO)

The Society's goals are to promote high standards of practice and instruction, facilitate communication among astrologers through meetings and publications and to foster cooperation among persons and organizations interested in astrology.

The NASO School of Astrology offers an intensive program of classes and workshops on astrology and sponsors lecturers from throughout the world.

INFORMATION: 205 Third Ave., Suite 2A, New York, NY 10003, (212) 673-1831.

● NATIONAL SPIRITUAL SCIENCE CENTER

Established 1941 in Washington By Reverend Alice Wellstood Tindall. Ordained at The Spiritual Science Mother Church in New York, Rev. Tindall directed Center activities 28 years. The Revs Henry and Diane Nagorka, trained by Rev. Tindall, were ordained by the Mother Church. Upon Rev. Tindall's disablement, the Revs Nagorka assumed Center direction in 1970.

A non-profit organization approved by the I.R.S., NSSC offers: regular services; four-year training course by its School of Spiritual Science; Holistic Medical Clinic (separate listing); Metaphysical reference Library; Bookstore; ESPress, a publishing division (separate listing).

INFORMATION: 5605 16th St., N.W., Washington, D.C. 20011, (202) 723-4510.

● NETWORK OF CONSCIOUS JUDAISM

The Network of Conscious Judaism is integrating the mystical, meditative and psychological teachings and practices rooted within traditional Judaism. Classes in Hassidism, Kabbalah, Jewish Meditation and Chanting are held in the San Francisco area, Los Angeles and around the Country. Teachers include Rabbi David Zeller (Network director), Rabbi Shlomo Carlebach, and others.

The Network is a resource center of classes, workshops, retreats, holyday celebrations, and counseling, and the Judaic Book Service, with books on all these subjects. For information of classes, counseling, book catalog or membership, call or write Rabbi David Zeller.

INFORMATION: 3825 Baldwin Dr., Dept. A, Santa Clara, CA 95051, (408) 247-7385.

● THE NETWORK OF LIGHT

The Network of Light is a network of many area groups which have programs based on New Age philosophy or spiritual development, emphasizing personal growth and responsibility. The Network includes groups from the

Washington, D.C., Maryland and Virginia areas, and from neighboring states.

The purpose of the Network is to strengthen ties between light centers and to promote the synergy needed for social transformation in the New Age.

The Network has planned monthly dinner-lectures, an annual Heart to Heart Festival featuring group presentations, and a Global Day of Meditation and Prayer for World Peace and Unity.

INFORMATION: 4617 Hunt Ave., Chevy Chase, MD 20815, (301) 986-1223.

● NEW AGE AWARENESS CENTER

The New Age Awareness Center is a networking information/resource center, a totally non-profit organization, and is a forum to increase awareness of alternatives for the spirit, mind, and body. The Center proposes no belief system, but rather, encourages each individual to find one's own path. Groups and individuals are invited to present their ideas through the Center and all New Age related subjects are welcomed at meetings, workshops and seminars. The focal center is located in Los Alamos, New Mexico and branches are being formed in Taos, Espanola, and Sante Fe. For more information contact Andronica or Mechail.

INFORMATION: P.O. Box 969, Los Alamos, NM 87544, (505) 662-4000.

● NEW AGE SCHOOL OF MASSAGE

The New Age School of Massage is a school of healing arts. The love that is shared during the training is the most powerful aspect of each student's experience. While maintaining a very high standard of technical proficiency, we focus on healing ourselves and our planet through love. The ten-week course, which includes Swedish/Esalen massage, Breema and Reflexology, leads to certification. We offer many workshops ranging from bodywork practices to Shamanism. Closely assocatied with the California School of Herbal Studies, we annually offer *Herbs and Massage:* The Simple Arts of Healing.

INFORMATION: P.O. Box 958, Sebastopol, CA 95472, (702) 823-1212.

● NEW COLLEGE OF CALIFORNIA

Accredited! Alternative! Independent! Unique! Public-Interest and Community-Oriented! Financial Aid Available! Credit for Prior Learning! Design your own courses; be responsible for your own education!

Program Options: Bachelor's Degrees in Humanities. Bachelor's Degrees/Master's Degree in Poetics. Master's Degree in Psychology. Weekend College for Working-Adults ... with 60-credits, you can complete your B.A. in 8 months. Pre-Professional Weekend Science Institute ... for: Chiropractic, Naturopathic, Podiatric applicants. West Marin Program. Public-Interest Law School. For information contact Mark Feldman, Director of Admissions or Sabira Scott, Coordinator of Admissions.

INFORMATION: 777 Valencia St., San Francisco, CA 94110, (415) 626-1694.

● THE NEW MEXICO ACADEMY OF ADVANCED HEALING ARTS

Sponsored by Dr. Jay Victor Scherer, the New Mexico Academy of Advanced Healing Arts (NMAAHA) offers training towards a degree in Homeopathy or Naturopathy. Our nine month full time program begins in September of 1982 and includes: Nutrition; herbology; homeopathy; ayurvedics; iridology; physiology; Molecular Biochemistry; Kineseology; Reflexology; Healing with sound, color and dance; yoga; Neuro-linguistic Programming; Human Centered Biology; natural childbirth; oriental medicine; meditation and energy work; and polarity.

Our program has been designed to achieve a balance of spirit and intellect, the opening of the heart going hand in hand with the ability to apply our knowledge in a practical way. We feel that it is only by the unfoldment of our spiritual self that we can truly become instruments of the Intelligent healing force of God and Nature, knowing with utter certainty when and how to apply the most appropriate healing tools to reestablish and maintain the being's natural harmony and health. Office hours are 3-6 p.m. Send $2 for our catalog.

INFORMATION: 133 Romero St., Santa Fe, NM 87501, (505) 982-6271.

● THE NEW VRINDABAN COMMUNITY -- ISKCON

Founded in 1968 by His Divine Grace Kirtanananda Swami Bhaktipada, a pure devotee of Lord Krishna, to provide a haven for seekers of the highest spiritual truths. The rural lifestyle is based upon the ancient and sublime teachings of the Bhagavad-Gita. The 400 happy residents live amidst 3000 acres of green rolling hills, and engage in farming, dairy, teaching, building and in dozens of trades and arts and crafts. Members have built the world famous Prabhupada's Palace of Gold. The community is open year round and a new 38 room guest house and vegetarian meals accommodate vistors and pilgrims.

INFORMATION: Rd. #1, P.O. Box 319, Moundsville, WV 26041, (304) 843-1600.

● NEW YORK ZEN CENTER

This is a Soto Zen Temple under the guidance of Rev. Kando Nakajima. Beginners are asked to attend a weekly introductory lecture given every Monday, after which they are welcome to participate in any of the activities of the center, which includes zazen, Monday and Friday evenings at 8 p.m.; lectures, Wednesday evening and Sunday morning; and an all-day sesshin the third Sunday of each month.

INFORMATION: 267 West 81 St., New York, NY 10024, (212) 724-4172.

● NURSES IN TRANSITION

We're nurses who are expanding our roles. The desire to fulfill our creative potential in nursing has brought us together. Collectively we are learning new ways to channel our healing energies, starting with healing ourselves. We support nurse colleagues in clarifying goals and in being strong, innovative change agents. Through national networking, we are realizing our vision of holistic autonomous, health oriented nursing practice. We welcome your membership in our growing organization. Information about chapters outside the Bay Area is available from the San Francisco Networking Center.

INFORMATION: P.O. Box 14472, San Francisco, CA 94114, (415) 282-7999.

● NYINGMA INSTITUTE

The Nyingma Institute was established in 1973 to convey the essence of Tibetan Buddhist teachings to a wide range of Western students.

Areas of study include Meditation, Kum Nye Relaxation, Buddhist Philosophy and Psychology, and Tibetan Language. The Nyingma approach to meditation includes many techniques to bring lightness and awareness into everyday living. Kum Nye, a gentle healing system, relieves stress, transforms negative patterns, facilitates balance, and increases enjoyment and appreciation of life. All practice instruction is tailored to the needs of each student.

Weekly classes are offered on the quarter system, and weekend seminars and special events are held frequently throughout the year. Week-long retreats include instruction, practice periods, counseling, vegetarian meals, and comfortable accommodations. Intensive training programs are also available for students seeking deeper connection with the teachings and their transformative power.

The primary goal of all instruction is to look at ourselves honestly, with complete openness, and by investigating the nature and functioning of our own mind, to gain enduring knowledge and understanding in our lives.

Free meditation and Dharma talk are held each Sunday at 5:00 p.m. All are invited.

INFORMATION: 1815 Highland Pl., Berkeley, CA 94709, (415) 843-6812.

O

● THE OJAI FOUNDATION

In 1927, the humanitarian Dr. Annie Besant, president of the Theosophical Society, envisioned a community where new ideas could be explored and realized, a place of peace on the planet where the qualities of intuition and intentional cooperation could be nurtured. Under the direction of Joan Halifax, Ph.D., The Ojai Foundation is working towards the realization of her vision. On 40 acres of semi-wilderness land in the Upper Ojai Valley

(80 miles from Los Angeles), the Foundation offers retreats with leading healers, scientists, artists and masters who represent diverse traditions and disciplines. Programs with Rolling Thunder, Paul Horn, Robert Bly, John and Toni Lilly, Jean Houston, Al Huang, Lama Sogyal Rinpoche, Peter Caddy, R. D. Laing, and others are planned for 1982-1983. A work-scholars residential program is available.

INFORMATION: P.O. Box 1620, Ojai, CA 93023, (805) 646-8343.

● OMEGA FELLOWSHIP

Omega Fellowship is an unique community offering psychological and spiritual growth opportunities focused on "lightening up". What makes us unique is our sense of oneness -- we see ourselves as an extended family, a support group of brothers and sisters who love and assist each other in our growth through weekly groups and special events. By clearing away the stuff that separates us from our beautiful inner selves, we're learning to play again and create joy and satisfaction in our lives. Call or write Rev. Baba Herrick.

INFORMATION: Omega Fellowship, 23800 Morrell Cutoff, Los Gatos, CA 95030, (408) 353-2545.

● ORGONOMY-WILHELM REICH

Born in Austria in 1897, Wilhelm Reich began his career as a disciple of Freud. He eventually broke with Freud, and formulated the Orgasm Theory. According to Reich, the orgasmic, rhythmic, pulsating movement was the basic, primordial function of all living units, and the very expression of life itself. He asserted that the organism's inability to combat disease was due to the repression of the orgasm.

In search of the force that activated the orgasm, Reich claimed that he discovered what he called Orgone energy, the Cosmic Life Force. He designed an Orgone Box for focusing this energy. Reich advocated that the right to sexual freedom be guaranteed by law, believing that man's salvation lay in again affirming life and harmonizing his evolution with the Cosmic Force. This scientist's theories have been put to practical use in Reichian therapy, massage and bio-energetics.

● OZ

Oz is an alternative energy community in the Northern California redwood forests for children, adults, and families. The residents offer workshops and camps introducing country living, tree houses, organic gardening and cooking, drama, wind and solar energy, music and hoedowns, canoeing, hot tubs, sauna, yoga, tai-chi, massage, herb walks, journal keeping, sports, New Games, treasure hunts, movie making, and more. There is no particular teacher or religion. The program integrates personal responsibility, over an earthy base of farm living (milking, animals, self-sufficiency). During the year there is a work/study program; during the winter they form a quiet cooperative.

INFORMATION: P.O. Box 147, Pt. Arena, CA 95468, (707) 882-2449.

● OZARK LIFE CENTER

Holistic health consultations in the medicinal use of Herbs, Nutrition, and supplements. Iridology diagnosis, Massage Therapy, Fasting, Energy Directed Healing, Aura Balancing, Bates Vision Therapy, etc.

State accredited correspondence (home study) or classroom courses in massage therapy, naturopathic medicine, and herbology.

Wholesale/retail herbal healing products, domestic bee pollen, salves, massage oils, massage tables. Powdered herb formulas harmoniously balanced for each organ, gland, blood, lymph, and energy systems. Products catalog -- $1.

Dr. Steve Schechter, N.D., co-director, is regularly published in national health magazines. We are available to teach workshops.

INFORMATION: Rt. 4, P.O. Box 540-S, Grandview Rd., Springdale, ARK 72764, (501) 361-2155.

P

● PACIFIC HEALING ARTS CENTER

The Pacific Healing Arts Center is a holistic chiropractic clinic dedicated to the goal of Abundant Good Health. We offer a wide range of services from nutritional counseling, correction of sports injuries, and conventional chiropractic care to advanced cranial balancing, coordinated jaw joint therapy with dental practitioners, and classical homeopathy.

We specialize in the treatment of chronic problems, especially those problems which have not been relieved by other therapeutic methods. Most of our patients are seeking Abundant Good Health, not merely the relief of symptoms. We believe that people must investigate all of the factors involved in their body and lifestyle which may affect their health. The body is an integrated vessel in which one part may affect or be affected by many other parts.

Our practitioners are highly trained in the advanced techniques of applied kinesiology, sacro-occipital technique, and craniopathy, and have developed an integrated approach using all these methods. Office hours are

"The beauty of the nuclear issue, at least in my own life, is that it's an opportunity to put spiritual practices in action. If you look at reverence for life as the basis of spiritual strength and then look at the nuclear threat, you're going to become active and speak out."

-- Patricia Ellsberg

Monday through Friday, 10 a.m. to 6 p.m., Saturday, 10 a.m. to 3 p.m. Please call for more information or an appointment to meet the doctors for a free consultation. William M. Mariner, D.C. is Clinical Director.

INFORMATION: 318 Ninth St., Suite A, Del Mar, CA 92014, (714) 481-2541.

● PAN -- PLANETARY ALIGNMENT NETWORK

PAN, the Planetary Alignment Network is an educational organization focused on planetary healing and on-going research into the nature of the earth's body and energy field -- linking the knowledge of the ancients with recent scientific discoveries and channeled information from Ascended Masters and cosmic beings serving the earth in her transition to a higher octave of vibration. The directors of PAN are available for lectures and audio - video presentations on planetary healing and earth energies. PAN also publishes a newsletter to facilitate networking.

INFORMATION: P.O. Box 21, Capitola, CA 95010, (408) 688-5935.

● PARAPSYCHOLOGY SOURCES OF INFORMATION CENTER

The Parapsychology Sources of Information Center serves as a clearinghouse for information on research findings, theories, organizations, publications, and personnel involved in parapsychology, mysticism, and consciousness studies. We collect, catalog, and index books, journals, articles, pamphlets, and unpublished manuscripts dealing with parapsychology and consciousness research, and provide fee-based information and bibliographic service. The PSI Center maintains a publishing program and compiles bibliographies on the subject of your choice. We also sell second-hand books, back issues of parapsychology periodicals, and reprints of articles and book reviews. A price list is available for $3. Write for free brochure. Rhea A. White, Director.

INFORMATION: 2 Plane Tree Ln., Dix Hills, NY 11746, (516) 271-1243.

● P.E.A.C.E. NETWORK

We will stop the arms race when enough of us -- all kinds of people in all countries -- realize our power of conscious choice, the power of the human spirit to act with One Vision, One Voice, One Purpose to determine our planet's future. P.E.A.C.E. Network offers a way to exercise that choice.

Each day, hold the shared *World Vision* in your mind: "I form a linkage with other P.E.A.C.E. Networkers around the world in visualizing our planet as seen from space -- beautiful and whole -- and enfolding it in an atmosphere of Peace, Love, and Light. I image it being lifted up with my own hands in gratitude for its service as humanity's home."

Each day, affirm the *Peace Pledge* within your heart: "Peace is my conscious choice. I choose to be peaceful and to stand for peace. I choose to make a difference in the world. In my own way and with the strength of my own convictions, I choose to act creatively and cooperatively for peace. This is my pledge!"

Each day, ask someone to join with us in our common purpose: "union of the human spirit As One to co-create an integrated World Spirit. We can, by linking with one another one by one, person to person, day by day, transform the destiny of mankind."

Coming together in this greater purpose as P.E.A.C.E. Networkers, with vision and commitment, we are discovering our own uniqueness as individuals, and expressing in new, creative ways. Join us. You are essential! Join in our daily time-synchronized World Vision. To know more, do more, and help the Network grow, send $2 for membership and P.E.A.C.E. Networker Action Packet (with flier, Action Guidebook, World Vision and Peace Pledge membership card, and Peace stickers).

INFORMATION: Truth Research Foundation, P.O. Box 7705, Stockton, CA 95207, (209) 478-7378.

● PHILOSOPHICAL RESEARCH SOCIETY

Founded in 1934 by Manly P. Hall, the Philosophical Research Society seeks to increase understanding of the nature of man through research in the areas of philosophy, comparative religion, and psychology. A quarterly program of seminars, workshops, and lectures is presented, featuring Manly P. Hall plus an international group of guest speakers. In addition to activities at the center in Los Angeles, there exists a number of study groups throughout the country which operate under the Society's supervision. The Society puts out an 80-page quarterly journal, published since 1941, and has an extensive library on its premises, containing over 50,000 volumes. The Society is always open to the public, and has no dues or membership list.

INFORMATION: 3910 Los Feliz Blvd., Los Angeles, CA 90027, (213) 663-2167.

● PLANETARY CITIZENS

Planetary Citizens was founded in 1974 by U. Thant (then Secretary-General of the United Nations), Norman Cousins and Donald Keys in response to the need for an organization to aid people in making the next major transition facing the Earth today: the movement from nationalistic and individualistic attitudes to a world community consciousness and active responsibility in determining the fate of the Planet.

Planetary Citizens provides avenues for people to discover for themselves ways in which they can contribute to the world community through publications, lecturing and a neighborhood-based international public education program on making the local-global connection.

INFORMATION: P.O. Box 1715, New Rochelle, NY 10802.

● PLAY MOUNTAIN PLACE

Play Mountain is a school that fosters self-discovery, self-discipline, and independence. Young people are respected as individuals with unique abilities, thoughts, and needs. Curriculum evolves from the interests of students and teachers.

On the school grounds are trees, earth, sand, private places, flexible structures, and open spaces. Our special human environment reflects the school philosophy: to allow the person's own impulse toward growth to function as freely as possible. Nursery and elementary ages; extended hours; parent involvement internships-teacher training seminars in non-authoritarian problem solving. Call for visiting time.

INFORMATION: 6063 Hargis St., Los Angeles, CA 90034, (213) 870-4381.

● POLARITY THERAPY

Dr. Randolph Stone, Doctor of Chiropractic, Osteopathy, and Naprapathy is the founder of Polarity. He began his career in the healing arts in 1912 in Chicago, and after receiving his degrees continued his studies all over the world. Among the systems he studied were Chinese Acupuncture, Naturopathy, Homeopathy, the Ayurvedic System of India and folk health practices of other countries. Polarity represents a synthesis of this transcultural health wisdom, that is simple, clear and a universally applicable approach to natural health care.

There are four major aspects to Polarity, the purpose of which is to balance the flow of life energy in the body. The first is a manipulative technique consisting of simple and gentle contacts on the body with both hands. These contacts are applied to pressure sensitive points which Dr. Stone identifies and maps out in his writings. The manipulation serves to stimulate energy centers in the body (called "Chakras" in Sanskrit), and to reestablish within each individual a sense of being "in Balance" with oneself and with one's environment.

The second aspect of Polarity is Polarity Yoga, a series of easy stretching postures combining movement and sound. These raising exercises are excellent for self-health care and easily integrated into daily life. Manipulations for oneself using Polarity techniques are also a part of Polarity Yoga. The Polarity diet, the third aspect of the system, consists of the use of foods and herbs to first cleanse and purify the digestive system and then to rebuild the body. Clear thinking is the fourth, the subtlest and most dynamic aspect of Polarity. It is what enables the individual to carry on by oneself, to consolidate the gains one has achieved through the other aspects of Polarity, and to retain one's own sense of energy flow and balance. Understanding the laws of energy will demonstrate that energy follows thought, and that as a person thinks so they are, at that time.

● POLESTAR INTERNATIONAL

Polestar International offers the spiritual teachings of Dr. Terry and Deb Chitwood. A student's spiritual development is accelerated through self-mastery sessions. Self-Mastery sessions consist of a dialogue between student and teacher where knowledge is transmitted by the presence of the teacher as well as by the spoken word. Residential intensives in self-mastery, meditation, yoga, inner breathing, postural restructuring, ki development, aikido, weight loss, natural foods nutrition, and vegetarian cooking are offered. Books, tapes and trainings are available. Polestar also has an urban spiritual community that lives, works, and shares on many levels, especially in working with feelings and dreams. Write or call for free information.

INFORMATION: 620 South Minnesota St., Suite 1, Sioux Falls, SD 57104, (605) 338-2888.

● THE PRISON-ASHRAM PROJECT

The Prison-Ashram Project is a free resource for prisoners and other shut-ins and is supported by the freewill donations made by a few thousand interested folks who wish to be on our mailing list and keep up with this work. The project distributes several books and tapes and a quarterly newsletter. By checking through our files, we can also usually help connect people to needs, resources, and opportunities for doing various forms of prison service. Director Bo Lozoff does prison workshops, training seminars, and public lectures in one or two tours each year throughout the country. (See article: *Growing Up In Prison* by Bo in this book.) Write for more information, materials, or to make donations.

INFORMATION: Bo & Sita Lozoff, Rt. 1, P.O. Box 201-N, Durham, N.C. 27705.

● THE PROVIDENCE ZEN CENTER

The Providence Zen Center, a residential community in rural Rhode Island, offers traditional Zen training under the direction of Zen Master Seung Sahn through daily meditation, monthly intensive retreats, and extended training programs. Teaching with Zen Master Seung Sahn are three Master Dharma Teachers, who are authorized to teach koan practice.

In the summer and winter, 90-day retreats are offered, divided into three-week sessions of sitting. In the summer workshops are offered in organic gardening, ecology, carpentry, vegetarian cooking, and stone carving, pottery, or another art.

INFORMATION: 528 Pound Rd., Cumberland, RI 02864, (401) 769-6464.

● THE PSYCHIC STUDIES INSTITUTE

PSI offers an opportunity to extend your *normal* perception into the realm usually considered *psychic*. We seek to help our students develop their sensitivity and self-knowledge as well as their perception; and our three most important tools are experience, affection and humor.

We conduct a Ten Month Intensive Training Program for those who wish to develop their clairvoyance and to undergo a rigorous process of self-examination and growth. Enrollment is continuous. The school offers eight week workshops, as well as student and professional aura readings/balancings.

INFORMATION: 535 Cordova Rd., Suite 164, Santa Fe, NM 87501, (505) 983-5681.

● THE PYRAMID CENTER OF BHAKTI YOGA

At the solar-energy pyramid center in the Santa Monica Mountains learn the science of Bhakti Yoga. Free Indian vegetarian feast, artik, bhajans,

Bhagavad-gita discussion, mantra meditation, and video presentations every Sunday 6:30 to 8:30 p.m. Also offered is a daily meditation program from 4:30 a.m. to 6:00 a.m., and Indian Vegetarian Cooking classes. A center for the International Society for Krsna Consciousness, founder acarya A. C. Bhakivedanta Swami Prabhupada; regional acarya Srila Ramesvara Swami Maharja.

INFORMATION: 20395 Callon Dr., Topanga, CA 90290, (213) 455-1658.

R

● RAINBOW TRIBE

The vision and the movement of the Rainbow Tribe is toward unity. It is away from separateness, away from discord and towards trust, away from greed and towards generosity, away from grasping and towards sharing. It is a return to the tribal way of life, a way of veneration and respect of all brothers and sisters equally, young or old, where every voice is heard within the council circle. To these ends, they hold gatherings where people come to meet each other and learn together in order to create new communities where people can live in harmony with each other and the Earth. Incorporated into the Rainbow Tribe is the Tribal Healing Council. Through the time-proven methods of the American Indians such as fasting, prayer, chanting, dancing, sweat lodges and healing herbs, the Rainbow Tribe endeavors to restore balance and harmony between the sick and Mother Nature. They are attempting to build a P.E.A.C.E. Village.

INFORMATION: P.O. Box 5577, Eugene, OR 97405.

● RAJ-YOGA MATH AND RETREAT

Raj-Yoga Math follows the flowing course of Divine Mother's Leela for those mature developing souls seeking their true Dharma. Each is taught how to begin removing impurities and ego games in order to become teacher/guides for young souls. The way is Kriya/Kundalini Yoga -- Eastern Old Catholic Rites -- Tibetan Bodhisattva training. The location is among tall evergreens, cold streams and intense vibrations. The teacher is Yogi father Satchakrananda Bodhisattvaguru who embodies the true Ecumenical spirit and uses the direct method (Jnana-Bhakti-Karma) like a Zen Roshi. Month by month workshops (small fee) available to unattached single entries with at least five years of work or training on their spiritual development.

INFORMATION: P.O. Box 547, Deming, WA 98244.

Growing Up In Prison
Bo Lozoff

For most people, doing time or even visiting in a prison can be the most negative experience of a lifetime. However, like anything else, it can also be the very most productive one. In the 1982 television movie, *Coming Out Of The Ice*, John Savage portrayed Victor Hermann, an American athlete who spent 45 years imprisoned in the Soviet Union, many of those years in the death-camps of Siberia. In the worst of those frozen prisons he met another American who taught him how to survive. "Red," played by Willie Nelson, was a real person, and in fact, died only a few years ago at a ripe old age. Hermann asked Red how long he had been there and when we would be getting out. Red replied that he never thought about such things, that he was just where he was for however long it was; he was right here. Hermann said he didn't think he could live a single day without relying on his hopes of getting out, to which Red (Willie Nelson) said, "Look at it this way, Victor. If you can make it here, I mean really make it, happily, then you've become a truly free man. When you get out, you won't need power, money, fame, or all the other stuff that you always thought you needed. You'll be able to live anywhere and do anything you want; you'll be a free man, and it's this place that will have made you free." Later in the film, when Red was being transferred to another camp, Victor Hermann was expressing all his appreciation before parting and said, "I love you, Red," to which Red replied, "I love you, too, Victor; isn't it great to have been here to meet each other?"

Those two scenes expressed essentially all that I try to get across in my prison workshops. No one (consciously) chooses to go to prison; prisons still have a long way to go before they can be considered at all civilized. They're brutal, unfair, unnatural environments which hopefully will some day be considered as incredible as the "snake pits" (mental asylums) of the 19th century. But rather than waiting for that day in the future when society thinks more clearly, todays inmates and staff and even the general citizenry have the same opportunities as did Red & Victor Hermann: The opportunity to take things just as they are, to strip ourselves of all our assumed needs, and to become truly free even though our culture is not.

As bad as prisons are, the flow of love can be enormous;

love between inmates, love coming in from the community, love from concerned prison workers. This flow of love is much greater than many of these folks would ever have felt under "normal" circumstances. The very bottom of the barrel, whether it's a prison, or people caught in an earthquake together, or victims of a senseless war, can be the place where our usual petty concerns fly out the window and we all meet right here, right now; where each moment becomes precious and appreciated.

I've had the good fortune to share millions of such moments in many prisons, and the effect it's had on my life has been too great to describe. At the very least, it's helped me to not sweat the small stuff in my life (and nearly everything we usually worry about turns out to be "small stuff"). It's also helped me to perceive the beauty hidden within ugliness; not only the "uglies" like prisons, but also cancer, death, heartbreak and the like. Reflecting on the fulfillment in the lives of many of my prison friends, has helped me to understand that I don't need power, money, fame and so forth; that there's really no condition that I need that I couldn't satisfy in a maximum security lock-up. What a relief, to realize that everything I have is pure gravy! If it comes, great; if it leaves me, that's fine because it wasn't a need in the first place. Prison continues to help me, in a very practical way, to become free.

Regardless of particular circumstance, any prisoner anywhere can take control over his or her life and use prison time for deep inner work. And regardless of special training or skills or lack thereof, anybody on the outside can find some way to become involved with prisons or prisoners and grow tremendously in the process. Helping people in both these directions, and with not losing their simplicity or sense of humor along the way, is the sole raison-d'etre for the Prison-Ashram Project. It is a joy for all of us to discover the prisons of mind and of body which can help us to grow up.

Bo Lozoff is director of the Prison-Ashram Project. See description in "Centers" section.

"*Despair can paralyze one, but when you share your despair and become active, you gain a kind of momentum and power that can really change the world, and I think we're doing it.*"

-- Patricia Ellsberg

● RAJNEESH FOUNDATION INTERNATIONAL

Rajneesh Foundation International is a church whose purpose is to spread the religious teachings and messages of the enlightened spiritual Master, Bhagwan Shree Rajneesh.

Until June 1981, Bhagwan resided at Shree Rajneesh Ashram in Poona, India, where for seven years he gave daily discourses to international gatherings of disciples and seekers. He spoke on Zen, Sufism, Taoism and other disciplines as well as the sayings of past enlightened Masters such as Buddha, Jesus, Krishna and Lao Tzu. He also answered questions covering every aspect of the spiritual quest, and of the human condition in general.

These discourses were all recorded and are now available to the public through Rajneesh Foundation International as audio cassettes and as hardback and softback books. Over 154 discourses were also recorded on videotape, and these are also available to the public.

Rajneesh Foundation International is a worldwide distributor of books and tapes about Bhagwan Shree Rajneesh, who is currently visiting the U.S.A. He is staying as a guest at the Rajneesh Neo-Sannyas International Commune in Rajneeshpuram, Oregon, where Rajneesh Foundation International is in the process of constructing a church building for meditations and religious celebrations.

INFORMATION: P.O. Box 12A, Antelope, OR 97001, (503) 489-3301.

● REIKI NATURAL HEALTH CENTER

Reiki Natural Health Center is a treatment center which, for the past four years, has utilized the highly effective natural healing system called Reiki. Reiki is a Japanese word meaning universal life force energy and it is this energy which flows through the hands of a certified Reiki therapist. This effective healing system has been used successfully on reversing physical, emotional and mental body dis-eases. All therapists have been fully certified by the American-International Reiki Association. Appointments suggested.

INFORMATION: 545 Pharr Road, N.E., Atlanta, GA 30305, (404) 233-5549.

● RELIGIOUS SCIENCE CENTER

"What you think and feel makes something happen. Your awareness can bring *What You Want* Into your life!"

We offer seminars, workshops, metaphysical bookstore, counseling and practitioner help by appointment, beginning classes in Science of Mind and advanced classes leading toward eligibility for practitioner and ministerial licenses. Sunday service is at 11:00 a.m. and there is also Sunday School.

Pastor is Reverend Betty Bailey. Office hours are Monday-Friday 9:30 a.m. to 4:00 p.m. How to get there: Mocine Avenue is off Harder Road between Mission and Soto Road.

Here with others you may move through your challenges into realization of New Goals.

INFORMATION: 26081 Mocine Ave., Hayward, CA 94544, (415) 886-5335.

● RINZAI-JI

Rinzai-ji, Inc. includes the Cimarron Zen Center in Los Angeles, Mt. Baldy Zen Center and other Zen centers in the U.S.A., Canada and New Zealand. They are religious institutes founded in the Rinzai tradition by Joshu Sasaki Roshi. The Mt. Baldy Center is open year-round and provides a total practice which includes zazen (sitting meditation), sanzen (private interviews with the Roshi), and Dai-Sesshin (intensive week-long meditation). The Center holds three-month intensive training periods (Seichu) each winter which enable the student to experience himself on a basic level. Each summer the Center provides a program of Buddhist studies which combines practice and academic study.

INFORMATION: Cimarron Zen Center, 2505 Cimarron St., Los Angeles, CA 90018, (213) 732-2263 and Mt. Baldy Zen Center, P.O. Box 526, Mt. Baldy, CA 91759, (714) 985-6410.

● ROCKY MOUNTAIN HEALING ARTS INSTITUTE

Rocky Mountain Healing Arts Institute has offered quality training in the healing arts since 1976, with a focus on massage and other bodymind therapies. People from all over the world train here to take responsibility for their level of wellness and to teach the same to others.

The largest component is the Boulder School of Massage Therapy, internationally known for excellence in professional massage training. BSMT is approved and regulated by: State of Colorado Board for Community Colleges and Occupational Education, American Massage and Therapy Association, Veteran's Administration.

INFORMATION: P.O. Box 4573, Dept. O, Boulder, CO 80306, (303) 443-5131.

● THE ROSELAND FOUNDATION

The Roseland Foundation informs of these times and conditions now and ahead. It gives its members the opportunity to learn of the prophecies of *now and in "The Golden Age",* (The millenium), through communications from those of higher dimensions, by Dr. Jeanne Kennedy.

Individuals can obtain insight into their life purpose through her life readings. Additional information for all mankind is given in the lectures she gives across the country. She has truly been given the gift of prophecy of that which is to come.

INFORMATION: 9722 Galston Ln., Spring, TX 77379, (713) 376-1892.

● THE ROSICRUCIAN FELLOWSHIP

The Rosicrucian Order, or Order of the Rose Cross, was founded in Central Europe by Christian Rosenkreuz, an Adept. Throughout the centuries, for the most part secretly, the Order transmitted a cosmic philosophy known as the Western Wisdom Teaching. In 1908, while Max Heindel was in Germany, he was chosen by the Brothers of the Rose Cross to receive the teaching later published in the book, *The Rosicrucian Cosmo-Conception,* and instructed to promulgate it to the world. The Rosicrucian Fellowship was organized in the city of Seattle, Washington.

It is the preparatory school for the Order, one of the Lesser Mystery Schools. It throws light on many perplexing passages in the Bible and bridges the chasm between science and religion.

The Fellowship distributes its teachings through correspondence courses, the magazine *Rays From The Rose Cross,* and numerous books and pamphlets. A summer school is conducted at its headquarters in Oceanside, California which the public may attend. The work is conducted on a freewill offering basis.

INFORMATION: 2222 Mission Ave., P.O. Box 713, Oceanside, CA 92054, (714) 757-6600.

● THE ROSICRUCIAN ORDER (AMORC)

The Rosicrucian Order, AMORC, is a worldwide fraternal, philosophical, cultural and educational organization of men and women devoted to investigating and applying natural laws for the benefit of themselves and those around them. Like most fraternal organizations it is based on a lodge system. However, the Rosicrucian Order also offers its members a philosophy and system of studies uniting such topics as psychology, parapsychology, science, the arts, metaphysics, mysticism, philosophy, history and so on. The Rosicrucian Order is not a religion. The information offered in the body of the Rosicrucian studies is not dogmatic. Members receive a weekly booklet offering an intellectual examination of certain topics. In addition, excercises and experiments are also offered to enable the individual to awaken the latent, dormant faculties, and to experience in a personal fashion the benefits to be derived from such studies.

INFORMATION: Rosicrucian Park, San Jose, CA 95191, (408) 287-9171.

● RUSSELL HOUSE

The Russell House is a haven for those people interested in juice fasting, detoxifying, learning and losing weight fast. Meet interesting people seeking a new and wonderful holistic experience.

The juice fasting program faithfully follows the recommendations of Dr. Paavo Airola. Freshly prepared juices of vegetables and exotic fruits, daily lectures, whirlpool, sauna and massage therapy, nutritional counseling and much more are provided for guests at this tropical old world paradise. Enjoy sunset on the Gulf of Mexico, Sunrise on the Atlantic, tropical foliage and cool sea breezes. Brochure on request.

INFORMATION: 415 William St., Key West, FL 33040, (305) 294-8787.

"I want to talk about the opportunity that the Bomb presents us with. It's pretty terrifying, but I want to talk about it in the sense of a spiritual teaching. The extraordinary thing about the situation we are in is that for the first time in history there is no private salvation. There is no place to hide. We're all in it together: we're all under the mushroom cloud."

-- Joanna Macy, Ph.D.

S

● SAKYA TEGCHEN CHOLING CENTER

This Tibetan Buddhist center for the study of Vajrayana Buddhism and Tibetan culture is under the guidance of Sakya Jigdal Dagchen Rinpoche. N. Trinlay Rinpoche and Dezhung Tulku Rinpoche also teach at the Center.
INFORMATION: 5042 18th N.E., Seattle, WA 98105, (206) 522-6967.

● SAT INSTITUTE

SAT Institute aims at training practitioners of human growth and offers a certificate program as well as events open to the community through its curriculum of integral education.

Activities include ongoing experiential groups and classes in educational and psychotherapeutic trends and the emerging world view -- along with major weekend events.

Claudio Naranjo, author of *The One Quest, The Healing Journey* and co-author of *The Psychology of Meditation,* is the Institute's founder. For a free brochure of SAT activities write.
INFORMATION: 63 Chattanooga St., San Francisco, CA 94114, (415) 285-2291 (Dionne Marx).

● SAWAN KIRPAL RUHANI MISSION

Darshan Singh is the living Master of the Surat Shabd Yoga, (Sant Mat), the simplest and most natural of spiritual paths. He is the successor of Kir-pal Singh, and was initiated into the mysteries of the beyond by Hazur Baba Sawan Singh. The living Master gives an experience of the inner Light and inner Sound at the time of initiation. He teaches a method of meditation by which the disciple rises above body-consciousness, traverses the inner spiritual planes and attains self-knowledge and God-realization. There is never any charge for instruction, initiation and meditation. The international headquarters where Sant Darshan Singh resides is: Kirpal Ashram, 2 Canal Road, Vijay Nagar, Delhi-110009, India.
INFORMATION: T. S. Khanna, General Representative, 8807 Lea Ln., Alexandria, VA   22309, (703) 360-9112; Sawan Kirpal Meditation Center, Dept. S., Rt. 1, P.O. Box 24, Bowling Green, VA 22427, (804) 633-9987.

● THE SAYBROOK INSTITUTE

The Saybrook Institute Graduate School wishes to announce program concentrations in Health Studies, Consciousness Studies, Study of the Person and Human Systems, leading to M.A. and Ph.D. degrees in Psychology and Human Sciences. The programs are designed for professionals who wish to continue working while earning an advanced degree. The Graduate School has an external degree format, offering self-paced study, individualized contact with faculty, and periodic residential meetings arranged to meet student needs. The Institute is State-approved and is a Candidate for accreditation with WASC.

INFORMATION: 1772 Vallejo St., A-7, San Francisco, CA 94123, (415) 441-5034.

● SCANDINAVIAN YOGA AND MEDITATION SCHOOL

A 3-month intensive is held every year in Sweden from January to April at the residential course place of the Scandinavian Yoga and Meditation School. The Kriya Yoga that Swami Janakananda teaches here combines the possibilities of developing yourself with your real goals in life -- uniting your everyday life with your spiritual reality.

Swami Janakananda's way of teaching meditation is the essence of the tantric tradition -- which begins with you, the very room you are in, your body and mind. By not rejecting any of it, by not escaping into wishful thinking about ideal states and fantasies about worlds that are nowhere, you are ensured a true and real experience all the way to the center of yourself and of life.

Swami Janakananda, born 1939 in Scandinavia, is teaching the tantric meditations; Inner Silence, Yoga Nidra and Kriya Yoga. His book *Yoga, Tantra & Meditation* (Ballantine) gives a practical knowledge of the physical, psychical and sexual sides of yoga. In 1970, he founded the Scandinavian Yoga and Meditation School.

In the Copenhagen, Arhus, Oslo and Stockholm schools there are weekly yoga classes year round, and at the residential course center in Sweden 14-day intensives are held. Swami Janakananda also teaches in America in the summer.

INFORMATION: 340 13 Hamneda, Sweden, (0372) 550 63.

● SCHOOL OF SPIRITUAL SCIENCE

Established in 1970, the School offers progressive training designed to expand consciousness and heighten awareness, guiding the individual into higher spiritual activity.

Studies emphasize Holistic concepts throughout four years. Prerequisite consists of a high school diploma or equivalency. Studies culminate in the third year with a Healer's certification. The fourth year ends with certification in the lay track, or ordination. On the premise that extrasensory capabilities correlate with total development and are not a special "talent," the staff has achieved exceptional results developing students' psychic and paranormal sensitivities.

INFORMATION: 5605 16th St., N.W., Washington, D.C. 20011, (202) 723-4510.

● THE SCHOOL OF T'AI CHI CHUAN

T'ai Chi is an ancient system of exercise and centering perfected and passed down for hundreds of years in China. The soft martial art, T'ai Chi develops strength like "steel wrapped in cotton," and, in slow relaxed movement re-connects us with our grounding earth.

The School was founded by Patrick Watson, a senior student of Cheng Man-Ch'ing, and offers beginning courses through Push Hands as well as special programs for older people, pregnant women and those with injuries or handicaps. We offer T'ai Chi in New York City, Gainesville, Los Angeles, Santa Cruz, Boston, Amherst, Washington D.C., Princeton, Baltimore and Atlanta, as well as Amsterdam, London and Dublin.

INFORMATION: 412 Avenue of the Americas, New York, NY 10011.

● THE SEARCH AT NORTHEON FOREST

A natural sanctuary, where a search for the real stuff of total existence occurs within the fabric of normality, was established in 1974 by Architect Paul Beidler continuing research begun under the aegis of Gurdjieff. Inner disciplines are designed to coordinate disparate elements in the human organism while transforming dissonant capacities into harmonious strength. Forest rites, prayerlike meditations, intensive rhythms, and daily choreographies consciously danced lead to a deep core of potential calm that gives equal validity to stress, joys, sorrows, rejoicings and sufferings. Ordinary life merges into linked occasions for inner affirmations of provisional reconciliation in a continuous now.

INFORMATION: P.O. Box 517, Hexenkopf Rd., Easton, PA 18042, (215) 258-9559.

● SEICHO-NO-IE

Seicho-No-Ie was founded in Japan by Dr. Masaharu Taniguchi in 1930. It teaches that Humans are Children of God, and Humanity is essentially sinless. Humans can experience freedom when they realize the Truth, and with this enlightenment comes a flow of Infinite Life, Infinite Wisdom and Infinite Abundance.

This Truth is expounded in a multi-volume *Truth of Life,* by Dr. Taniguchi. Although healing is not the major emphasis, many Seicho-No-Ie followers have been healed by merely reading *Truth of Life* or other Seicho-No-Ie publications.

Prayerful meditation, Shinsokan, enables one to break through to a conscious awareness of one's Truth, Jisso, as a Child of God. The movement has over 4,000,000 members throughout the world.

INFORMATION: 14527 S. Vermont Ave., Gardena, CA 90247, (213) 323-8486.

● SELF IMPROVEMENT INSTITUTE (SII)

SII teaching is *not* a dogma, religion or technique. It is, rather a New Age process of natural growth from within you, according to your needs, capabilities, potentials, evolution, and roots. Focus is on your achieving a continuous flow with life's spontaneity -- independent of teacher, technique, or theory. Its goals are to foster harmony with life and fulfillment for the individual and society; for inner peace and world peace. The Institute is directed by Dr. Elan Z. Neev (Ph.D & D.D.).

133

Highlights Of The Self Improvement Oneness Process:

Powerful fusion of the best in New Age growth and awareness with Kabala secrets, channeled through Dr. Neev, in accord with the readiness of the individual and the group consciousness. Regression and progression for loving liberation from limitations on all levels to realize oneness and fulfill our missions. Energy linkage with the Highest, and synergy for God-given power to perform *miracles.* Multi-sensory, multi-dimensional balancing through sound, color, breath, movement, and more -- futuristic and ancient techniques. Practical integration and application of all knowledge, including nutrition, art, science, and metaphysics, for goal achievement, and to prevent or heal "spiritual indigestion." Safe acceleration of energies, to manifest peace, healing, abundance, love, joy, wisdom ... and to be ready for the Great Changes. Taped review and conditioning. See Classified Section under *miscellaneous.*

INFORMATION: P.O. Box 6300, Beverly Hills, CA 90212-1300, (213) 933-NEEV.

● SELF REALIZATION FELLOWSHIP

Paramahansa Yogananda founded SRF in 1920 to disseminate the science of Kriya Yoga meditation. The goal of the Self-Realization Kriya Yoga teaching is direct personal experience of God. For those who wish to know more about the life and teachings of Yogananda, we recommend his Autobiography Of A Yogi. Columbia University Press's *Review of Religions* wrote: "There has been nothing before, written in English or in any other European language, like this presentation of Yoga." For free literature on SRF's Lessons, books and/or recordings contact us.

INFORMATION: 3880 San Rafael Ave., Los Angeles, CA 90065, (213) 225-2471.

● THE SEVA FOUNDATION

The Seva Foundation was founded in 1978 by a group of individuals who participated in the global eradication of smallpox or were inspired by this remarkable feat. *Seva* is the Sanskrit word for service and reflects our guiding principle: to help reduce suffering through service. Members of Seva come from many spiritual traditions. Seva's major support project is the Nepal Blindness Program, a five year effort to reduce preventable and curable blindness by 90 percent and to provide Nepal with self-sufficiency in eye care. Other projects are supported in India and the U.S.

INFORMATION: 108 Spring Lake Dr., Chelsea, MI 48118, (313) 475-1351.

● SEVERAL SOURCES FOUNDATION

Several Sources Foundation is a small group of people who are receiving Messages from God. The purpose of the organization is to help others grow spiritually through a sharing of the Messages which they have received. The volunteers through the knowledge they have gained from the Messages have helped individuals on a one-to-one basis who are depressed, blind, suicidal, sick at heart and badly in need of the Lord's love, knowledge and guidance. The volunteers through their own incomes are sponsoring *A Book of Messages* and a radio program called "Inspirational Messages." If you are merely curious, if you are in need of spiritual renewal, if you are wondering if there is a God, then please write for details.

INFORMATION: 182 Prospect St., Ramsey, NJ 07446.

● SHASTA ABBEY -- ORDER OF BUDDHIST CONTEMPLATIVES

Shasta Abbey, Headquarters of the Order of Buddhist Contemplatives of Soto Zen Church, is a Zen Buddhist seminary and monastery located in northern California. Shasta Abbey was founded in 1970 by Rev. Roshi Jiyu Kennett, Abbess and Spiritual Director, who received the Dharma Transmission from the Very Reverend Keido Chisan Koho Zenji, the late Chief Abbot of Dai Hon Zan Soji-ji Temple in Japan. At present there are 49 male and female monks in residence at the Abbey.

Shasta Abbey also has a variety of programs for the lay person. These include daily meditation instruction, and introductory and advanced retreats throughout the year held for serious lay trainees who wish to learn and practice Zen Buddhist training. The program of study and training includes morning and evening services, ceremonies, classes in Zen training, and manual work, with a particular emphasis on zazen, the traditional meditation practice of Zen Buddhism. The emphasis is on personal experience and its direct application in one's daily life.

INFORMATION: The Guestmaster, P.O. Box 478, Mt. Shasta, CA 96067, (916) 926-4208.

● SHENANDOAH VALLEY HEALTH RANCH

When you pass through the gates of Shenandoah Valley, you're entering 1600 acres of pristine beauty, surrounded by State Forest abundant in wildlife, streams, rivers and flower gardens. In essence, those things supplied by nature. We encourage you to use this land. We have horseback riding, cross-country skiing/hiking and jogging trails. This land provides the necessary seclusion from man-made stresses, allowing us to work with you to achieve a new understanding of your total being.

During your stay with us, we would like you to receive the optimum program conducive to physical, mental and spiritual well-being. You have only one body and one life. They aren't separate entities. How you care for one reflects directly on the other. Following our holistic approach could add length to your life. You will certainly improve the quality of life you lead through better diet and our methods to deal with and lessen the stress in your life.

INFORMATION: Flowing Well Rd., Route #1, Kalkaska, MI 49646, (616) 258-2750.

● THE SHEPHERD'S BUSH CENTRE

The Centre is a non-denominational training center/community. Our purpose as a training center is to love, serve, and surrender to Spirit. Our mission is to change the world by creating value and demonstrating more loving ways of living. The Centre has served Spirit and the community in various capacities for 12 years. Services include classes, workshops, counseling, meditations, quarterly newsletters, tapes, and an active volunteer program which includes computers and word processing activity. We are especially dedicated to spiritual healing for psychosomatic dis-eases and disorders.

We have created the Centre in the urban environment and plan a work/retreat auxiliary in New Mexico. Long term plans involve relocating the main centre to New Mexico with a service centre in Dallas. We are now open to new members/associates to further our purposes.

INFORMATION: 5416 Gaston Ave., Dallas Texas 75214, (214) 823-0292.

● SHIATSU CENTER AT HARBIN HOT SPRINGS

The Shiatsu Center offers drop-in classes at Harbin and in San Francisco, workshops, and a weekend or residential program which leads to certification through Harbin's Niyama School of Massage. Tuition and expenses can be covered under Harbinger work study program. Harbin, two hours north of the Bay Area, is a new age community in its own valley with pools, gardens, sundecks and 1400 acres of woods and streams. Transportation is available. The Center's director, Harold Dull, was trained in shiatsu by the Zen priest, Reuho Yamada; by Wataru Ohashi; and, in Japan, by Shizuto Masunaga, author of *Zen Shiatsu.*

INFORMATION: Harold Dull, 1479 5th Ave., San Francisco, CA 94122, (415) 731-5652.

● SHIATSU MASSAGE SCHOOL OF CALIFORNIA

To Practice Shiatsu massage is an artistic deed, one of great value of communication, and Shiatsu brings greater understanding to the family, community and one's whole universe.

At the school we have set up several different levels of Shiatsu for the serious practationer or for the layman homecare. We offer a 102 hour professional license course Shiatsu I with optional training in swedish massage. Next, we have more advanced programs and an intern clinic under the director's guidance. We also have a short informal 40 hour course for those interested in learning in a more relaxed manner for self and homecare.

Our teachings in Shiatsu are based on traditional Acupuncture principles of Yin & Yang & The Five Element Theory. Our method of Shiatsu is based on Anma meridian massage, an original form of Acupressure & Shiatsu that involves not only pressing points but rubbing, kneading, exercises, adjusting and tapping.

DoAhn T. Kaneko is the founder-director of the "Tao Healing Arts Center and Shiatsu Massage School Of California. He is a California State licensed acupuncturist and instructor.

See the other listing under Tao Healing Arts Center.

INFORMATION: 2309 Main St., Santa Monica, CA 90405, (213) 396-4877.

● SILVA MIND CONTROL

During intensive training classes, students are taught to produce and maintain tranquil, positive mental states and to develop ESP. This is done by learning to function at alpha and theta frequencies of the brain. The training is accomplished without the use of bio-feedback equipment. Classes are available throughout the world.

INFORMATION: 1110 Cedar Ave., P.O. Box 2249, Laredo, TX 78040, (512) 722-6391.

● SINO-AMERICAN BUDDHIST ASSOCIATION

The Sino-American Buddhist Association (SABA) was formed in 1959 to bring the orthodox teachings of the Buddha to the entire world. At all of its monasteries, SABA offers a rigorous schedule of Buddhist practice seven days a week which includes at least three hours of group meditation, two and a half hours of group recitation, and an hour-long lecture on the Buddhist scriptures each day. There are also daily courses in Buddhist and canonical language studies, and week-long intensive recitation and meditation sessions every other month, and a three to ten week meditation session in the winter. Residents get a thorough understanding of the main teachings of all the major schools of Mahayana Buddhism, develop skill in scriptural languages, and become adept at a wide variety of spiritual practices. These activities are offered through a government approved three-year Sangha (monastic) and two-year Laity Training Program. The Sangha Training Program leads to ordination as a Bhikshu or Bhikshuni.

One of SABA's major tasks is the translation of the major Buddhist scriptures into the world's languages, primarily English. SABA also publishes a monthly bi-lingual journal of Buddhist studies, *Vajra Bodhi Sea,* which contains its most recent translation work.

SABA has established various educational and social service programs to bring peace and happiness and promote a high standard of ethical conduct for the world. At its headquarters, the City of 10,000 Buddhas, are housed Dharma Realm Buddhist University, Cultivating Virtue High School, and Instilling Virtue Elementary School. SABA is also a founding member of the Buddhist Council of Refugee Rescue and Resettlement. The 3-month training program, with 100-150 refugees in residence at the City of 10,000 Buddhas, has received high acclaim from various government and social service agencies. The spiritual guide of SABA is its founder, the most Venerable Tripitaka Master Hsuan Hua.

INFORMATION: City of 10,000 Buddhas, P.O. Box 217, Talmage, CA 95481, (707) 462-0939; Gold Mountain Monastery, 1731 15th St., San Francisco, CA 94103, (415) 861-9672; Gold Wheel Monastery, 1726 W. Sixth St., Los Angeles, CA 90017, (213) 483-7497.

● SIRIUS

Sirius Community was founded in 1978 by former Findhorn Community members Gordon Davidson and Corinne McLaughlin on 86 acres of forest and gardens. Everyday life is our spiritual teacher, and we govern ourselves by group consensus and meditation. Our purpose is to live in harmony with the earth, with all humanity, and with God, and to help others to do so.

We are currently 12 adults and 6 children, with an extended family of Supporting Members nearby. Community Members have started a lecture and meditation tape business, a cooperative solar construction company, and a health food bakery. We offer slide shows and workshops on spiritual themes. You are welcome to visit us! Write for a free brochure.

INFORMATION: P.O. Box 388-G, Amherst, MA 01004, (413) 256-8015.

● SIVANANDA YOGA VEDANTA CENTER

The Sivananda Yoga Vedanta Centers bear the name and spirit of Swami Sivananda, the great saint of modern India. Sivananda is famous for his many good works, as well as for writing more than 200 books on all aspects of Yoga. In 1957, he sent his close disciple, Swami Vishnu Devananda, to the West.

Author of the *Complete Illustrated Book of Yoga,* Swami Vishnu founded this organization to propagate the ancient teachings of Yoga. Its aims are to help individuals prepare for meditation and Self-realization through the practices of Hatha and Raja Yogas and the study of Yogic philosophy.

Ashram headquarters are in Val Morin, Canada with ashrams in Woodbourne, New York and Paradise Island, Bahamas. There are centers in most major cities. A four-week Yoga Teachers' Training Course is given at the various Ashrams throughout the year.

INFORMATION: Sivananda Yoga Camp, 8th Ave., Val Morin, P.Q., Canada, (819) 322-3226.

● SKY FOUNDATION

The Sky Foundation, under the direction of Dr. Vijayendra Pratap, offers a program of Yoga in the Classical tradition designed for both those new to Yoga and for those with previous experience. It is suitable for all ages and backgrounds, with the only requirement a personal commitment to self-improvement.

There is a regular series of weekly classes, and there are workshops, seminars, lectures and summer retreats, often including distinguished visiting teachers and experts in related fields. As taught at Sky, Yoga is strictly non-denominational, respecting and supporting the personal and religious beliefs of each practitioner.

Sky is a non-profit foundation, chartered by the Commonwealth of Pennsylvania in 1972. Since that time it has taught thousands of men and women a system faithful to the traditional Yoga discipline advanced by the

---

"We need not only to transform the disarmament movement by bringing spirituality into it, we need to create a spiritual society that understands the nature of conflict, the deep sources of conflict, that understands and accepts the fact that conflict is a creative energy that can be used to move us forward in the evolutionary process as a species and as people."

-- Gordon Feller

Kaivalyadhama, India's famed Yoga institute which was founded in 1924 by Swami Kuvalayanandaji, a pioneering exponent of the modern scientific approach to classical Yoga.
INFORMATION: 527 South St., Philadelphia, PA 19147, (215) 923-5946.

● SOCIETY FOR THE PROTECTION OF THE UNBORN THROUGH NUTRITION

The Society for the Protection of the Unborn through Nutrition attributes the large majority of maternal complications and birth defects to the widespread neglect to recognize the critical importance of satisfying the nutritional stress of pregnancy. An institutionalized nutritional nonchalance and the widespread use of drugs and employment of technologically advanced monitoring and diagnostic equipment are responsible for the crippling of hundreds of thousands of new lives every year. The Society advocates certain positive alternatives.
INFORMATION: 17 North Wabash St., Suite 603, Chicago, IL 60602, (312) 332-2334.

● SOMA

Soma was established in 1971 as a holistic health and education center serving the Cambridge community. Over the years it has evolved into a Clinical Counseling Center.

Soma practitioners provide psychodynamic, gestalt, bioenergetics, art, and body oriented therapies in individual, couple, family and group sessions. Soma also provides Alexander Technique, nutritional counseling, massage, and pregnancy and birth counseling.

Soma also offers a counselor-training program of practical and theoretical training for people working or planning to work in a helping capacity for others.
INFORMATION: 99 Bishop Allen Dr., Cambridge, MA 02139, (617) 491-8694.

● SOMA INSTITUTE

Soma Practitioner Training -- A six month, residential program for outstanding candidates, taught by a distinguished team of physicians, therapists, scientists and professional educators. Degree credit for Soma University, Touch for Health Instructor Certification, Soma Practitioner Certification, Nautilus Training, and preparation for successful private practice are included in this program.

Some bodywork is a process of deep tissue manipulation, designed to facilitate body-mind integration. Included are studies in applied kinesiology, autogenic training, specific spinal technique and psychological facilitation.

Soma School of Massage Therapy -- Holistic program, Clinical supervision, Athletic injury, Nautilus training program. Also available ... Sports Therapy Clinical Internship.

Soma University -- Offers state authorized residential and external degree

programs including B.S. in Manual Therapy, M.A. in Yoga, M.S. in Holistic Health Science, M.S. in Structural Integration, Ph.D. in Holistic Health Science, and Ph.D. in Neuromuscular Integration. Students actively participate in designing a specific program to meet individual needs and interests. Soma University is in Pasadena, California. For a complete catalog send $4.
INFORMATION: Dept. WCS, P.O. Box 12624, Gainesville, FL 32604.

● THE SOYFOODS CENTER

The Soyfoods Center, founded by William Shurtleff and Akiko Aoyagi Shurtleff, is the world's leading source of information and materials related to soyfoods, with emphasis on traditional, low-technology soyfoods such as tofu, tempeh, soymilk, miso, natural shoyu and tamari, soynuts, soy sprouts, and other related foods. We have published nine books about these foods, the most popular of which are *The Book of Tofu* (350,000 copies in print), *The Book of Miso, The Book of Tempeh,* plus craft and technical manuals accompanying each of these basic books which describe how you can start your own business making these foods.

Our Center has been very active in helping people to start soyfoods companies. The results have been remarkable. As of July 1982 there are over 200 tofu shops in North America and 47 more in Europe and Australia, plus 51 tempeh shops, 11 miso makers, and 19 soyfoods restaurants and delis. These businesses have joined to form the Soyfoods Association of North America, which holds large annual conferences, publishes a quarterly magazine (*Soyfoods,* circulation 8,500), and a monthly newsletter, and has national headquarters in Massachusetts.

We feel that soyfoods are going to be the protein source of the future since they are low in cost, highly nutritious, tasty, remarkably versatile, great meat and dairy replacers, and time tested for 2,000 years. Most important, they make best use of the world's precious farmland to help combat world hunger.

For a free catalog of our publications and some of our favorite tofu recipes, just send a stamped, self-addressed long envelope to us.
INFORMATION: P.O. Box 234, Lafayette, CA 94549.

● SPECTRUM WORKSHOPS/CLUB SPECTRUM

Club Spectrum is a "community of communities." Its purpose is to provide its members, and the public, with access to the best teachings and seminars available in personal growth. SW/CS creates and promotes monthly trainings and invites teachers from diverse disciplines to present their particular understanding of a particular theme, such as "relationships," or "body awareness," etc. The Club's financial success and growth is shared with its members by way of a unique, multi-level marketing structure. This "spectrum connection" supports diversity and celebrates community and empowers its members and supporters to share in teaching, learning, playing, loving and earning.
INFORMATION: 959 DeSoto Ln., Foster City, CA 94404, (415) 349-6946.

140

● SPIRITUAL ADVANCEMENT OF THE INDIVIDUAL (SAI)

SAI, the Spiritual Advancement of the Individual Foundation, Inc., is dedicated to spreading the teachings of Sri Sathya Sai Baba, who is believed by his followers to be the living Avatar of this Age. For 35 years Sai Baba has been working to bring about the spiritual regeneration of humanity, healing comforting, and inspiring people to love and serve God. Activities at the Sai Baba Center include group meditation, lectures, films, and *bhajans* -- prayer and song meetings and education in human values for children. A book shop is operated in conjunction with the center, offering all of Sai Baba's discourses, photos, tapes, films, and video cassettes. Catalog available.

INFORMATION: 7911 Willoughby Ave, Los Angeles, CA 90046, (213) 656-9373.

● THE SPIRITUAL HEALING CENTER

The Spiritual Healing Center offers classes and lectures in the art of spiritual healing and psychic surgery and private healing sessions. Reverend Joseph Martinez, founder and director of the Center is a gifted healer from the Philippines. Rev. Martinez works with the etheric body or life field surrounding the physical body to alleviate ailments and clear up health problems. Spiritual healing is combined with etheric surgery to release the causitive factors in illness and bring about permanent positive change.

Students who attend classes at the Spiritual Healing Center are thoroughly versed in all aspects of psychic healing. The theory and background of each healing discipline is presented, healing processes are demonstrated and students are given the opportunity to work with these methods on themselves and their classmates. Among the skills learned are channeling of cosmic energies, grounding, chakra and aura cleansing, attracting spirit guides, color healing, sound therapy, etheric surgery and other esoteric and yogic disciplines.

INFORMATION: 1739 Anza St., San Francisco, CA 94118, (415) 221-4058.

● SPIRITUAL LIFE INSTITUTE

The Spiritual Life Institute has two centers, one just south of Sedona, Arizona, and a second in Nova Scotia, Canada. The aim of these centers is to foster religious contemplation, offering short-term retreats or long-term residence. Founded by Fr. William McNamara, it is an ecumenical institute desiring to achieve a renewal of the spirit of the Christian Church. It stresses a contemplative life similar to that of the Carmelite hermits, and believes that in isolated locations, such as the desert, man is able to achieve his greatest degree of communion with God. The Institute puts out a quarterly magazine entitled *Desert Call,* and a series of cassette tapes dealing with contemplation in the modern world.

INFORMATION: Nada Contemplative Center, Star Rt. 1, Sedona, AZ 86336, (602) 282-7668.

● SPIRITUAL SCIENCE CENTER

The Spiritual Science Center offers worship services, discussion groups, special workshops and seminars, and a program of progressive training designed to expand the consciousness, heighten awareness, and guide the individual into higher levels of spiritual activity. The study emphasizes holistic concepts throughout four years. It is designed for the adult with no prerequisites in previous training in metaphysics or spiritual studies. However, a high school diploma or equivalency is required.

INFORMATION: Pastor/Founder Rev. Stefanie Nagorka, P.O. Box 755, Wall Street Station, New York, NY 10268, (212) 227-2154.

● SPIRITUAL UNITY OF NATIONS

The Spiritual Unity of Nations (S.U.N.) is an organism serving as an instrument for Unity. The S.U.N. serves organizations with the sole objective of coming together in Harmony for purposes of sharing perspectives of truth. Each participating group has the opportunity of broadening their horizons without sacrificing their individuality.

S.U.N. introduces a new flexibility in the approach to spirituality by encouraging people to open their minds to the Ancient Wisdoms and new truths and examine them in the Light. The S.U.N. shall not dictate to any person, church, religion, philosophy or nation any dogma or doctrine but instead we espouse Universal Principles.

INFORMATION: 1735 Pinnacle St., S.W., Wyoming, MI 49509.

● THE SPROUTLETTER

The Sproutletter works to spread the many benefits of sprouting, live foods and a healthful lifestyle. We publish a 12 page newsletter which covers these topics and networking information. Our goal is to provide current, reliable and useful information and present it in a way which is both enjoyable and inspiring. We also supply sprouting screens, charts and racks to individuals and to co-ops and stores throughout the country. Subscriptions to The Sprout-letter are $10/year or $8 for low-income persons.

INFORMATION: P.O. Box 10985, Eugene, OR 97440, (503) 689-7566.

● SRI AUROBINDO'S ACTION CENTER

A collective dedicated to the evolutionary vision of Sri Aurobindo and the Mother and to support the evolving township of Auroville.

"Our aim is not, either, to found a religion or a school of philosophy or a school of Yoga, but to create a ground of spiritual growth and experience and a way which will bring down a greater Truth beyond the mind but not inaccessible to the human soul and consciousness. All can pass who are drawn to the Truth, whether they are from India or elsewhere, from the East or from the West." -- Sri Aurobindo.

Auroville Review, published twice a year in Auroville, is available from Sri Aurobindo's Action Center ($8/yr.). The Center provides information for Auroville, the Sri Aurobindo Ashram and World Union. A comprehensive library is maintained and a weekly meditation is held. All are welcome.

INFORMATION: P.O. Box 1977, Boulder, CO 80306, (303) 499-3313.

● SRI CENTRES INTERNATIONAL

Founded in 1975, SRI Centre International operates human growth centers in New York City, Princeton, New Jersey; Amsterdam, Holland; and Brussels, Belgium. The centers offer a comprehensive approach to human development and fulfillment.

A wide range of programs is available in both New York City and Princeton. Regularly scheduled classes include Chakra Psychology, Inner Tuning, sound therapy, relaxation and stress management, hatha yoga, yantra painting, Pressure Point and Lymphatic Massage, Vegetarian Cuisine and Tambura Tuning. Private seminars and workshops are also available to business, private groups of professionals, and other organizations.

Shyam Bhatnagar is the founder of InnerTuning, a therapeutic system. He is the Director of of SRI Centre International, and the Director of the Department of the Chakra Studies at the International University of Lugano, Switzerland.

He leads special programs in Chakra Psychology and InnerTuning for psychiatrists, physicians, therapists and the general public, in America and Europe. These courses are designed to teach participants techniques that can broaden their effectiveness as professionals in their respective fields. He also conducts a private practice in InnerTuning, in Princeton, New Jersey.

INFORMATION: 45 East 51st St., New York, NY 10022, (212) 688-6452 and P.O. Box 3016, Princeton, NJ 08540, (201) 359-7383.

● THE SRI CHINMOY CENTRE

The Sri Chinmoy Centre, whose members practice meditation and spiritual disciplines under the guidance of spiritual Master Sri Chinmoy, includes 60 branches throughout the U.S.A. and the world, with a central headquarters in New York City. On a community level, each Centre offers the public free courses in meditation and yoga philosophy, concerts of inspirational music and athletic events such as road races and tennis classics.

Spiritual Master Sri Chinmoy conducts free meditation sessions open to the public on Wednesdays in New York City, and meets daily with his private students. He also conducts twice-weekly meditations at the United Nations (for diplomats and staff). On select occasions throughout the year, both in New York City and while visiting his world-wide Centres, Sri Chinmoy offers free public concerts in which he performs on the esraj and flute and sings his original devotional music. Over 500 books of yoga philosophy, poetry, music and fiction has been written by Sri Chinmoy and tapes have been made of a number of his musical performances.

INFORMATION: P.O. Box 32433, Jamaica, NY 11431.

● STELLAR CRYSTAL COMMUNICATIONS

Stellar Crystal Communications is designed to unite speakers having backgrounds and expertise in New-Age Thought and Scientific Frontiers, with organizations who in turn require these kinds of sensitive speakers. The purpose is to bring to humanity a greater awareness of spiritual principles through networking practices. Rev. Yvonne J. Johnson is president of Stellar Crystal Communications.

INFORMATION: 431 N. Armistead St., Suite 101, Alexandria, VA 22312, (703) 941-0965 or 941-7799.

● STELLE -- CITY OF TOMORROW

The intentional community of Stelle, Illinois is evolving into an ecumenical center of New Age thinking where all the many different resources for personal and social transformation will be available in a mutually supportive and constructive environment.

Founded upon the philosophy and world view in *The Ultimate Frontier,* Stelle welcomes other individuals and philosophical groups interested in advancing New Age concepts to take advantage of the foundation the community provides. Many intentional communities have been formed for various reasons, each with its own particular slant on survival, religion, health, ecology, etc. Stelle is different from these in that it pursues a balanced holistic upgrading of all aspects of living which involves the conscious evolution of economics, politics, social structures, education, health, technology, spiritual and psychological growth, commerce, construction, agriculture, and futurist undertakings. At present the community consists of 42 homes on 240 acres, exceptional educational programs, participatory democracy, factory and businesses, holistic health center, cooperative, greenhouse and telephone mutual. We invite people of all ages, races, creeds, and origins who are ready to meet the challenges of pioneering the New Age to join us.

INFORMATION: The Stelle Group, P.O. Box 27, Stelle, IL 60619, (815) 256-2200.

● STILL MOUNTAIN SOCIETY

Still Mountain Society is a non-profit educational organization sponsoring programs at White Spruce Farm and workshops throughout Canada. White Spruce Farm is a learning center near Fernie, B.C. Canada where programs in natural living are held. White Spruce Farm is a *homestead* situated on 250 acres of wooded land in the Canadian Rocky Mountains.

A yearly summer camp and summer residential courses are offered in organic gardening and natural agriculture, natural foods cooking, herbs and wild plants, folk medicine and natural healing, shiatsu, do-in, and macrobiotic philosophy.

INFORMATION: RR #1, Fernie, B.C. Canada, VOB 1MO, (604) 423-6406.

● THE STROKING COMMUNITY NETWORK

Touch heals body, mind, and spirit. We believe people never outgrew their need to touch and be touched, and since 1975 we've created a support network for personal growth, open communication, trust, and taking charge of our own lives, based on caring for ourselves and others through touch. Groups meet regularly in several centers to share meals and exchange non-sexual massage. Our monthly newsletter, *The Stroking Times* ($8 per year; sample $1) lists groups and events "for people who knead people" nation-

wide. Our retreats, workshops, and outreach programs teach massage as a way of love. To get in touch, write.
INFORMATION: 1247 Palethorp St., Philadelphia, PA 19122.

● SUBUD

Subud is the contraction of three sanskrit words; Susila Budhi Dharma, which roughly translates as "right living in accordance with the will of the One Almighty God." It is a way which involves direct religious experience. It is not a teaching. It is a receiving. It is a progressive, deepening process of submission to the will of God. It is indonesian in origin. This "contact" was first given to Mhmd. Subuh (Bapak) in 1933 and has been in the west since the late '50's.

In Subud one follows no teachings or dogmas, nor does one meditate. One simply receives the Latihan, which is that which has been passed through Bapak to all of us, via "helpers" who are to be found in each group and designated as such. Eventually, the Latihan opens up the connection between inner and outer.

Anyone interested in joining Subud need only ask any group to be admitted as probationers. As probationers, they must wait three months during which time all of their questions can be answered. After three months they may be opened, which simply means they do Latihan for the first time. Afterwards, Latihan is done usually twice a week.
INFORMATION: C/O Chairman Locksin Thompson, 4 Pilot Rd., Carmel, CA 93924, (408) 659-4818.

● SUFI ISLAMIA RUHANIAT SOCIETY (SIRS)

Closely allied with the tradition of Sufism are the Dervish Brotherhoods, known for their dances and their music. Consistent with this tradition, Sufi Ahmed Murad Chisti (Murshid Samuel L. Lewis), a disciple of Hazrat Inayat Khan and an American Sufi leader from San Francisco, California, made the Dances of Universal Peace a central feature of contemporary Sufism. Murshid Lewis, who "danced away from his body" in 1971, emphasized the pragmatic approach to spiritual awakening of an often quoted and old master who said, "Sufism is based on experience and not on premises." The work of Spiritual Walk and Dance is carried on by the Sufi Islamia Ruhaniat Society, under the guidance of Murshid Lewis' spiritual successor, Murshid Moineddin Jablonski.

The Society sponsors an annual summer camp at which Spiritual Dance and Walk, *zikr,* healing and other elements of Sufi practice are taught for the general public. Through its centers, it sponsors meetings of the Dances of Universal Peace and Sufi *zikr* throughout the world. Intensive instruction in the Dance and leading the Dance is available through The Center for the Study of Spiritual Dance and Walk in San Francisco. In addition, an active program of publishing the works of Murshid Samuel L. Lewis and Hazrat Inayat Khan as well as recording music of the Sufi Choir, Dances of Universal Peace and Sufi *zikr* goes on through Sufi Islamia/Prophecy Publications at the address below.
INFORMATION: C/O Mentorgarten, 410 Precita Ave, San Francisco, CA 94110, (415) 285-0562.

Spiritual Awakening
Darshan Singh

Mankind has always dreamed of a Golden Age. Some imagine it as having existed in the remote past, while others project it into a distant future. For those who have the eyes to read the signs, the Golden Age of spirituality has already begun, and we are witnessing its dawn. Already, young and old throughout the world are beginning to seek spiritual awakening.

People today are realizing as never before the ephemeral nature of material life. Although we have made great strides in science and technology, we find humanity is no closer to happiness. The world is still strife-torn, the crime rate is ever-increasing, wars continue to be fought between people of one religion and another, between people of one color and another, between one country and another. Even within the family there is unhappiness.

Not only family life, but community life is also vanishing. There is such an emphasis on individuality that we are not concerned about our neighbors. A man may fall seriously ill and need help -- even die -- and those living next door may not learn of it for weeks.

With our material advances we have been able to acquire so many luxuries, but we have not been able to bring peace to the world, to our countries, to our communities, to our families, or to our own souls. We may build the tallest building in the world, possess the costliest diamond, become president of the richest nation, and fulfill all our sensuous cravings, but such achievements, we find to our dismay, do not give us lasting peace and happiness. We then begin to ask, "Can we not seek something which will give us permanent happiness and bliss?"

This quest is leading us to explore numerous paths and movements which promise peace to the soul. In this age of spiritual awakening we find people returning to more healthy ways of living: vegetarian and natural diets, physical exercises, hatha yoga, natural remedies for disease, wellness and fitness programs, and abstinence from smoking, drinking and intoxicating drugs which harm the body. Others who long for world peace join organizations to further that end: ecological groups, organizations to deal with world hunger, social welfare societies, world peace organizations and human rights movements are a few examples.

Others are trying to raise the moral and ethical values of mankind, especially in the fields of politics, education and business.

More and more people are turning to spiritual paths. Meditation is no longer something obscure; it is being practiced by people of all religions, ages and avocations. These people are joining different groups and are practicing various forms of yoga, transcendental meditation, Zen Buddhism, Sufism, and the like. Some forms of meditation are becoming a daily feature in the lives of doctors, educators, scientists, lawyers, businessmen, politicians, those in the creative arts and all other walks of life. Meditation is now being recognized as a means to relieve depression and reduce the tensions of daily life. It is being used by many to increase productivity on the job, to help the concentration of students who have learning difficulties, and to give those who were addicted to drugs a natural means to overcome their problems. While many practice meditation to relieve anxiety and become more productive, a growing number of serious seekers are turning to meditation to solve the mystery of life and death.

As more and more people take to meditation and learn to transcend their limited physical consciousness, they will begin to see that all are children of the same Father, of the One God. The walls which separate man from man will gradually crumble and we will create a world in which every individual -- no matter how humble -- is respected and cared for.

We are witnessing the dawn of a spiritual revolution. By definition, such a revolution, unlike political, social or economic ones, cannot be enforced from without. It is an inner revolution which centers on a change of consciousness. We cannot convert others, we can only convert ourselves. If we can accomplish this transformation we will not only hasten the spiritual dawn, but will ourselves bask in its full glory.

Excerpted from the book Spiritual Awakening *by Darshan Singh. Published by Sawan Kirpal Publications. Darshan Singh is the head of Sawan Kirpal Ruhani Mission.*

"*A human being is part of the whole, called by the 'Universe,' a part limited in time and space. He experiences himself, his thoughts and feelings as something separated from the rest, a kind of optical delusion of his consciousness. This delusion is a kind of a prison for us, restricting us to our personal desires and to affection for a few persons nearest to us. Our task must be to free ourselves from this prison by widening our circle of compassion to embrace all living, creatures and the whole nature in its beauty.*"

-- Albert Einstein

• THE SUFI ORDER

The Sufi Order, founded in 1910 by Hazrat Inayat Khan, is the continuation of a direct line of spiritual transmission stretching back to antiquity. Stressing the ideal of living a deeply spiritual life in the midst of the world, the order offers the public access to the meditation techniques developed by Pir Vilayat Inayat Khan, present head of the order. Further training for members includes personal guidance in a program of regular meditation practice.

The Sufi Order is an interreligious body revering the scriptures and the great teachers of all religious traditions. Its aim is the unity of humanity.

INFORMATION: 1570 Pacheco St., Santa Fe, NM 87501, (505) 988-4411.

• SUFISM REORIENTED

Sufism Reoriented is a formal spiritual school in the Sufi tradition, adapted to life in the Western world. This particular Sufi school traces its history from the Sufi Order initiated in the West in 1910 by Hazrat Inayat Khan, continued through (1947) by Murshida Rabia Martin, and sustained by its current head, Murshida Ivy O. Duce. The applied mysticism of Sufism Reoriented focuses on the nurturing of a link with God through love and remembrance of him. Students (mureeds) learn from pure Sufi teachings to strive for spiritual self-discipline, development of character and selfless service, all to be applied in the context of esoteric wisdom and ordinary life. The school is so called because of its reorientation in 1952 by Meher Baba, whom mureeds consider the Avatar of the age. Meher Baba universalized the school, confirmed Murshida Duce's status, and gave detailed instructions on its spiritual practices and future role.

INFORMATION: 1300 Boulevard Way, Walnut Creek, CA 94595, (415) 938-4820.

• THE SUMMIT LIGHTHOUSE

The Summit Lighthouse was founded in Washington, D.C., in 1958 by Ascended Master El Morya of Darjeeling, India, for the express purpose of publishing the teachings of the ascended masters dictated to the Messengers Mark and Elizabeth Prophet.

A unique nondenominational religious and philosophical organization, The Summit Lighthouse, publisher for Church Universal and Triumphant, has become a forum for the ascended masters and their students throughout the world. Its authority is derived from the order of devotees comprised of the ascended masters and their unascended chelas known as the Great White Brotherhood. Having mastered time and space and ascended into the white light of the Presence of God, the ascended masters have fostered the exploration of reality and the defining of individual self-mastery since the dawn of civilization. With international headquarters and Summit University in Los Angeles, California, and study groups and teaching centers in the major cities, the ascended masters and their students are disseminating the ancient wisdom to every nation.

Since 1958, The Summit Lighthouse has published the weekly letters of the ascended masters to their students throughout the world. Called *Pearls of Wisdom,* these letters are the intimate contract, heart to heart, between the guru and the chela. They contain instruction on cosmic law, commentary on current conditions on earth, and whatever the hierarchy of the Great White Brotherhood deems necessary to the individual initiation of those who form a part of this great movement of light-bearers on earth. The Summit Lighthouse is a movement and a momentum of light and light-bearers determined not to leave the earth as they found it!

INFORMATION: P.O. Box A, Malibu, CA 90265, (213) 880-5300, Weekly *Pearls of Wisdom* (free will love offering).

● **SUMMIT UNIVERSITY**

Summit University was founded by Mark and Elizabeth Prophet in 1971 in Santa Barbara, California. Conceived in the heart of Gautama Buddha, it is a modern mystery school, a place where disciples of both East and West come to sit at the feet of their own Real Self, the inner Guru, to be God-taught by the ascended masters. The ascended masters are sons and daughters of God who have risen from every race and religion, transcended the cycles of karma and rebirth, mastered time and space, and returned to the Great Source of Life through the accelerated consciousness of the ascension.

At Summit University, the ascended masters initiate students in cosmic law through their messenger, Elizabeth Clare Prophet, who wears the mantle of the embodied Guru side by side with the "Ever-Present Guru," Lanello (Mark L. Prophet, who made his ascension February, 1973). The teaching is the way of enlightenment through contact with the inner Christ Self, the individual reality that knows itself as God. Twelve weeks of personal initiation, meditation, and study secure within the soul the living teachings of the Great White Brotherhood. Seven courses correspond to the seven rays or states of God-consciousness, including Buddhic and Christic meditation for the raising of the Mother light in the chakras and scientific techniques for the acceleration of consciousness on the path of the ascension through invocation of the sacred fire in the science of the spoken word. Summit University also sponsors special two-week summer seminars for the recreation of body, mind, and soul.

INFORMATION: P.O. Box A, Malibu, CA 90265, (213) 880-5300.

● **SUNBURST -- THE ANCIENT BUILDERS**

The Ancient Builders reflects the positive return of ancient theocratic societies into a new age of universal enlightenment; an age where love and concern for the sacredness of all life shall reign again in the hearts of men. Our people live and work together in the spirit of brotherhood, and are caretakers of all life forms entrusted to us. We have acquired over 500,000 acres in northern Nevada, where we cultivate and raise an assortment of organic orchards, vegetables, grains, horses, cows, chickens, goats, and sheep. We also explore the seas in our large wooden sailing schooner. State-registered schools have been established for our children.

The Ancient Builders was founded on the visions and inspirations of

Norman Paulsen, who, as a young man, was a disciple of Paramhansa Yogananda. At age 21, shortly after Yogananda passed away, Norman had his first mystical death and rebirth experience in the luminous Body of Christ, the Eternal Light. Almost 20 years later, in 1969, he founded one of the world's most successful communities.

It is the goal of our society, by demonstration and images, to help rekindle the flame of desire in mankind for self-realization and the knowledge of, and the eventual meeting with a personal Mother-Father Creator Spirit.
INFORMATION: 77 E. St., Salt Lake City, UT 84103, (801) 363-1222.

● SURATAO

Suratao, the School of Universal Religious Arts of The Aquarian Order, is a non-profit religious educational and humanitarian fellowship dedicated towards manifesting the Commandment of "Simplicity" being the essence of Uranian power and Divine Will for the next 2,000 years as transmitted by Iotashe. Through living Group experience, awareness of cyclic manifestation is understood and mastered by application of astrological and esoteric principle. Beyond personal desire and Neptunian dissolution is Divine Synthesis through Group Activity and Humanitarian Service. Publications include *The Aquarian Mandate, The Story of Joy,* and *Timeless Mysteries-Mexico Ruin Series* photographs.   ·
INFORMATION: P.O. Box 19847, Los Angeles, CA 90019, (213) 931-0371.

● SYDA FOUNDATION -- SIDDHA MEDITATION

Siddha Meditaton is a natural method of contacting one's inner source of creativity and well-being. It was introduced to the West by Swami Muktananda, a Siddha master and one of the most respected and renowned teachers in the world today.

In Siddha Meditation the inner meditative state is experienced effortlessly and spontaneously. People who use it in their daily lives find that it benefits their health, effectiveness and clarity of mind.

Ashrams and centers around the world have regular free programs that include meditating and chanting. You are always welcome to visit and participate.
INFORMATION: P.O. Box 11071, Oakland, CA 94611, (415) 655-8677
and P.O. Box 600, South Fallsburg, NY 12779, (914) 434-2000.

"Conversion is an interesting word because it is both a spiritual and an economic word ... Conversion is a process of transformation: the process, as we see it, of transforming socially destructive technology to socially useful purposes, the ones that give life rather than make plans for its destruction.
Conversion as an approach gives a positive, hopeful vision. It values and affirms people who are caught in all of the structures, and it works in a serious way on positive alternatives."

-- David McFadden

● TAO HEALING ARTS CENTER

Chinese medicine is understood as experiencing a way of life based on Taoism. In our workshops we experience awareness of body, mind, spirit and therefore one's whole universe, in the process of balancing energy flow through Shiatsu & Anma massage, Acupuncture & Moxibustion. Consequently, we learn to heal ourselves and others in order to share happiness and peace in nature.

We offer classes in Shiatsu and an internship for people interested in becoming professionals as well as just for home care. In addition we offer Natural Healing Arts workshops & classes; Breathing & Meditation, Tai Chi Ch'uan, Yoga, Touch for Health, Doin (self exercise and healing), Preservation for health -- Japanese methods, etc. We also have a clinic that specializes in Acupuncture & Moxibustion treatments, Shiatsu & Anma, herbal remedies, and a low cost Shiatsu intern clinic. DoAhn T. Kaneko is the founder-director and also a California State licensed acupuncturist and instructor.

"Without stagnation, water flows into the ocean. It is simple yet great. To understand its love and peace is a key of our healing arts." See other listing under Shiatsu Massage School Of California.

INFORMATION: 2309 Main St., Santa Monica, CA 90405, (213) 396-4877.

● TAOIST INSTITUTE

The Taoist Institute is a center established for the practice and education regarding various aspects of the Taoist Holistic Tradition. Our focus is on the enhancement of optimal human development through the meditative arts, martial arts, and healing arts. All programs emphasize Chi Kung internal energy cultivation, health promotion, and body/mind integration through the harmony of vision, mind, breath and movement.

Classes are available in Taoist meditation and yoga, kung fu, Tai Chi Ch'uan, holistic healing, acupressure massage, Tai Chi Ruler and philosophy. Services are available in hypnosis, holistic counseling and healing, rebirthing, past life regression, and The Symbol-Linking Process. Call, visit or write for more information.

INFORMATION: 10632 Burbank Blvd., North Hollywood, CA 91601, (213) 760-4219.

● TEACHING OF THE INNER CHRIST

The Teaching of the Inner Christ is a metaphysical new thought teaching designed to help each person contact their own Inner Self and become a channel of love, light and healing. The Inner Christ -- your mystical higher nature -- can guide you through intuition, feed you universal love, and help you take dominion over your life.

Weekly classes include inner sensitivity, parapsychology, and prayer healing. There are also Sunday worship services. For information and location of TIC centers contact Rev. Ann Meyer, D.D.

INFORMATION: 3869 42nd St., San Diego, CA, (714) 280-7770.

● TEMENOS INSTITUTE, INC.

Temenos Institute, a center for psychotherapy and experiential learning, offers a Training Program In Humanistic/Transpersonal Psychotherapy. The Temenos Training Program is designed for human service professionals who wish to deepen their understanding of holistic process and for students who are entering the helping professions. The program is unique in that it offers experiential training in several therapeutic disciplines with particular attention given to major transpersonal depth psychologies such as Jungian Analysis and Psychosynthesis; to integrative body therapies; and to interpersonal and group approaches based on holistic principles.

INFORMATION: 29 East Main St., Westport, CT 06880, (203) 227-4388.

● TEMPLE OF COSMIC RELIGION

The Temple of Cosmic Religion (Sanatana Vishwa Dharma) is dedicated as a place where people of all faiths may come worship, meditate, and sing God's name. To achieve world peace through love, to understand the teachings of world religions, and to help the individual grow into a universal person are the goals of the Temple. The Temple has branches all over the world including Washington D.C., Pittsburgh, Michigan, Houston, and Santa Ana. Oakland Temple offers Gayatri Vidya Mandir which promotes educational and cultural programs. The founder and President is Sadguru Sant Keshavadas. A catalog of books and recordings by Sant Keshavadas and more information are available on request from the Oakland center.

INFORMATION: 174 Santa Clara Ave., Oakland, CA 94610, (415) 654-4683.

● THE TEMPLE OF MAN

The Temple of Man was formed in dedication to the sentient individual, creative man and woman and for the presentation and preservation of their creative works, in order to help broaden perception and increase the understanding between all men and women everywhere, who, being unified by the vital and supreme force of life, are working toward a higher social and spiritual evolution.

The Temple was founded with the knowledge that religion is that which should enable us to liberate ourselves from meaningless dogmas and superstitions and live as free spirits. The essence of all religion is an inner personal experience, an inner individual relationship with the Divine. It is not worship so much as a quest. It is a way of becoming, of liberation. The

152

Temple welcomes sentient beings, regardless of faith, to come together and share in the experience of be/coming.

The Temple offers no rigid doctrines or philosophy, no dogmatic concepts or intellectual disciplines, but only certain in/out sights through which you may engage the unknown.

The Temple functions in many areas, both spiritual & temporal with an esoteric humanitarian focus. To quote Albert Einstein:
"The most beautiful and most profound emotion we can experience is the sensation of the mystical. It is the source of all true science. Those beings to whom this emotion is a stranger, who can no longer wonder and stand rapt in awe, are as good as dead. To know that what is impenetrable to us really exists, manifesting itself as the highest wisdom and the most radiant beauty which our dull faculties can comprehend only in their most primitive forms -- this knowledge, this feeling, is at the center of true religiousness."

And finally, to quote Rabbi Nachman of Bratzlav:
"Man is afraid of things that cannot harm him, and he knows it, and he craves things that cannot be of help to him, and he knows it; but in truth the one thing man is afraid of is within himself, and the one thing he craves is within himself."

If there is any way in which we may serve you, please call or write to us. We will respond with the best we have to offer.

"The temple of man is within you." -- David Meltzer

INFORMATION: Revs. Robert and Anita Alexander, Co-Pastors, 1439 Cabrillo Ave., Venice, CA 90291, (213) 399-9747 or 396-6438 and Rev. Don Roberts, Pastor, 3921 France Ave., South, Minneapolis, MN 55416, (612) 929-9049.

● TERRA, INC.

Terra is a non-profit organization dedicated to the improvement of humanity. Only through the practice of the responsibility does the individual learn to fulfill his potential. Only through the expression of that potential will the individual find personal meaning. Terra seeks to join these experienced people together into a new society ..., that shall be as strong as truth.

We work towards the creation of a new culture and eventually the birth of a new civilization.

INFORMATION: 17 W. Biddle St., West Chester, PA 19380, (215) 692-6318.

● THE THEOSOPHICAL SOCIETY

The Theosophical society which was first established in New York City in 1875 by Helena Petrovna Blavatsky (HPB), Henry S. Olcott, William Q. Judge and others remains an international and spiritually oriented group composed of students bound together by Brotherhood of Humanity, without distinction of race, creed, sex, caste or color. To encourage the study of Comparative Religion, Philosophy and Science. To investigate unexplained laws of nature and the powers latent in man.

The Society is completely nonsectarian; it welcomes as members individuals from all religio-philosophical systems, and encourages total freedom of search and belief for its members.

The headquarters of the American Section of the Society (in Wheaton, Illinois) houses the largest library in the West on spiritual development, occultism and comparative religion, with over 25,000 volumes, and is a valuable resource center for scholars researching ancient wisdom -- religions and mystery traditions. This center also provides ongoing workshops and seminars on the spiritual background of man and the universe.

INFORMATION: The Theosophical Society in America, P.O. Box 270, Wheaton, IL 60187, (312) 668-1571.

● THOMAS INSTITUTE OF METAPHYSICS

Thomas Institute of Metaphysics was founded in 1976 to sponsor research in the transpersonal sciences and to offer related classes to the general public. "T.I.M." upholds the principle that advancement of universal consciousness results from cross cultural integration of the world's wisdom teachings, through dialogue among the various disciplines and heritages. As a non-sectarian metaphysical center, T.I.M. unites academic, spiritual, and esoteric sciences while being committed to the complete freedom of individual belief and search for truth. The center encourages comparative study of world religions, philosophies, humanistic psychologies, and esoteric traditions that promote peace, love and progress both within and about the individual.

In considering the esoteric ideas the center attempts to discover basic laws that help give a better understanding of the substance, the energy and the direction of the universe. Thomas Institute of Metaphysics works to raise the vibration of individual and group consciousness and bring about the New Age. For more information on classes and activities write us.

INFORMATION: 659 S. St. Andrews Pl., Los Angeles, CA 90005, (213) 387-1353.

● 3HO DRUG PROGRAM

The 3HO Drug Program represents a holistic approach to overcoming substance abuse and addictions. This residential treatment program is designed to rehabilitate a person naturally, without the use of chemical substances. It is based on the practice of yoga and meditation, nutrition, acupressure, self-awareness therapy and a positive family environment.

The program is only one facet of the spiritual community of Maha Deva Ashram. The Ashram consists of many families and individuals interested in living with others who have similar spiritual goals and ideals.

The 3HO Drug Program is accredited by the Joint Commission on Accreditation of Hospitals.

INFORMATION: Maha Deva Ashram, 1050 N. Cherry Ave., Tucson, AZ 85719, (602) 327-1734.

● 3HO FOUNDATION -- YOGI BHAJAN

The 3HO Foundation, Healthy, Happy, Holy Organization, founded in 1969, is an international, educational and spiritual organization offering instruction in Kundalini Yoga, Tantric Yoga, meditation and other subjects for improving the quality of life. Under the direction of the Siri Singh

Sahib, Harbhajan Singh Khalsa Yogiji (also known as Yogi Bhajan), 3HO centers around the world offer a wide variety of community services such as drug rehabilitation programs, free kitchens to feed the poor, schools, clinics and workshops in healing, massage therapy, natural childbirth, natural foods cooking and other subjects. Gatherings, courses and camps are open to all. These include: summer and winter solstices, Children's Camps, Women's Camp.

The Siri Singh Sahib (Yogi Bhajan) came to America in 1969, recognizing the need for a technology of mind and spirit to balance the technology of industry which pervades the Western World. He brought the ancient teachings of Kundalini Yoga and Tantric Yoga so that people could experience fulfillment and happiness in their lives in spite of the pressures and tensions of modern life. He came to America not to gather disciples, but to train teachers who in turn could reach out to serve within their own communities.

The 3HO Foundation requires no vows or "initiation," but serious students commit themselves to a regular routine of sadhana (daily spiritual discipline), involving Kundalini Yoga, meditation before dawn, hard work (to earn an honest living), and active sharing within the community. Many students have committed themselves to live as "Sikhs," exemplifying the high standard of righteous living and service to humanity that is the foundation of the Sikh Dharma (a world-recognized religion founded in India during the late 15th Century).

The focal point of the teachings of the 3HO Foundation is *Kundalini Yoga*. This ancient scientific technique works on the basic systems of the body to strengthen the nerves, purify the blood and regulate the glands, making the individual healthy, radiant and happy. Kundalini Yoga is also known as the "Yoga of Awareness" because it works directly to awaken the power of intuition, the basic tool of spiritual awareness.

Tantric Yoga is a science of interpersonal relationship based on polarity meditation, i.e., men and women together. Working at a meditation level (not the sexual practices often associated with the word "tantric") it cleanses the subconscious mind of fears and blockages, giving clarity of understanding and a strong sense of compassion in all relationships. Tantric Yoga is taught only by Mahan Tantric, Yogi Bhajan.

The Sikh Dharma had its beginnings in the late 15th century as an application of universal spiritual concepts into a practical daily routine. Guru Nanak, founder of Sikh Dharma, taught a basic triad of consciousness: Meditate, Work and Share. His successors (there were a total of ten Gurus from the 15th to the 18th centuries) emphasized other laws of consciousness including: "Live humbly, stand for righteousness and defend Truth everywhere." For a Sikh there can be no compromise with lower consciousness, and the concept of "Saint-Soldier" is a living reality in day to day life. Sikhs can be recognized by their outward form; turbans, uncut hair and white clothes, and by their actions and attitudes in daily life, for, above all, a Sikh lives to serve humanity.

INFORMATION: 3HO International Headquarters, Guru Ram Das Ashram, P.O. Box 35006, 1620 Preuss Rd., Los Angeles, CA 90035, (213) 550-9043; 3HO East Regional Headquarters, Guru Ram Das

Ashram, 1740 Whitewood Ln., Herndon, VA 22070, (703) 435-4411; 3HO Hacienda de Guru Ram Das, Rt. 1, Box 132D, Espanola NM 87532, (505) 753-9438; 3HO Canada, Guru Ram Das Ashram, 346 Palmerston, Toronto, Canada M6G 2N6, (416) 964-0612; and 3HO European Regional Headquarters, Guru Ram Das Ashram, Den Texstraat 46, Amsterdam, Holland 1017zc, telephone: 24-19-77.

● THE TIBET SOCIETY

The Society is directed by Thubten Jigme Norbu Tagster Rinpoche who is the older brother of the Dalai Lama. Former Abbot of Kumbum Monastery in Eastern Tibet, he is now an author and professor.
INFORMATION: Goodbody Hall, 101, Indiana University, Bloomington, IN 47405, (812) 335-2233.

● T.O.P. TRAINING: THE OMNISION PROGRAM

The T.O.P. Training: The Omnision Program by Jiun.

Throw Your Glasses Away -- And Learn to *see*! See For Yourself! Complete Training in one weekend workshop for natural, balanced, whole vision. Available in major metropolitan areas. Satisfaction guaranteed or money refunded. Teacher wore glasses 18 years, attaining perfect vision in *three* days. Although you are focusing wrongly, you can learn to focus correctly. Free introductory guest evenings in major cities. Various contribution options. Comprehensive brochure available.
INFORMATION: Call Jiun *Person-to-Person* Collect at (808) 572-0666 for local availability across the continent.

● TRAGER PSYCHOPHYSICAL INTEGRATION AND MENTASTICS

Trager Psychophysical Integration And Mentastics is the innovative learning approach to movement re-education created and developed over the past 50 years by Milton Trager, M.D. The Trager approach utilizes gentle, non-intrusive movements to facilitate the release of deep-seated physical and mental patterns which may inhibit free-flowing motion and full self-expression. In the climate of trust and cooperation engendered by The Trager Approach individuals usually experience an increased sense of well being, greater mobility, and a renewed capacity to relax. For more information, referrals, and training schedules contact us.
INFORMATION: 300 Poplar Ave., Suite 5C, Mill Valley, CA 94941, (415) 388-2688.

● THE TREE OF LIFE

The Tree Of Life New Age learning center has reopened at the Sojourner Truth School on the corner of 118th Street & Lennox Avenue. The center has been a beacon of light for the people of Harlem for many years. Its director and founder is Kanya Kekumbha.

Activities include use of its reading room with a collection of rare and unusual books on spiritual education for body, mind and spirit. Through reading these books it is hoped the youth will be inspired to useful service to themselves and mankind and turn from a path of drugs, crime and early death. Programs will also be directed towards senior citizens with seminars on health, nutrition and positive lifestyles. We invite all people of good will to join with us to work together to bring into fruition a New Age of love, wisdom and prosperity for all.

INFORMATION: 34 W. 118th St., Room 211, New York, NY 10026, (212) 222-1100.

● TRUTH CONSCIOUSNESS

The heart and substance of Truth Consciousness resides in the teachings of its founder and Spiritual Master, Swami Amar Jyoti. In the age-old classic way, Swamiji guides each seeker through his or her own way to the Divine, teaching no one theology or technique but catering to each one's individual temperament and needs. Swamiji maintains that all religions are one and that all paths lead to the same One. His purpose is no less than the complete regeneration of mankind, the establishment of Life Divine on earth for every soul who comes openhearted and yearning to know.

Truth Consciousness Ashrams are located in Boulder, Colorado; Tucson, Arizona; and Rockford, Michigan. Satsangs (Communion with Truth) are open to the public twice weekly the year round, as well as meditation classes, retreats, special events, and religious celebrations. Truth Consciousness also publishes books, cassette tapes of Swamiji's Satsangs, and *Chants to the Divine.*

Above all, Truth Consciousness is the vehicle for establishing a genuine relationship between the seeker for God, Truth, Self-Realization, and the Guru who shows the way, step by step, in infinite wisdom and love.

INFORMATION: Gold Hill, Salina Star Route, Boulder, CO 80302, (303) 447-1637.

● THE TWELVE RAYS OF THE GREAT CENTRAL SUN

This organization was originally founded in 1972 under the name, Teachings of the New Age. Sanat Kumara (Ancient of Days) is the Administrator with Christ Jesus as the World Teacher. Laws are taught that enable individuals to make direct contact with Sanat Kumara, who is one with the Creator, the Father Mother God of the Great Central Sun. This training center prepares leaders to operate their own Light Center through studies of Laws, weekly Etheric Operations (dissolution of karma), Akashic Readings, Books, Booklets, and Tapes.

The University of the Twelve Rays of the Great Central Sun provides a four year course through weekly tapes and pamphlets to assist one in further knowledge and enlightenment to become a teacher, writer, counselor, speaker, leader and train in channeling the Ascended Masters (Administrators within the University). Upon graduation, Ordination Certificates will be awarded enabling each to perform weddings and transitional services.

INFORMATION: 3427 Densone Pl., Charlotte, NC 28213, (704) 598-0692.

Peace Affirmations
& Meditations

Blessed are the peacemakers: for they shall be called the children of God.

The Great Invocation

From the point of Light within the Mind of God
　　Let light stream forth into the minds of men.
　　　　Let light descend on Earth.
From the point of Love within the Heart of God.
　　Let love stream forth into the hearts of men.
　　　　May Christ return to Earth.
From the center where the Will of God is known
　　Let purpose guide the little wills of men --
　　　　The purpose which the Masters know and serve.
From the center which we call the race of men
　　let the Plan of Love and Light work out
　　　　and may it seal the door where evil dwells.
Let Light and Love and Power restore the Plan on Earth.

Triangles asks you to join with two friends (in thought, but not necessarily simultaneously or in one location) to voice the "Great Invocation". (See Lucis Trust in *Center* section)

A Prayer For Peace

Lead me from death to life, from falsehood to truth.
Lead me from despair to hope, from fear to trust.
Lead me from hate to love, from war to peace.
Let peace fill our heart, our world, our universe.

Prayer for Peace, 21 Little Russell St., London WC1A 4HF (tel. 01 242 3486) distributes this prayer. They urge people to use it in their prayer and meditation work. Make a special effort to offer this prayer for one minute at noon every day, local time.

A Prayer For World Peace

The Christ Light fills all the leaders of America and Russia.
The Christ Light establishes a channel of Light,
Love and Peace between the leaders now.
The Christ Light directs the leaders to peace now.

United Research, P.O. Box 1146, Black Mountain, NC 28711 does prayer work for peace and conducts prayer tours for peace throughout the world. They recommend the preceding prayer be repeated over and over, preferably in groups. You can substitute any other countries.

The Prayer of Saint Francis of Assisi

Lord, make me an instrument of thy peace.
Where there is hatred, let me sow love;
Where there is injury, pardon;
Where there is doubt, faith;
Where there is despair, hope;
Where there is darkness, light;
Where there is sadness, joy;
O divine Master, grant that I may not so much seek
To be consoled as to console,
To be understood as to understand,
To be loved as to love;
For it is in giving that we receive;
It is in pardoning that we are pardoned;
It is in dying (to self) that we are born to eternal life.

U

● UNITY CENTER

We are a spiritual, non-profit organization which exists to bring an environment and opportunity for Spiritual growth to people in the San Francisco Bay Area. As well, we are a Community which practices the Presence of God/Spirit as an ongoing awareness in all that we do. We offer classes year-round. We also have a metaphysical bookstore, biofeedback, and Sunday services.

INFORMATION: 1871 Geary Rd., Walnut Creek, CA 94596, (415) 937-2191 and Dial-a-thought: (415) 937-0777.

● THE UNITY-IN-DIVERSITY COUNCIL

The Unity-in-Diversity Council is a worldwide coordinating body of organizations, individuals and networks fostering the emergence of a new universal person and civilization based on unity-in-diversity among all peoples. The work of the Council, begun in 1965 under the International Cooperation Council, has developed toward the emergence of a "People's United Nations", in which participants are accountable not to "national concerns", but to their own inner truths and the "good of the whole."

Membership in U.D.C. invites: access and visibility in (1) the *Directory for a New World,* a worldwide annual directory of groups and individuals contributing to a more cooperative, humane and healthful world (100,000 circulation), (2) the *Spectrum,* a quarterly newsletter including all Council information, human interest stories, important events and display ads (presently 25,000 circulation); full participation in (3) the Peacemaker Series, a monthly action forum and exposition designed to explore, understand and actualize the process of creating peace in our world today. Various programs and interactive processes will bring into focus the inner and personal, as well as the outer, a societal and planetary aspects of peacemaking, (4) the Mind, Body, Spirit Festival '83 to be held February 11-13 in Los Angeles and March 25-27 in San Francisco, (5) the U.D.C. General Assembly, (6) all Specialized and Geographic Councils, (7) all special events, projects and other services such as the "Transformation On Wheels" program series designed for 1982-83; (8) Voting rights and powers, and (9) discounts on a wide variety of books, tapes, and events.

INFORMATION: World Trade Center, 350 South Figueroa St., Suite #277-D, Los Angeles, CA 90071, (213) 626-2062.

● UNITY WOODS YOGA CENTER

Unity Woods Yoga Center, situated on 47 acres of rolling fields and forest in the foothills of the Catoctin Mountains of Maryland, is dedicated to the promotion of physical, mental, and spiritual health and awareness.

Founded in 1978 by its Director, John Schumacher, who has studied yoga in India with B. K. S. Iyenger, Unity Woods conducts hatha yoga classes and workshops in surrounding Frederick and Montgomery Counties year around, and during the summer months offers a program of silent retreats and weekend workshops featuring guest instructors in yoga related disciplines such as massage, acupressure, and cooperative relationship.
INFORMATION: 11432 Old Frederick Rd., Thurmont, MD 21788, (301) 898-5909.

● UNIVERSAL GREAT BROTHERHOOD, SOLAR LINE (U.G.B.)

The U.G.B., Solar Line is a non-profit educational and cultural institution founded by Sat-Guru Dr. Serge Raynaud de la Ferriere. It is established throughout the Americas and Europe. Its work emphasizes balance and health in individual life through the establishment of centers teaching yoga, meditation, vegetarian cooking, astrology, women and children classes and humanistic studies for people of all ages and backgrounds.

The Solar Yoga offered at the U.G.B. Centers is a synthesis of Eastern and Western techniques; thereby being Universal. The organization has opened more than 200 yoga centers worldwide.
INFORMATION: International H.Q. Avenida Insurgentes Sur 226, Mexico 7, D.F. Mexico and U.S.A. H.Q., P.O. Box 9154, St. Louis, MO 63117.

● UNIVERSAL LIFE CHURCH

An ex-Bapist minister from North Carolina arrived in Modesto, California after traveling and living around the country. Being a carpenter by trade, he converted the garage of his home into a chapel and put a sign over it that simply read "Church." Passersby would ask him what kind of church it was. He would ask them what religion they were. If they said Baptist, he would answer, "It is a Baptist church," and to the Pentacostal, "It is a Pentacostal church." Thus Kirby Hensley conceived the idea of The Universal Life Church. In 1962 he legally incorporated ULC and began to ordain ministers without questions and without charge, proclaiming that individuals have the right to interpret God according to their own theories or concepts. The idea grew and received national press coverage. To date, ULC claims 12 million ministers and 55,000 affiliated congregations. ULC ministers can legally perform weddings, funerals, baptisms, etc. Kirby Hensley continues to ordain ministers free of charge. Anyone interested in starting a church can send for a charter, and pledge a $2 monthly donation to be kept in the records.
INFORMATION: 601 3rd St., Modesto, CA 95351, (209) 527-8111.

● UNIVERSITY OF THE TREES

University Of The Trees is a community whose purpose is to serve the One and in that way to return consciousnss to its Source. Members of the community are engaged in running several businesses, including University Of The Trees Press, whose resources are ultimately dedicated to spiritual purposes. Christopher Hills, founder and director of the University Of The Trees, has spent the last 25 years researching Spirulina plankton as an answer to the problem of hunger in the world. One of the purposes of the community is to bring this dream into manifestation.

University Of The Trees offers correspondence courses in meditation and other aspects of consciousness research. The Press publishes books by Christopher Hills and by other members of the community, as well as taped lectures and meditations. It also markets divining instruments for purposes of research. Making these materials available to spiritual seekers around the world is part of the service to which the community members have committed their lives.

INFORMATION: P.O. Box 66, Boulder Creek, CA 95006, (408) 338-2161.

V

● VAJRADHATU

Vajradhatu is the international organization of Buddhist study and meditation centers under the direction and guidance of Vajracarya the Venerable Choyam Trungpa Rinpoche. The teachings of the Ven. Trungpa Rinpoche, which incorporate all three major traditions of Buddhism, Hinayana, Mahayana and Vajrayana, warn against "spiritual materialism," an approach to spirituality based upon enriching ego through seeking "salvation, miracles and liberation." Students are encouraged to surrender their struggle for self-improvement and fully encounter their own confusion and suffering in order to see things as they are and live fully and directly in the world.

Two major contemplative centers have been established: Karme-Choling in Vermont and Rocky Mountain Dharma Center in the Colorado Rockies. Karma Dzong, the largest Vajradhatu Center, is located in Boulder, Colorado. There are also numerous centers for meditation and study in cities throughout the U.S. and Canada, called Dharmadhatus. In 1974, the Ven. Trungpa Rinpoche was confirmed by His Holiness the XVIth Gyalwa Karmapa as "Vajracarya" a spiritual master of the highest level. He is also the author of numerous books.

INFORMATION: 1345 Spruce St., Boulder, CO 80302, (303) 444-0190.

● VALLEY LIGHT CENTER

The Valley Light Center is dedicated to the dissemination of the highest spiritual truths and of their useful application in daily life. The Center is a true center of light whose service is manifested through the written word in an effort to assist all seekers of Truth in their own personal spiritual evolution. The Valley Light Center's first manifested work was the publication of *Sadhana In Our Daily Lives* -- A Handbook For The Awakening Of The Spiritual Self. Other projects include: *Conscious Marriage/Conscious Divorce* ceremonial booklet; *More Light* book catalog; and the Madonna Project (job training for ex-prostitutes).

INFORMATION: P.O. Box 355, Oak View, CA 93022-0355, (805) 649-3393.

● VEDANTA CENTRE -- ANANDA ASHRAMA

The Vedanta Centre -- Ananda Ashrama community is probably the oldest Eastern spiritual community in America, having been founded in 1909, by Swami Paramananda, a disciple of Vivekananda and a monk of the Ramakrishna Order. The Ananda Ashrama near Pasadena and the Vedanta Centre near Boston both provide a spiritual home for men and women monastics. Public services and group meditations are held, and retreat facilities are available for those with committed interest in the Vedanta teachings. The active spiritual head is Mother Gayatri Devi, who has been teaching Vedanta in America since 1927, the first Indian woman to do so. Vedanta Centre also publishes books.

INFORMATION: 130 Beechwood St., Cohasset, MA 02025, (617) 383-0940 and Ananda Ashrama, P.O. Box 8555, La Crescenta, CA 91214, (213) 248-1931.

● VEDANTA SOCIETIES -- THE RAMAKRISHNA ORDER

The Vedanta movement was started in the United States by Swami Vivekananda, who came to represent Hinduism at the World's Parliament of Religions in Chicago in 1893. He founded the Vedanta Society of New York in 1896 and that of San Francisco in 1900. At present, there are 16 Vedanta Centers in this country run by monks of The Ramakrishna Order of India.

Vedanta, which forms the basis of the various sects of Hinduism, is one of the major living philosophies and religions of the world. The word "vedanta" means literally the concluding portion of the Vedas, India's most ancient scriptures. The books that comprise Vedanta consist of the accumulated knowledge of God, Soul and the World as derived from the spiritual experiences and discoveries of generations of India's *Rishis* (Seers). Vedanta teaches that man's real nature is divine, a manifestation of the infinite, immortal Reality or Godhead, which is within each person and every creature and object. The aim of man's life on earth is to realize this divinity. Through spiritual practice he can discover his true Self, which is pure consciousness distinct from the body and mind, perfect, free and blissful. Having found the Divine Being within himself, he sees Him likewise in others, regarding his fellow men as the very embodiments of God. Vedanta holds that man is both the maker and master of his destiny, and prescribes various tested and effective methods of spiritual practice suitable to individual needs and temperaments. Vedanta also maintains, as does Christianity, that God sometimes specially manifests His power and grace through a human personality, to teach us the way, and to provide a focal point for our love and devotion to Him.

Whereas Christianity teaches that Jesus Christ was the one incarnation for all time, Vedanta believes that God has come to earth repeatedly in times of man's greatest need, and will continue to do so in the future. However, the idea of Divine incarnation is not obligatory to students of Vedanta.

There are three main systems within the Vedanta philosophy, namely, Dualism (Dvaita), Qualified Monism (Vishitadvaita) and Monism (Advaita). In the first, God is different from his creation. In the second, the created universe is a part of God. In the third, the most lofty school of Vedantic thought, man, universe and God in their ultimate nature are non-different. A spiritual Seeker starts with dualism, passes through qualified monism and ends in monism. Sri Ramakrishna and Vivekananda stood for the harmonization of these three systems.

INFORMATION: Vedanta Society of Northern California, 2323 Vallejo St., San Francisco CA 94123, (415) 922-2323 and Vedanta Society of Southern California, 1946 Vedanta Pl., Hollywood, CA 90068, (213) 465-7114.

● VEGETARIAN SOCIETY, INC.

Vegetarian Society, Inc. is an educational, humanitarian, lively, non-profit organization, in its seventh year. A $12 annual membership fee gives you a quarterly newsletter, information on the monthly events (including free health lectures), vegetarian recipes, bumper sticker, two free books, and nutritional counseling. The group takes booths at health and other conventions, sells books. C.C.C. Division = College Campus Chapters. Send $32, and a subscription to *Vegetarian Times,* monthly magazine, will be added. $100 gives you a life membership (and a big bonus box of books is your gift for this donation.) Founder-President: Blanche Leonardo, Ph.D.

INFORMATION: P.O. Box 5688, Santa Monica, CA 90405, (213) 396-5164 or 477-0050.

● VIETNAMESE BUDDHIST TEMPLE AND FOREST RETREAT CENTER

Vietnam had two major Buddhist meditation traditions: Vietnamese Zen and Vietnamese Theravada Vipassana. As the Vietnamese people are being reshaped by the American experience, the remarkable *Buddha-Dharma* teachings they bring with them emerge in our culture as a wholesome and enlightening contribution to the New Age revolution.

The Vietnamese Buddhist Temple in Seattle was founded by its abbot, Ven. Thich Nguyen Dat, a Vietnamese Zen monk. For beginners and newcomers, meditation instruction and initial sitting practice is offered on Thursday evenings and you are also welcome to join in the Traditional Service for the Vietnamese community on Saturday afternoons. The Tapovana Forest Retreat Center, a meditation sanctuary near Cinebar, Washington (98533), is for intensive retreats and residential practice.

INFORMATION: 1651 S. King St., Seattle, WA 98144, (206) 323-2669 and Ven. Rahula, 863 S. Berendo, Los Angeles, CA 90005, (213) 384-9638.

● WAKING UP IN THE NUCLEAR AGE

Waking Up In The Nuclear Age is a project of and is located at Fort Mason Center. We are a cadre of therapists asking the questions: who have we become in the Nuclear Age and how can we begin to transform ourselves and our world into the Post-Nuclear Age? We offer workshops and seminars to move beyond psychic numbing about the nuclear threat; to explore our feelings and ideas about nuclear events, survival and living in this Age; and to find more loving and creative ways to work for change.
INFORMATION: P.O. Box 23, Fort Mason Center, San Francisco, CA 94123, (415) 885-5038.

● WALDORF INSTITUTE

Since 1967 we have offered programs, based on Rudolf Steiner's anthroposophical spiritual science, to people actively desiring the renewal of our society. We have a spacious, wooded campus featuring a large bio-dynamic garden with flower borders and fruit trees. Our faculty includes visitors from many nations who are leaders in their professions. Students come from throughout North America and other parts of the world.

We offer full time college-accredited programs in Waldorf education, including an M.A. program; also a part time, non-credit Life Studies Program. We warmly welcome inquiries and visitors.
INFORMATION: 23399 Evergreen Rd., Southfield, MI 48075, (313) 352-8990.

● THE WASHINGTON BUDDHIST VIHARA

The Washington Buddhist Vihara is a religious center set up for the teaching and practice of Theravada Buddhism, the most ancient Buddhist lineage best known for its system of insight meditation. The resident monks at the Vihara offer instruction in Buddhist doctrine and meditation, lecture, and provide spiritual services. The Vihara publishes a quarterly newsletter with articles on Buddhism, *The Washington Buddhist.* It also operates a book service selling a large selection of domestic and foreign books on Buddhism, hard to find elsewhere. A brochure and booklist are available on request.

INFORMATION: 5017 16th St., N.W., Washington, D.C. 20011, (202) 723-0773.

● WASHINGTON PSYCHIC INSTITUTE

Washington Psychic Institute offers techniques and a safe place to explore your psychic abilities, with eight week classes in healing, meditation, body magic, female healing and male energy. A one-year Intensive Training Program is offered for one wishing to pursue his spiritual communication with the God of his heart. This includes using your psychic and clairvoyant abilities through aura readings. Introductory workshops, demonstrations, healing clinics, aura readings plus all day workshops at our island retreat are also available.

Call the Institute nearest you for more information: Seattle (206) 782-3617, Tacoma (206) 759-7460, Spokane (509) 534-5444, Bellingham and Vancouver, B.C. (206) 671-4291, Portland (503) 232-3443, Everett (206) 258-1449.

INFORMATION: 10924 S.W. 168th, Route 5, P.O. Box 479, Vashon, WA 98070, (206) 463-9671.

● WELL BEING COMMUNITY CENTER

The Well Being Community Center is a non-profit community resource center. It produces a monthly publication, *Well Being Community Calendar,* which features articles, classes and businesses in Sonoma County area that deal with health, the arts, personal and spiritual growth, and the transformation of our planet. It sponsors two Festivals a year as well as lectures, workshops, concerts, and community celebrations.

The Health & Harmony Festival is held the 3rd weekend in May each year at Santa Rosa Fairgrounds, California. It features a Health Exposition, Crafts Faire and an all day Music Concert with local and national talent. The Spirit of Christmas Crafts Faire & Celebration is held weekends in December, also at Santa Rosa Fairgrounds. It is a unique marketplace and Christmas Celebration. (Well Being Center is an office only and does not have facilities for housing.)

INFORMATION: P.O. Box 940, Sebastopol, CA 95472, (707) 823-1489.

● WHOLISTIC COUNSELING

Wholistic Counseling is a therapeutic community focusing on individual growth and social change based on a natural approach utilizing herbs, gestalt therapy, creative emotions, interpersonal communications, group process, body awareness, nutritional education and spiritual connection. Founded by Ethan Nebelkopf, a family therapist, herbalist and author of *The Herbal Connection* and *The New herbalism,* the Wholistic Counseling network directly addresses the problems of drug and alcohol abuse in teenagers and adults. The Wholistic Counseling center provides training for herbalists and family counselors as well as for human service groups with a social consciousness.

INFORMATION: 1614A Harmon St., Berkeley, CA 94703, (415) 652-2724.

● WILLOW GOLD

Willow Gold is a small community averaging ten people living at Willow Gold farm itself. There is also a network of friends locally and throughout the globe, including informal affiliations with the Lorian Association, Findhorn Community, the Love Project, and Auroville, India.

Workshops, celebrations, and classes take place regularly, which are geared to opening individual and group energy. These events are open to anyone drawn to share in them. The community also maintains an organic garden and cares for the land, forest and animals with a sense of cooperation with nature.

Several residents at Willow Gold operate Global View a retail store, mail order service and wholesale distribution for fine products, hand crafted at Findhorn, Auroville, and elsewhere in Asia. By personally selecting articles from Asian cottage industries, we together synthesize traditional crafts with functional design, thus creating a tangible creative link with a world neighborhood.

We believe our business relationships should improve the quality of life for craftspeople. In maintaining marketing networks, we hope to nurture a personal relationship between buyer and producer.

Working together helps us grow with greater direction and clarity. Through acknowledging, encouraging, and reinforcing the clarity in ourselves and in each other, we find a tool for individual and group growth.
INFORMATION: Route 3, Spring Green, WI 53588, (608) 583-5311.

● WILMOT CENTER

Wilmot Center, a residence community and meeting place, provides an atmosphere of collaboration and integral development of the spiritual truth of the individual and the integrated personality of man. Wilmot Center is non-sectarian, leaving each person free to find within himself the truth which speaks to his own inner development; while concurrently, the Center welcomes and supports all spiritual teachings. All aspects of human development are taken up in the center's activities, in furtherance of which we are developing a school, library, newsletter, organic garden, new age businesses, healing center, and classes in various aspects of life in the new age. Leadership is collaborative. Each individual is encouraged to take responsibility for his own growth and the community growth. Freedom, growth, responsibility and progress are the goals and the methods of spiritual integration and true personality expression.
INFORMATION: 30626 112th St., Wilmot, WI 53192, (414) 862-6968.

● WIN SYSTEMS

Win Systems was established to provide young adults with special seminars in which guided imagery, role playing, motivational exercises and internal/external teachers are used to provide enlightened awareness and in-

creased feelings of high self-esteem. The common goal of inter-connection with each other, the universe and the Life Force is given special emphasis.
INFORMATION: P.O. Box 1234, Sacramento, CA 95806, (916) 922-2202.

● THE WINGED HEART HOMESTEAD

The Winged Heart Homestead is a community with a school on a 283 acre piece of property in the Blue Ridge Mountains of Virginia. We are open to all religions, non-denominational, unattached to any existing institution. We plan to build a *Universel* -- a temple of art.

We emphasize spiritual growth; health ecological living and eating; research in the area of medicine and healing; different methods of organic gardening and farming; developing new ways of architecture, new ways of handling psychological conflict, etc. We would like to have families here, each living in their own house.
INFORMATION: Rt. 67, P.O. Box 47, Alum Ridge, VA 24051, (703) 763-3137.

● WOMEN AND WISDOM

At Women And Wisdom we seek a new manifestation of spirituality for our time. At our Center, which is home for our workshops, classes, meditations, celebrations, events and newsletter, we are dedicated to breaking through our fears and defenses to discover Who We Really Are. With a new sense of peace and Oneness, we are freeing and empowering our Selves. At Women And Wisdom we are claiming our heritage as Divine Co-Creators, healing one another and, thereby, the planet. It is toward this joyful remembering that we journey together, and we welcome you. Gabrielle Beard is Director and Founder.
INFORMATION: 155 Bank St., 12th Fl., New York, NY 10014, (212) 807-1222.

● WOMEN'S CONFERENCES

Directed by Linda Barone, M.A., M.F.C.C., we produced *Women: The Leading Edge Of The New Age,* a healing and spirituality conference in Los Angeles, California in April, 1982, attended by over 400 women nationwide. October 22-24, 1982 we will present *The Heart Of The Matter,* a Los Angeles conference with over 60 workshops, including rituals, meditations, dance, martial arts, visual thinking, acupressure, herbs, gestalt, polarity, tai chi, and goddess consciousness. We welcome all inquiries.
INFORMATION: 12581 Venice Blvd., Suite 206, Los Angeles, CA 90066, (213) 455-1472.

● THE WORD FOUNDATION, INC.

A non-profit organization publishing and distributing the four spiritual self-guidance books of the late Harold W. Percival. The information offered by Percival was obtained by transcendent noetic illuminations and by an unusual mental power he called "real thinking". His major work is *Thinking*

And Destiny, a comprehensive 1,000 page book outlining his singular metaphysical and spiritual system of thought. Covers the purpose and plan of the Cosmos, ultimate destiny of the individual, powers of the Self, degrees of being conscious, the law of thought as destiny, classes of elementals, etc.
INFORMATION: P.O. Box 18235-S, Dallas, TX 75218, (214) 348-5006.

Y

● YASODHARA ASHRAM

Yasodhara Ashram was founded in 1956 by Swami Sivananda Radha, a direct disciple of Swami Sivananda of Rishikesh, India. The Ashram gives those who are serious about spiritual life an opportunity to discover their own paths and to serve those who seek the Most High. They provide a retreat where people of all religions may come to find their center.

The ashram gives courses in yoga and workshops in Self-development including a three-month Yoga Teachers Course. Hatha, Mantra, Karma, Raja and Kundalini are the principal aspects of yoga that they teach. Swami Radha has adapted several Eastern techniques for self-development to the group situation, creating workshops which emphasize the unity of the spiritual with the mental, emotional and physical levels of being.
INFORMATION: P.O. Box 9, Kootenay Bay, B.C., Canada V0B 1X0, (604) 227-9224.

● YESHE NYING PO -- ORGYEN CHO DZONG

Yeshe Nying Po is the American seat of His Holiness Dudjom Rinpoche, head of the Nyingmapa Order of Tibetan Buddhism, and the parent organization for Orgyen Cho Dzong, a meditation retreat and practice center in upstate New York.

There are also centers in Ashland, Oregon (run by Gyatrul Rinpoche) and in other parts of the country.
INFORMATION: Yeshe Nying Po, 19 W. 16th St., New York, NY 10011, (212) 691-8523; Orgyen Cho Dzong, Rd. 1, P.O. Box 555, Greenville, NY 12083, (518) 926-4228; Yeshe Nying Po, 36 S. Second St., Ashland, OR 96520, (503) 688-2993.

● YOGA AND GROWTH CENTER OF BERGEN COUNTY

The Yoga and Growth Center of Bergen County is an organization devoted to the education, awareness and personal growth of the individual and the community. We offer daily Hatha Yoga sessions with Sauna, as well as a wide variety of classes, evening programs and workshops. Our diversified offerings include: nutrition, herbology, massage, shiatsu, reflexology, Tai Chi, Feldenkrais, etc.

An integral part of the Center is the Upstairs Herb Shoppe selling bulk herbs, spices and foods, books, magazines, herbal body products, records, and tapes, all-cotton clothing and much more.

Call or write for free brochure listing our current offerings. Easy public transportation access.

INFORMATION: 84 East Ridgewood Ave., Ridgewood, NJ 07450, (201) 447-2474.

● YOGA RESEARCH SOCIETY

The Yoga Research Society provides a neutral platform where students of the science of Yoga, along with others, may explore the potentials of human development with a wide range of teachers, researchers, physicians and therapists.

Each year since 1975, YRS has conducted an annual October conference featuring internationally respected scientists, authors, and religious leaders. These conferences have clarified the relationship of Yoga to fields such as medicine, religion, psychology, sports, and the arts. The Society additionally conducts ongoing research independently and through like-minded institutions in this country and abroad, publishing results as funds are available.

INFORMATION: 527 South St., Philadelphia, PA 19147, (215) 923-5946.

Z

● ZEN CENTER OF LOS ANGELES

The Zen Center of Los Angeles offers daily sitting meditation and private instruction under the direction of Zen Master Taizan Maezumi and his senior students. Maezumi Roshi has received certification in both the Soto and Rinzai traditions and blends the methods of both in his teaching. The Center holds intensive meditation retreats (sesshin) and Introduction to Zen Practice workshops each month. A residential training program continues throughout the year for those interested in devoting a month or more to full-time Zen practice. Public talks and beginners' instruction are given each week.

INFORMATION: 905 South Normandie Ave., Los Angeles, CA 90006, (213) 387-2351.

● THE ZEN CENTER OF ROCHESTER

Ven. Philip Kapleau, Roshi, teaches an integral Zen grounded in the doctrines and disciplines of both the Soto and Rinzai sects, which includes koan practice for experienced students. The Rochester center offers a daily schedule of meditation and chanting with periodic four and seven-day sesshins open to members. Introductory workshops are also available.
INFORMATION: 7 Arnold Park, Rochester, NY 14607, (716) 473-9180.

● THE ZEN CENTER SAN FRANCISCO/TASSAJARA

The Zen Center of San Francisco holds Zazen, gives lectures on Zen, and in general makes the teachings of Zen Masters available to the public. More specifically, it prepares serious students for a retreat experience at Tassajara. Baker Roshi is Spiritual leader.

The Zen Mountain Center of Tassajara was founded to make possible the practice of the Middle Way in America. Suzuki Roshi, a Zen Master, opened it in 1967 so that individuals could temporarily withdraw from everyday life to experience in themselves something beyond mind and body, feeling and will. Zen technique seeks to transcend doctrine, ideology and philosophies. The individual sits perfectly still, conscious of his breathing, and experiences himself at the source of action. Once the technique is internalized, withdrawal is no longer necessary, and he takes back his *Satori,* or Enlightenment, to everyday life.
INFORMATION: Zen Center, 300 Page St., San Francisco, CA 94100, (415) 863-3136 or 626-3697 and Zen Mountain Center, Tassajara Hot Springs, Carmel Valley, CA 95705.

● THE ZEN STUDIES SOCIETY

The Zen Studies Society has two zendos (Zen training centers) one in the New York City and another in the Catskill Mountains. At each zendo, study and practice in the Rinzai tradition is under the guidance of Eido Roshi and his master, Soen Roshi, who visits periodically. New York Zendo Shobo Ji (City Zendo) offers part time Zen practice for those who live and work in the city, while Dai Bosatsu Zendo Kongo Ji (Catskill Monastery) is the first Zen Buddhist Monastery in this country to offer traditional full-time Zen monastic life in a Japanese-style temple.
INFORMATION: 223 E. 67th St., New York, NY 10021, (212) 861-3333.

Yogi Bhajan and Daniel Ellsberg do not have a corner on the 'How Do We Get Out of the Predicament' market. If we do get out of this predicament, we do it together. No one person can do it alone: no one small group even can do it alone. If they give the Nobel Peace Prize because there are no more nuclear weapons left on this planet in five or ten years, and if at the same time we have been able to do away with chemical weapons and biological weapons and are pretty far along the way to reducing pollution, the Peace Prize will have to go to humanity."

-- John Steiner

The figure of the coming **Buddha Maitreya,** *the Great Loving One, is one of those future-building forces, which in ever increasing strength penetrates the consciousness of humanity. The tremendous changes which this exalted figure has brought about in the milleniums of spiritual history of Buddhism is a sure proof of its vitality and effectiveness -- which nowadays goes far beyond the confines of traditional Buddhism.*

-- Lama Govinda

172

Community
Directory

NEW AGE MAILING LISTS

Promote your products or programs by renting our mailing lists. Thousands of New Age: Centers & Communities • Natural Foodstores & Restaurants • Wholistic Health Groups • Bookstores • Periodicals • Individual Book buyers • Therapists & More.

What is NAM?

NAM/New Age Mailing Lists is a modern computerized service providing up-to-date mailing labels to help you in your sales, promotion and fund raising activities.

How and why is NAM done?

NAM Mailing Lists are compiled from various sources including our regular work on the **New Consciousness Sourcebook** and **A Pilgrim's Guide to Planet Earth.** Over the years many have used the **Guides** for mailing, and we have come to realize that our books could never provide as extensive and up-to-date a mailing list as was required. Continual updating, and expanding is being done to insure maximum usefulness to the renter.

What can NAM do for you?

NAM Mailing Lists are a unique and effective way to reach the New Age community, whether it be to increase the sales market for your products and services, promote your conferences and activities or expand your advertising and readership.

Why use NAM over other lists?

There are no other lists available which cover the New Age community and its businesses as comprehensively and accurately as NAM. We've been a New Age information center since 1971; one of the first. Developing the lists has been a lengthy and thorough effort on our part.

In What form does Nam come?

Nam Mailing Lists are available in both categorical and/or geographical-regional form on four-up Cheshire labels or Avery Pressure sensitive labels.

What is the Cost?

$55.00 per thousand on four-up perforated Chesire labels. $5.00 extra per thousand on Avery self-adhesive labels. The minimum order is $60.00. After minimum order, a fraction of the basic unit of 1000 will be prorated. NAM Lists rentals are for ONE TIME USE ONLY. Special rates for multiple use can be arranged.

How to order

Contact us immediately by mail or telephone. Let us know the categories you need. Ask any questions you have. We will give you category counts, mailing advice, costs, and any other information you need. Then send us a check and within ten days you'll have your labels.

Write or telephone:
**PS Khalsa NAM lists P.O. Box 1067
Berkeley, CA 94701
(415) 644-3229**

Alabama

Birmingham *Center* 3HO -- GRD, 1172 16th Ave., S., 35205, (205) 322-7337.
Foodstore GOLDEN TEMPLE NATURAL FOODS & RESTAURANT, 1901 11th Ave. South, 35205, (205) 933-6333. Complete foodstore and fast vegetarian lunches.
Huntsville *Bookstore* BOOKS AS SEEDS, 200 1/2 Andrew Jackson, 35801, (205) 533-0270.
Restaurant PEARLY GATES, 2308 Memorial Parkway, S.W., 35801, (205) 534-6233. Also natural foods market and holistic health school.

Alaska

Anchorage *Center* 3HO -- GRD, 467-H-Bayview Dr., 99507, (907) 345-1339.
MORNINGSONG, (Priti Lorand, Dir.) 504 W. 25th Ave., 99503, (907) 277-8549. Holistic education, yoga, natural healing.
Bookstore THE SOURCE, 336 E. 5th Ave., 99501, (907) 274-5850. Metaphysical books & supplies.

Arizona

Flagstaff *Center* 3HO -- GRD, P.O. Box 1134, 86002, (602) 774-8517.
Phoenix *Center* 3HO -- GURU NANAK DWARA, 2302 N. 9th St., 85006, (602) 271-4480, 256-9731.
INTERNATIONAL HOLISTIC CENTER, INC., P.O. Box 15103, 85060, (602) 957-3322.
Prescott Valley *Center* HOHM, P.O. Box 5839, 86312, (602) 778-9189. Real apprenticeship programs in various arts for spiritual enlivenment.
Scottsdale *Center* COSANTI FOUNDATION, 6433 Doubletree Rd., 85253, (602) 948-6145.
Sedona *Center* SPIRITUAL LIFE INSTITUTE, Nada Contemplative Center, Star Route 1, 86336, (602) 282-7668.
Instruction JAY STEINBERG TAPES, P.O. Box 2282, 86336, (602) 282-2373. High quality, low cost cassette tapes; seminars and workshops on music, color, humor, medicine wheel.
Tempe *Bookstore* CHANGING HANDS BOOKS, 414 S. Mill Ave., 85281, (602) 966-0203. New & used books.
Foodstore GENTLE STRENGTH COOP, 38 E. 5th St., 85281, (602) 968-4831. Dairy, produce, herbs, grains, bulk. Non-member OK. Open everyday.
Tucson *Center* 3HO -- MAHA DEVA, 1050 N. Cherry Ave., 85719, (602) 795-7346.
3HO DRUG PROGRAM, Maha Deva Ashram, 1050 N. Cherry Ave., 85719, (602) 327-1734.
Health DENT INFO, 2509 N. Campbell #S262, 85719, (602) 432-3081.

Arkansas

Melbourne *Center* DIMENSIONS OF EVOLVEMENT, S.R. 3, P.O. Box 47, 72556, (501) 368-4468.

Nail *Center* SUFI ISLAMIA RUHANIAT SOCIETY, Heartsong Farm, Star Route, 72056, (501) 428-5503.

Springdale *Center* OZARK LIFE CENTER, Route 4, P.O. Box 540-S, Grandview Rd., 72764, (501) 361-2155.

California

Altadena *Center* 3HO -- GRD, 1059 E. New York Dr., 91001, (213) 794-4148.
School NATURAL VISION IMPROVEMENT INSTRUCTOR TRAINING: BATES METHOD PLUS, Janet Goodrich, Ph.D., P.O. Box 1973, 91001, (213) 986-0886. Intensive apprenticeship course to professionally teach naturally clear vision.

Anaheim *Bookstore* PSYNETICS BOOK STORE, 1212 E. Lincoln Ave., 92805, (714) 533-2311. ESP, Metaphysics, and Mysticism.

Arcata *Center* SUFI ISLAMIA RUHANIAT SOCIETY, Garden of the Heart, 2270 Western Ave., 95521, (707) 822-3179.

Arleta *Center* AQUARIAN AGE CHURCH & SPIRITUAL UNITY MOVEMENT CENTER, 9575 Canterbury Ave., 91331, (213) 892-1832.

Berkeley *Center* 3HO, 2669 LeConte, 94706, (415) 540-6332.
3HO -- HOUSE OF GRD, 1642 Francisco, 94703, (415) 849-3794.
THE ACUPRESSURE WORKSHOP, 1533 Shattuck Ave., 94709, (415) 845-1059.
THE AQUARIAN MINYAN, P.O. Box 7224, 94707, (415) 848-0965.
BESHARA, 2448 Prospect St., 94704.
THE GRADUATE THEOLOGICAL UNION LIBRARY, New Religious Movements Research Corporation, 2400 Ridge Rd., 94709, (415) 841-8222.
JUNGIAN-SENOI INSTITUTE, 1525J Shattuck Ave., 94709, (415) 848-0311.
NYINGMA INSTITUTE, 1815 Highland Pl., 94709, (415) 843-6812.
SUFI ISLAMIA RUHANIAT SOCIETY, Garden of Bismillah, 851 Regal Rd., 94708, (415) 527-2569.
VEDANTA SOCIETY OF BERKELEY, 2455 Bowditch St., 94704, (415) 848-8862.
School ACUPRESSURE WORKSHOP, 1533 Shattuck Ave., 94709, (415) 845-1059. Certified Training Program.
KHALSA CHILDREN'S CENTER, 2669 Le Conte, 94709, (415) 843-9106. A New Age spiritual school designed to nourish body, mind and spirit. Montessori based pre-school and elementary. El Cerrito-Richmond area.
Foodstore EDEN NATURAL FOODS, 2050 University Ave., 94704, (415) 845-7000. Organic produce. Juice-sandwich bar. Vitamins-herbs.
Service NANCY FREEDOM, P.O. Box 3072, 94703, (415) 653-3123 (messages). Neurolinguistic Programming (tm), therapeutic yoga, rebirthing.
Instruction YEHUDIT GOLDFARB, 2020 Essex St., 94703, (415) 848-0965. Instructor of T'ai Chi Chih and T'ai Chi Ch'uan.
Counseling WHOLISTIC COUNSELING, 1614A Harmon St., 94703, (415) 652-2724.
Media NAM -- NEW AGE MEDIA, P.O. Box 1067, 94701, (415) 644-3229.

Beverly Hills *Center* THE INTERGROUP COMMITTEE, P.O. Box 5105, 90210, (213) 379-9990, 540-8689.

SELF IMPROVEMENT INSTITUTE (SII), P.O. Box 6300, 90212-1300, (213) 933-NEEV.
Counseling DR. ELAN Z. NEEV (Ph.D. & D.D.), P.O. Box 6300, 90212, (213) 933-NEEV. A holistic healing of most problems; goal-realization; parapsychological communications and readings. See center section under Self-Improvement Institute and classified under Miscellaneous.

Big Sur *Center* ESALEN INSTITUTE, 93920, (408) 667-2335.

Bonsall *Center* GENESA, P.O. Box 327, 92003.

Boulder Creek *Center* UNIVERSITY OF THE TREES, P.O. Box 66, 95006, (408) 338-2161.

Burlingame *Center* EARTHBEAM NATURAL FOODS, 1399 Broadway, 94010, (415) 347-2058.

Campbell *Health* DRS PETER W. ROSS, O.D. AND GARY R. STOCKER, O.D., 1725 South Bascom #108, 95008, (408) 371-2020 (Milpitas 263-2040). Vision care and improvement: preventive techniques, orthokeratology and vision therapy.

Canoga Park *Restaurant* FOLLOW YOUR HEART NATURAL FOODS, 21825 Sherman Way, 91303, (213) 348-3240. Vegetarian restaurant, complete store, produce, grocery, herbs, bulk, clothing, love.

Capitola *Center* PAN -- PLANETARY ALIGNMENT NETWORK, P.O. Box 21, 95010, (408) 688-5935.
SUFI ISLAMIA RUHANIAT SOCIETY, Nur Manzil, 122 Central Ave., 95010, (408) 462-1512.

Carmel *Center* SUBUD, c/o Chairman Locksin Thompson, 4 Pilot Rd., 93924, (408) 659-4818.

Carmel Valley *Center* THE ZEN CENTER SAN FRANCISCO/TASSAJARA, Tassajara Hot Springs, 95705.
Foodstore CARMEL VALLEY NATURAL FOODS, Village Center, 93924, (408) 659-2811. Complete selection of natural foods, vitamins, supplements, sandwiches, salads, juices.

Chico *Service* PURCELL/CLAIR, 1602 Laburnum, 95926, (916) 342-4451. See classified ads under Astrology and Handicrafts.

Corte Madera *Center* HEAVENSONG, P.O. Box 605, 94925, (415) 459-7119.
Bookstore PAPERSHIP BOOKS, 69 Tamal Vista Blvd., 94925, (415) 924-4212. New Age music, crystals, jewelry and metaphysical books.

Cotati *Center* HAWTHORNE UNIVERSITY, 315 East Cotati Ave., Suite F, 94928, (707) 795-7168; (415) 521-6126, 239-0887.

Covelo *Center* MISHAKAI CENTER FOR THE STUDY OF SHAMANISM, P.O. Box 388, 95428.

Davis *Bookstore* ORPHEUS BOOKS, 204 E St., 95616, (916) 758-4040.

Del Mar *Center* MANDALA SOCIETY, P.O. Box 1233, 92014, (714) 481-7751.
Center PACIFIC HEALING ARTS CENTER, 318 Ninth St., Suite A, 92014, (714) 481-2541.

Dulzura *Center* MADRE GRANDE, Star Route 118, 92017, (714) 468-3810.

Duncan Mills *Restaurant* THE BLUE HERON INN, Hwy. 116 between Guerneville and Jenner, 95430, (707) 865-2269. A culinary jewel in a country setting, featuring International Vegetarian specialities, homemade soups and pastries, beautiful gardens & a turn-of-the-century tavern.

Emigrant Gap *Foodstore* ALIVE POLARITY'S VEGETARIAN RESTAURANT, Interstate 80 & Emigrant Gap Exit, 95715, (916) 389-8237. Located East of Sacramento near Donner Summit.

Escondido *Center* THE LIGHT OF THE DOVE FOUNDATION, World Organization And Healing Ministry, 1120 E. Washington St. #22, 92025, (714) 747-5085.

Fairfax *Restaurant* THE SLEEPING LADY CAFE, 58 Bolinas Rd., 94930, (415) 456-2044. Entertainment evenings.

   Health HOMEOPATHIC MEDICINE, 4 Sherman Ave., 94930, (415) 457-8851.

Fallbrook *Center* GENESA, 4702 San Jacinto Ter., 92028, (714) 728-2822.

Foster City *Center* SPECTRUM WORKSHOPS/CLUB SPECTRUM, 959 DeSoto Ln., 94404, (415) 349-6946.

Fullerton *Center* 3HO -- GRD, 419 W. Commonwealth Ave., 92632, (714) 738-9556.

Garberville *School* HEARTWOOD: CALIFORNIA COLLEGE OF THE NATURAL HEALING ARTS, 220 Harmony Ln., 95440, (707) 923-2021.

Gardena *Center* SEICHO-NO-IE, 14527 S. Vermont Ave., 90247, (213) 323-8486.

Glendale *Bookstore* CHURCH OF RELIGIOUS SCIENCE, 2146 E. Chevy Chase Dr., 91206, (213) 244-8171.

Greenbrae *Therapy* HYPNOTHERAPY, 1125 South Eliseo Dr., 94904, (415) 461-5937. Morton Rossman, certified hypnotherapist; Shirley F. Rossman, certified hypnotherapist, registered nurse. Value fulfillment hypnosis.

Guerneville *School* CALIFORNIA SCHOOL OF HERBAL STUDIES, P.O. Box 350, 95446.

   Bodywork PACIFIC SCHOOL OF MASSAGE AND HEALING ARTS, 44800 Fish Rock Rd., 95445, (707) 884-3138.

Hawthorne *Center* INTERGALACTIC LOVETRANCE CIVILIZATION CENTER, 5113 W. 134th St., 90250, (213) 675-1464.

Hayward *Center* RELIGIOUS SCIENCE CENTER, 26081 Mocine Ave., 94544, (415) 886-5335.

Healdsburg *Center* DADA CENTER PUBLICATIONS, 2319 West Dry Creek Rd., 95448, (707) 433-2161.

Hermosa Beach *Bookstore* EITHER/OR BOOKSTORE, 124 Pier Ave., 90254, (213) 374-2060. Leading The Way in Semi-Consciousness.

Hollywood *Center* VEDANTA SOCIETY OF SO. CALIF., 1946 Vedanta Pl., 90068, (213) 465-7114.

   Bookstore VEDANTA PRESS AND BOOKSHOP, 1946 Vedanta Pl., 90068, (213) 465-7114. Free catalog available.

Hopland *Center* SUFI ISLAMIA RUHANIAT SOCIETY, Allah's Acres, P.O. Box 606, 95449, (707) 744-1422.

Julian *Health* MOHAVE SUN LODGE -- TISHA, P.O. Box 12, 92036, (714) 765-1926. See Health & Healing in classified ad section.

Kensington *Center* EWAM CHODEN TIBETAN BUDDHIST CENTER, 254 Cambridge Ave., 94708, (415) 527-7363.

La Crescenta *Center* VEDANTA CENTRE -- ANANDA ASHRAMA, Ananda Ashrama, P.O. Box 8555, 91214, (213) 248-1931.

Lafayette *Center* THE SOYFOODS CENTER, P.O. Box 234, 94549.

La Habra *Service* REV. BARBARA BARTOLE, 1221 North Orange St., 90631, (213) 691-0131. Psychic, trance medium, freelance writer, spiritual counselor: private sittings, psychic development, past lives, consciousness awareness/sensitivity training; lectures, classes, seminars, home parties; metaphysical baptisms, weddings, funerals, special ceremonies.

La Mirada *Center* INTERNATIONAL BABAJI YOGA SANGAM, 14011 Mansa Dr., 90638, (213) 921-5575.

Long Beach *Center* 3HO -- GRD, 2211 Ocean Blvd., 90803, (213) 433-9477.

   MORNINGLAND, 2600 E. 7th., 90804, (213) 433-9906.

   Other FUTON DESIGN, 2636 E. 7th St., 90804, (213) 433-8749. Beautiful 100% cotton futons, zabutons, rice paper shades, buckwheat hull pillows, and MORE!

Los Angeles Area (See Listings Under: Altadena, Anaheim, Beverly Hills, Canoga Park, Fullerton, Gardena, Glendale, Hawthorne, Hermosa Beach, Hollywood,

La Habra, La Mirada, Long Beach, Los Angeles, Malibu, Manhattan Beach, North Hollywood, Northridge, Pasadena, Pomona, Santa Monica, Studio City, Sun Valley, Tujunga, Venice.)

Los Angeles *Center* 3HO -- ADI SHAKTI, 839 Hilldale Ave., 90069, (213) 550-9238.
3HO -- GRD, 5273 S Broadway, 90037, (213) 232-8850.
3HO -- GURU ARJUN DEV, 1945 Preuss Rd., 90034, (213) 558-9767.
3HO -- SIRI GURBANI SADAN, 1912-1914 Preuss Rd., 90034, (213) 558-9255.
3HO FOUNDATION, 3HO International H.Q., Guru Ram Das Ashram, P.O. Box 35006, 1620 Preuss Rd., 90035, (213) 550-9043. Founded by Yogi Bhajan. Kundalini Yoga, White Tantric Yoga, holistic health and New Age lifestyle. Also a chance to observe Sikh Dharma in the West. Gurudwara Sunday mornings -- call first.
BUILDERS OF THE ADYTUM, 5105 N. Figueroa St., Dept. NC, 90042, (213) 255-7141.
CENTER FOR THE HEALING ARTS, 11081 Missouri Ave., 90025, (213) 477-3981.
CENTER FOR MATURING AND EVOLVING, 5402 Franklin Ave., 90027.
CENTER FOR YOGA, 230 1/2 Larchmont Blvd., 90004, (213) 464-1276.
CENTER OF BEING -- HER HOLINESS SRI MARASHAMA DEVI, P.O. Box 3384, 90028, (213) 874-2661.
CHURCH OF LIGHT, P.O. Box 76862, 90076, (213) 487-6070.
EAST-WEST CULTURAL CENTER, 2865 W. 9th St., 90006, (213) 480-8325.
FREE FOR ALL, 1623 Granville Ave., Suite 11, 90025, (213) 826-9665.
INT'L SIVANANDA YOGA COMMUNITY, 8157 Sunset Blvd., 90046, (213) 650-9452.

Cassette Recordings of
YOGI BHAJAN'S LECTURES

Also available: Kundalini Yoga Classes, Self Improvement, Gurbani Kirtan, 3HO Music & Sikh history.

GOLDEN TEMPLE RECORDING
1654 PREUSS ROAD
LA, CA 90035
213/274-0963
Send for free catalog

*Books to
illuminate
the Heart and Mind*

BODHI TREE BOOKSTORE

8585 Melrose Avenue
Los Angeles, Calif. 90069
(213) 659-1733 (New Bks)
(213) 659-3227 (Used Bks)

Books (New & Used), New Age Music Recordings, Incense, Tarot Cards, Herbs & Teas, Crystals, Meditation Pads, and Children's Toys

MAIL ORDER AVAILABLE

INTERNATIONAL BUDDHIST MEDITATION CENTER, 928 South New Hampshire Ave., 90006, (213) 384-0850.

KARMA CHANGJUB LING, Rumtek Monastery, 90069, (213) 276-4207.

KARMA THEGSUM CHO LING, 9057 Harland Ave., 90069, (213) 276-4207.

THE MAZDAZNAN ELECTOR, 1159 S. Norton Ave., 90019, (213) 734-4359.

MOVEMENT OF SPIRITUAL INNER AWARENESS (MSIA), P.O. Box 3935, 90051, (213) 733-4055.

PHILOSOPHICAL RESEARCH SOCIETY, 3910 Los Feliz Blvd., 90027, (213) 663-2167.

RINZAI-JI, Cimarron Zen Center, 2505 Cimarron St., 90018, (213) 732-2263.

SATHYA SAI BABA CENTER, 7911 Willoughby Ave., 90046, (213) 656-9373. Books, films, cassettes, photos, weekly bhajans. Films Friday at 8 p.m.

SELF REALIZATION FELLOWSHIP, 3880 San Rafael Ave., 90065, (213) 225-2471.

SINO-AMERICAN BUDDHIST ASSOCIATION, Gold Wheel Monastery, 1726 W. Sixth St., 90017, (213) 483-7497.

SRI AUROBINDO YOGA INSTITUTE, 4230 Brooklyn Ave., 90063.

SURATAO, P.O. Box 19847, 90019, (213) 931-0371.

THOMAS INSTITUTE OF METAPHYSICS, 659 South St. Andrews Pl., 90005, (213) 387-1353.

THE UNITY-IN-DIVERSITY COUNCIL, World Trade Center, 350 South Figueroa St., Suite #277-D, 90071, (213) 626-2062.

VIETNAMESE BUDDHIST TEMPLE AND FOREST RETREAT CENTER, Ven. Rahula, 863 S. Berendo, 90005, (213) 384-9638.

WOMEN'S CONFERENCES, 12581 Venice Blvd., Suite 206, 90066, (213) 455-1472.

ZEN CENTER OF LOS ANGELES, 905 S. Normandie Ave., 90006, (213) 387-2351. Zen Master Maezumi Roshi. Daily Zazen talks, retreats.

School PLAY MOUNTAIN PLACE, 6063 Hargis St., 90034, (213) 870-4381.

Bookstore BODHI TREE BOOKSTORE, 8585 Melrose Ave., 90069, (213) 659-1733 (new), (213) 659-3227 (used). Books (new and used), records, and tapes -- "To Illuminate The Heart And Mind". Also, incense, tarot cards, herbs/teas, meditation pillows, and children's toys. Mail Order is available.

Restaurant GOLDEN TEMPLE CONSCIOUS COOKERY, 7910 W. 3rd. St., 90048, (213) 655-1891. Superb international vegetarian natural foods in dining.

Health MALCOLM J. LEWIS, C.A., 1273 Westwood Blvd., Suite 205, 90024, (213) 479-2284. Certified acupuncturist combining integrative bodywork, acupressure, deep muscle release & nutritional guidance.

Service PENELOPE SMITH, 834 N. Occidental Blvd., 90026, (213) 413-3626. Animal consultant. Communication with animals restoring spiritual and physical harmony.

Instruction MOVEMENT EXPRESSION, 4237 Michael Ave., 90066, (213) 391-9641, 450-1744.

Counseling LINDA WAKE, MFCC, #MB14381, 3431 Club Dr., Suite 4, 90064, (213) 559-7587. Child and adult counseling; educational consulting.

LOS ANGELES INFORMATION & REFERRAL CENTER, 8380 Melrose Ave., 90069, (213) 878-2105. Psychotherapy, Counseling, Human Development.

Media THE LA LIGHT DIRECTORY, 4026 Beverly Blvd., 90004, (213) 739-0190. A Southern California resource directory for healing, growth and transformation. Over 250 listings in 15 catagories including the Arts, Healing & Bodywork, Growth & Psychology, Events, Schools, Spiritual Practices, etc. Our FORUM Section also carries articles and poetry related to health, personal growth, community service, and planetary transformation. 40,000 copies are distributed quarterly through over 300 outlets including health food stores, bookstores, libraries, and natural food restaurants, etc. Mail subscriptions are available for $1.50/copy, $5/year, or $9/2 years.

THE MOVEMENT NEWSPAPER, P.O. Box 19458, 90019, (213) 737-1134. A high-spirited paper for down-to-earth living.

WHOLE LIFE TIMES, 18 Shephard St., 02135, (617) 783-8030. Directory of health care, natural foods, spiritual growth, personal development, national and local products and services.

Los Gatos *Center* OMEGA FELLOWSHIP, Omega Fellowship, 23800 Morrell Cutoff, 95030, (408) 353-2545.

Lynwood *Center* BRAHMA KUMARIS RAJA YOGA CENTER, 11600 Atlantic Blvd., 90262, (213) 635-4846.

Malibu *Center* THE SUMMIT LIGHTHOUSE, The Summit Lighthouse, P.O. Box A, 90265, (213) 880-5300, Weekly *Pearls of Wisdom* (free will love offering).
School SUMMIT UNIVERSITY, P.O. Box A, 90265, (213) 880-5300.

Manhattan Beach *Center* ARCANA WORKSHOPS, P.O. Box 506, 90266, (213) 379-9990, 540-8689.

Menlo Park *Center* CALIFORNIA INSTITUTE OF TRANSPERSONAL PSYCHOLOGY, 250 Oak Grove Ave., 94025, (415) 326-1960.
Bookstore EAST WEST BOOKSHOP, 1170 El Camino Real, 94025, (415) 325-5709. Metaphysics, astrology, New Age music tapes, crystals, children, healing, Jung, Theosophy, Gurdjieff, world religions, consciousness expansion, psychic phenomena, Tarot cards.

Middletown *Center* HARBIN HOT SPRINGS NEW AGE COMMUNITY, Residency SG, P.O. Box 782, 95461, (707) 987-3747.
Community HEART CONSCIOUSNESS CHURCH, At Harbin Hot Springs, P.O. Box 782, 95461, (707) 987-3747, 987-2477. New Age community -- work or room/food. Call or write.

Mill Valley *Center* TRAGER PSYCHOPHYSICAL INTEGRATION AND MENTASTICS, 300 Poplar Ave., Suite 5C, 94941, (415) 388-2688.
School COLUMBIA PACIFIC UNIVERSITY, 150 Shoreline Hwy., Suite 15NC, 94941, (415) 332-7832.
BERNARD CHIROPRACTIC OFFICE, 10 Willow St., 94941, (415) 383-5676.
THE TRANSFORMATION INSTITUTE, DR. SUKI RAPPAPORT, 70 Hilarita Ave., 94941.
Service CAMP SUNBURST, Geri Brooks-Ciosek, M.A., Executive, Director, 150 Shoreline St., 94941, (415) 332-7832 (office), 898-1158 (home).

Modesto *Center* UNIVERSAL LIFE CHURCH, 601 3rd St., 95351, (209) 527-8111.

Monte Rio *Center* HOLYEARTH FOUNDATION, P.O. Box 873, 95462.
Bookstore LAND HOUSE, P.O. Box 801, 95462, (707) 865-2463.

Monterey *Center* 3HO, P.O. Box 2115, 93943, (408) 646-1493.

Morro Bay *Bookstore* STARLIGHT BOOKS, 230 Harbor St., 93442, (805) 772-2880.

Mount Baldy *Center* RINZAI-JI, Mt. Baldy Zen Center, P.O. Box 526, 91759, (714) 985-6410.

Mt. Shasta A very powerful and mysterious place. Many tales and organizations related to The Great White Brotherhood, Lemuria, Big Foot and UFO's in the area.
Center SHASTA ABBEY, Summit Dr., Guestmaster, P.O. Box 478, 96067, (916) 926-4208. Shasta Abbey is a seminary and training monastery for the Zen Buddhist priesthood under the direction of Rev. Jiyu-Kennett Roshi, Abbess. The Abbey offers a comprehensive lay program which includes daily meditation instruction, weekend retreats and a three-month lay training program. Shorter stays may also be arranged. The program of study and training includes morning and evening services, ceremonies, classes in Zen training, and manual work, with particular

181

emphasis on zazen, the traditional meditation practice, of Zen Buddhism. The emphasis is on personal experience and its direct application in ones daily life. Publishes *Journal of Shasta Abbey* with articles on Zen and Buddhism.

Mountain View *Center* CHURCH OF ANTIOCH, 257 Castro St., 94041, (415) 965-3753.

HAIKU ZENDO, 292 College Ave., 94040, (415) 948-5020.

Murrieta Hot Springs *Foodstore* ALIVE POLARITY'S VEGETARIAN RESTAURANT, 92362, (714) 677-7411. Enjoy the services of California's only vegetarian health spa.

Napa *Center* SAWAN KIRPAL RUHANI MISSION, 1115 3rd Ave., 94558, (707) 226-7703.

National City *Bookstore* THE MAGICK BOOKSTORE, 2304 Highland Ave. SG82, 92050. Occult books and supplies. $1 catalog.

Nevada City *Center* ANANDA, 14618 Tyler Foote, 95959, (916) 292-3494.

INSTITUTE FOR THE DEVELOPMENT OF THE HARMONIOUS HUMAN BEING, P.O. Box 370, Dept. S, 95959.

THE FLOWER ESSENCE SOCIETY, P.O. Box 459, 95959, (916) 265-9163.

Newberry Springs *Center* AUM TEMPLE OF UNIVERSAL TRUTH, 45837 Deva Ln., 92365, (714) 257-3255.

Newport Beach *Service* HOLISTIC HEALTH EDUCATION/A.S. FELD, P.O. Box 2145, 92663, (714) 631-6377. Network information referral services.

North Hollywood *Center* BUDDHIST WATS (TEMPLES) OF THAILAND, Wat Thai, 12909 Cantara St., 91605, (213) 780-4200.

INTERNATIONAL COUNCIL OF SPIRITUAL SCIENCES, 12936 Welby Way, 91606.

TAOIST INSTITUTE, 10632 Burbank Blvd., 91601, (213) 760-4219.

Instruction LEIGH GARNER-FLUTE & PIANO INSTRUCTION, 91601, (213) 762-4355.

Northridge *Center* 3HO -- GRD, 17441 Cantara, 91324, (213) 996-1235.

Novato *Center* THE INNER LIGHT FOUNDATION, P.O. Box 761, 94948, (415) 897-5581.

SUFI ISLAMIA RUHANIAT SOCIETY, Garden of Inayat, 910 Railroad Ave., 94947, (415) 897-5426.

Oak View *Center* VALLEY LIGHT CENTER, P.O. Box 355, 93022-0355, (805) 649-3393.

Oakland *Center* HYPNOSIS CLEARING HOUSE, INC., 1504 Franklin St., Suite 303, 94612, (415) 451-6440.

SYDA FOUNDATION, P.O. Box 11071, 94611, (415) 655-8677.

TEMPLE OF COSMIC RELIGION, 174 Santa Clara Ave., 94610, (415) 654-4683.

Bookstore QUEST BOOKSHOP AND THEOSOPHICAL LIBRARY, 1416 Alice St., 94612, (415) 465-3909.

Instruction ODISSI DANCE CENTRE, 590 66th St., 94609, (415) 658-5729. Classes in Odissi Dance -- one of India's ancient spiritual styles of classical dance.

Occidental *Community* OCEAN SONG INSTITUTE, P.O. Box 659, 95465, (707) 874-2274. Followers of Paramahansa Yogananda. Sister community of Ananda, Nevada City, CA, under direction of Swami Kriyananda. Health center and retreat planned. Vegetarian. No dogs, drugs, alcohol. Classes in yoga. Sunday service, 9 a.m.

Oceanside *Center* THE ROSICRUCIAN FELLOWSHIP, 2222 Mission Ave., P.O. Box 713, 92054, (714) 757-6600.

Ojai *Center* DJARMA LEARNING COMMUNITY, P.O. Box 263, 93023, (805) 646-2021.

KRISHNAMURTI FOUNDATION OF AMERICA, P.O. Box 216, 93023, (805) 646-2726.

MEDITATION GROUP FOR THE NEW AGE (MGNA), P.O. Box 566, 93023, (805) 646-6300.

THE LIBERAL CATHOLIC CHURCH, P.O. Box 598, 1610 Grand Ave., 93023, (805) 646-2960.

THE OJAI FOUNDATION, P.O. Box 1620, 93023, (805) 646-8343.

Olema *Center* VEDANTA RETREAT, P.O. Box 215, 94950, (415) 663-1258. Ramakrishna and Swami Vivekananda.

Orinda *School* JOHN F. KENNEDY UNIVERSITY, Graduate School of Consciousness Studies, JFKU, P.O. Box 1, 12 Altarinda Rd., 94563, (415) 254-0200, ext. 47.

Oroville *Center* GEORGE OSHAWA MACROBIOTIC FOUNDATION, 902 14th St., 95965, (916) 533 7702.

Palm Springs *Health* EXPERIENCES IN AWARENESS, P.O. Box 296, 92263, (714) 320-1517, 323-3033. Marcia AKAL KAUR Wieting, See Health & Healing in classified ad section.

Palo Alto *Center* CENTER FOR VISION IMPROVEMENT, 616 Ramona St., 94301, (415) 321-9525.

THE ECCLESIA GNOSTICA, 3437 Alma St. (The Alma Plaza Shopping Center), Suite 23, 94306, (415) 494-7412.

INNER GROWTH SEMINAR, P.O. Box 1107, 94302, (415) 328-8552.

SUFI ISLAMIA RUHANIAT SOCIETY, c/o Sheikh Mohammed Iqbal Lewis, (415) 821-3306.

Counseling VIKI MARKHAM, 808 Green, 94303, (415) 328-0567. Transpersonal counseling and support group, focusing on self-trust. M.A. Psychology -- stress management. B.A. Nutrition.

Therapy JUDITH BELL MANGOLD, R.N., M.N., P.O. Box 1001, 94301, (408) 378-2133. Mind-Body-Spirit Integration and Talismans.

Palo Cerdo *Center* AMERICA VEDANTA SOCIETY, 6150 Rusty Ln., 96073.

Pasadena *Bookstore* THE MAGIC CIRCLE OCCULT SHOP, 1274 N. Lake Ave., 91104, (213) 794-6013.

Petaluma *Center* SUFI ISLAMIA RUHANIAT SOCIETY, Noor Mahal, 758 D St., 94952, (707) 763-7271.

Counseling CAROL ADRIENNE, 4955 Lake Ville Hwy., 94952, (707) 762-7231. Numerology ... name changes, partnerships, yearly, monthly guides.

Placerville *Center* AJAPA YOGA FOUNDATION, Shri Janardan Ajapa Yoga Ashram, P.O. Box 1731, 95667, (916) 626-1585.

Pt. Arena *Center* OZ, P.O. Box 147, 95468, (707) 882-2449.

Pomona *Center* 3HO -- GURU GOBIND SINGH SADAN, 575 N. Hamilton Blvd., 91768, (714) 622-9249.

ATMANIKETAN ASHRAM & AUROMERE, 1291 Weber St., 91768, (714) 629-8255. Sri Aurobindo teachings and books.

Richmond *Center* UNITY CHURCH OF RICHMOND, 351 28th St., 94804, (415) 236-2924. Meditations, classes, workshops. Sunday Service, 11:00 a.m.

Riverside *Bookstore* ANANDA BOOKSTORE, 3663 Canyon Crest Dr. #E, 92507, (714) 686-3471.

Sacramento *Health* VEDANTA SOCIETY OF SACRAMENTO, 1337 Mission Ave., 95608, (916) 489-5137.

JOHN B. ADAMS, P.O. Box 2914 (Near Madison and Manzanita), 95812, (916) 332-7022. Trager Psychological Integration and Mentastics: private sessions and group demonstrations.

SACRAMENTO HOLISTIC HEALTH INSTITUTE, 1822 21st St., 95814, (916) 454-4470.

Counseling WIN SYSTEMS, P.O. Box 1234, 95806, (916) 922-2202.

San Anselmo *Service* AUGIE BLUME & ASSOC, P.O. Box 190, 94960, (415) 457-0215. Promotion, public relations, bios, press releases, national radio/press mailing lists and labels, consulting.

San Bernadino *Center* 3HO -- GRD, 630 N. "G" St., 92410. (714) 885-4781.

San Diego *Center* 3HO -- GRD, 1421 Myrtle Ave., 92103, (714) 299-4196.

BRAHMA KUMARIS RAJA YOGA CENTER, 4536 Maryland St., 92116, (714) 296-4403.

CENTER FOR PSYCHOLOGICAL REVOLUTION, 1525 Hornblend St., 92109, (714) 273-4673.

GRIEF MANAGEMENT CENTER, 6310 Alvarado Ct., 92120, (714) 286-1010.

SUFI ISLAMIA RUHANIAT SOCIETY, Garden of the Quest, 3661 1/2 Villa Terrace, 92104, (714) 296-2691.

TEACHING OF THE INNER CHRIST, 3869 42nd St., 92105, (714) 280-7770.

THE LOVE PROJECT, Arleen Lorrance (OSO) & Diane K. Pike, P.O. Box 7601, 92107, (714) 225-0133.

Bookstore CONTROVERSIAL BOOKSTORE, 3021 University Ave., 92104, (714) 296-1560.

San Francisco Bay Area (See Listings Under: Berkeley, Burlingame, Corte Madera, Cotati, Fairfax, Foster City, Greenbrae, Hayward, Kensington, Lafayette, Los Altos, Menlo Park, Mill Valley, Mountain View, Novato, Oakland, Olema, Orinda, Palo Alto, Petaluma, Richmond, San Anselmo, San Francisco, San Jose, San Rafael, Santa Clara, Santa Rosa, Stanford, Tiburon, Walnut Creek.)

San Francisco *Center* 3HO-GURU RAM DAS ASHRAM, 1390 Waller St., 94117, (415) 864-9642. Kundalini Yoga classes in the heart of Haight-Ashbury.

ACTUALIZATIONS, 3632 Sacramento St., 94118, (415) 563-1006.

ANANDA CENTER, 2900 Judah St., 94122, (415) 753-2556, 567-1125. Teachings of Paramahansa Yogananda; meditation, Yoga postures, Yoga teacher training course.

THE AVADHUT, P.O. Box 27582, 94127, (415) 588-7907. Bhagavan I.M. Nome is identical to His Guru, Bhagavan Ramana Maharshi and His Brother Sage, Sri Nisargadatta Maharaj. Satsang is open dialogue -- That Truth expressed in Advaita Vedanta (Ajatavada) and Ch'an Buddhism. No physical or mental disciplines. *Absolutely Free!*

BIOFEEDBACK INSTITUTE, 3428 Sacramento St., 94118.

BRAHMA KUMARIS RAJA YOGA CENTER, 1619 Clement St., 94121, (415) 668-3487.

THE CENTER FOR SELF HEALING, 1718 Taraval St., 94116, (415) 665-9574.

CULTURAL INTEGRATION FELLOWSHIP, 2650 Fulton St., 94118, (415) 648-6777.

GURDJIEFF FOUNDATION OF CALIFORNIA, P.O. Box 549, 94101, (415) 921-0218.

THE HOFFMAN QUADRINITY PROCESS, 2295 Palou St., 94124, (415) 397-0466..

HOLY ORDER OF MANS, International Headquarters, 20 Steiner St., 94117, (415) 431-1917.

I.C.S.A., NADA-BRAHMANANDA ASHRAM, 2872 Folsom St., 94110, (415) 285-5537.

INNER RESEARCH INSTITUTE -- School Of T'ai Chi Ch'uan, 1133 Mission St., 94103, (415) 521-2681.

INSTITUTE FOR THE STUDY OF CONSCIOUS EVOLUTION, 2418 Clement St., 94121, (415) 221-9222.

KAGYU DRODEN KUNCHAB, 1892 Fell St., 94117, (415) 386-9656.

KERISTA CONSCIOUSNESS CHURCH, 543 Frederick St., 94117, (415) 566-6502, 665-2988.

MAHIKARI-NO-WAZA, 2489 19th Ave., 94116, (415) 661-2505.

MOVEMENT PUZZLES INSTITUTE, 2575 Washington St. #1, 94115, (415) 922-8809.

MYERS INSTITUTE FOR CREATIVE STUDIES, 3827 California St., 94118, (415) 668-1555.

NURSES IN TRANSITION, P.O. Box 14472, 94114, (415) 282-7999.

SAT INSTITUTE, 63 Chattanooga St., 94114, (415) 285-2291 (Dionne Marx).

THE SAYBROOK INSTITUTE, 1772 Vallejo St. A-7, 94123, (415) 441-5034.

SHIATSU CENTER AT HARBIN HOT SPRINGS, Harold Dull, 1479 5th Ave., 94122, (415) 731-5652.

SINO-AMERICAN BUDDHIST ASSOCIATION, Gold Mountain Monastery, 1731 15th St., 94103, (415) 861-9672.

SRI CHINMOY CENTRE, 2438 16th Ave., 94116, (415) 861-4148. Classes in meditation offered by disciples of Sri Chinmoy. Free.

SUFI ISLAMIA RUHANIAT SOCIETY, 410 Precita Ave., 94110, (415) 285-5208. Sufi seminars, camps, instruction in Dances of Universal Peace, Sufi Choir information, worship/healing services, mail order books/records.

THE ZEN CENTER SAN FRANCISCO, 300 Page St., 94100, (415) 863-3136, 626-3697.

VEDANTA SOCIETY OF NORTHERN CALIFORNIA, 2323 Vallejo, St., 94123, (415) 922-2323.

WAKING UP IN THE NUCLEAR AGE, P.O. Box 23, Fort Mason Center, 94123, (415) 885-5038.

WASHINGTON RESEARCH CENTER, 3101 Washington St., 94115.

Community SAN FRANCISCO CHRISTIAN COMMUNITY (Holy Order of Mans), 720 Duboce St., 94117.

School CALIFORNIA INSTITUTE OF INTEGRAL STUDIES, 3494 21st St., P.O. Box CS, 94118.

THE INTERNATIONAL SCHOOL OF MASSAGE THERAPY, 2872 Folsom St., 94110, (415) 285-5040.

NEW COLLEGE OF CALIFORNIA, 777 Valencia St., 94110, (415) 626-1694.

Bookstore ATLANTIS METAPHYSICAL TAPE, RECORD & BOOK STORE, 584 O'Farrell St., 94102, (415) 775-7166.

Foodstore NEW WEST NATURAL FOODS, 970 Market St., 94102, (415) 775-4995. Flower Essences, Homeopathic Remedies, General Information, Herbs.

Restaurant THE CHAC CAFE, 3870 17th St., 94114, (415) 861-1878.

DIPTI NIVAS, 216 Church St., 94114, (415) 626-6411. Full-fare vegetarian restaurant featuring gourmet casseroles, curries, sandwiches, shakes, salads & desserts. Best in San Francisco.

Health IRENE NEWMARK, 181 Noe St., 94114, (415) 552-3813. Health education, nutritional, herbal counseling, flower essences, radiesthia. Breema energy balancing, Shiatsu. Classes.

LINDA JENNINGS, 494 27th Ave., 94121, (415) 752-6749. Reflexologist.

VEGETARIAN SOCIETY OF SAN FRANCISCO, 1450 Broadway, 94109, (415) 775-6874. Send $1 for Information Packet.

Service FREE HOLISTIC HYPNOSIS, 717 Hyde #6, 94109, (415) 885-4752. Consultation/Brochure. Certified.

H.S. DAKIN COMPANY, 3101 Washington St., 94115. Computer Services.

RANCHO ASPEN, 242 Turk St. #416, 94102, (415) 771-7640. Residence for troubled youth, ages 6-16. Problems: Home/Law/School.

ROLAND CAMPOS, 3245 24th St., 94110, (415) 731-2356. Higher consciousness facilitation.

VEGETARIAN SOCIETY OF SAN FRANCISCO, 1450 Broadway, 94109, (415) 775-6874. For health & humanity nutritional information available $1.

Instruction BIOFEEDBACK INSTITUTE, 3428 Sacramento St., 94118, (415) 921-5455. Biofeedback Certification and Training Programs.

CHOY LI FUT KUNGFU, Hung Sing style. Guru Dev Singh Khalsa-instructor. (415) 566-1390.

INTEGRATED TAI CHI CHUAN, 227 22nd Ave., 94121, (415) 668-1397. Basic Exercises, Solo Form, Hand-to-Hand Practices, Sanshou (Partner Form).

TIBET LAMA HOPGAR STYLE KUNG-FU, 909 Geary St. #418, 94409, (415) 441-6432. Combat Kung-fu.

Counseling ST JAMES CHURCH, ULC INC., P.O. Box 18100, 94118, (415) 386-4737. Rev. Dr. Carroll Marsey, Metaphysical Counseling working with auras and spiritual healing.

Media WHOLE LIFE TIMES, 18 Shephard St., 02135, (617) 783-8030. Directory of health care, natural foods, spiritual growth, personal development, national and local products and services.

Other ASIAN ART MUSEUM OF SAN FRANCISCO, The Avery Brundage Collection, Golden Gate Park, 94118.

San Jose *Center* 3HO -- GRD, 14695 Story Rd., 95127, (408) 272-3277.

THE ROSICRUCIAN ORDER (AMORC), Rosicrucian Park, 95191, (408) 287-9171.

Other ROSICRUCIAN PARK (AMORC), Egyptian style buildings and museum.

San Rafael *Center* THE HEALING CIRCLE, ULC, P.O. Box 2819, 94901, (415) 435-0383.

SUFI ISLAMIA RUHANIAT SOCIETY, 61 Blossom Dr., 94901, (415) 456-1950.

School ALI AKBAR COLLEGE OF MUSIC, 215 West End Ave., 94901, (415) 454-6264. Concerts and lessons by masters of North Indian classical music.

Health MARCIA R STARCK, P.O. Box 893, 94915, (415) 457-7837. Medical astrologer using astrology as a diagnostic tool with holistic health. Author of *Astrology Key to Holistic Health* **($9.95)**.

Santa Barbara *Center* INTEGRAL YOGA INSTITUTE/SATCHIDANANDA ASHRAM, 1705 San Marcos Pass Rd., 93105, (805) 964-9964.

THE INSTITUTE FOR HOLISTIC STUDIES, 33 W. Canon Perdido, 93101, (805) 963-5005.

INWARD JOURNEY, P.O. Box 2592, 93120, (805) 969-1254 or (415) 845-9498 (Berkeley).

SANTA BARBARA TEMPLE, 927 Ladera Ln., 93108, (805) 969-2903.

SRI CHINMOY CENTER, 3111 Calle Cedro, 93105, (805) 687-8844.

Bookstore STARLIGHT BOOKS, 33 E. Victoria St., 93101, (805) 963-5444.

Santa Clara *Center* NETWORK OF CONSCIOUS JUDAISM, 3825 Baldwin Dr., Dept. A, 95051, (408) 247-7385.

Santa Cruz *Center* THE AVADHUT, P.O. Box 574, 95061, (408) 338-3923.

Bookstore GATEWAYS NEW AGE BOOK AND GIFT, 815 Pacific Ave., 95060, (408) 429-9600.

Therapy ELISABETH A. ULATOVSKA WORKSHOPS, 215 Beach St. #307, 95060, (408) 427-0243.

Santa Maria ACCELERATED LEARNING SYSTEMS, P.O. Box 862, 93456, (805) 925-0355. Seminars, workshops and in-service training on right/brain learning & relationships.

Santa Monica *Center* HUNA INTERNATIONAL, 1535 Sixth St. #202, 90401, (213) 394-8913.

SHIATSU MASSAGE SCHOOL OF CALIFORNIA, 2309 Main St., 90405, (213) 396-4877. Shiatsu Massage license course and home shiatsu course.

TAO HEALING ARTS CENTER, 2309 Main St., 90405, (213) 396-4877. Classes, treatment and product sales of natural healing arts.

VEGETARIAN SOCIETY, INC., P.O. Box 5688, 90405, (213) 396-5164, 477-0050.

Bookstore ALEPH BOOKS & GIFTS, 2825 Main St., 90405, (213) 392-3605.

Santa Rosa *Therapy* ELIZABETH EILERMAN, PH.D., C.M.H., 1041 Second St., 95405, (707) 523-3011. Hypnotherapist, Doctor of Humanistic Psychology.

Sebastopol *Center* SUFI ISLAMIA RUHANIAT SOCIETY, Psalmgarden, 9195 Barnett Valley Rd., 95472, (707) 823-7106.

WELL BEING COMMUNITY CENTER, P.O. Box 940, 95472, (707) 823-1489. Sponsors of the annual Festivals; the Spirit of Christmas Crafts Faire and Celebration and the Health & Harmony Festival.

School NEW AGE SCHOOL OF MASSAGE, P.O. Box 958, 95472, (707) 823-1212.

Sierraville *Center* CONSCIOUSNESS VILLAGE, P.O. Box 234, 96126, (916) 994-8984, 994-3677.

Solana Beach *Health* HOLISTIC HEALING ARTS CLINIC, 312 South Cedros, 92075, (714) 755-6681. A complete health care clinic emphasizing natural health care. One of the largest and most respected holistic clinics.

Soquel *Center* DHYANYOGA CENTERS INC., 3500 Rodeo Gulch, 95073, (408) 462-4225.

Stanford *Center* THE ASSOCIATION FOR TRANSPERSONAL PSYCHOLOGY, P.O. Box 3049, 94305, (415) 327-2066.

Stockton *Center* P.E.A.C.E. NETWORK, Truth Research Foundation, P.O. Box 7705, 95207, (209) 478-7378.

Studio City *Restaurant* CHEZ NATURAL, 11838 Ventura Blvd., 91604, (213) 763-1044. Truly gourmet wholefood dining -- the finest in Los Angeles.

Sun Valley *Center* CHURCH OF THE HEALING WAY, 11050 Lorne St., 91352, (213) 995-8591.

Talmage *Center* SINO-AMERICAN BUDDHIST ASSOCIATION, City of 10,000 Buddhas, P.O. Box 217, 95481, (707) 462-0939.

Tiburon *Center* CENTER FOR ATTITUDINAL HEALING, 19 Main St., 94920, (415) 435-5022.

Topanga *Center* THE PYRAMID CENTER OF BHAKTI YOGA, 20395 Callon Dr., 90290, (213) 455-1658.

Health JUMUNA DASI, P.O. Box 112, 90290, (213) 455-1678. Reflexology in the canyon.

Torrance *Center* SUFI ISLAMIA RUHANIAT SOCIETY, Khankah Nuri Mohammed, 3714 W. 173rd St., 90504, (213) 538-4037.

Trabuco Canyon *Monastery* RAMAKRISHNA MONASTERY, P.O. Box 408, 92678, (714) 586-7932.

Tujunga *Center* MAHIKARI-NO-WAZA, 6470 Foothill Ave., 91042, (213) 353-0071.

Tustin *Bookstore* CHIP'N BOOKS, 14181 Newport Ave., 92680, (714) 838-6008. Metaphysical books and supplies, computerized charts, numerology, etc.

Twain Harte *Service* LYN PROCTOR, P.O. Box 1667, 95383, (209) 586-7995. Rebirthing, High Sierra Vision Quest, Transformation -- Personal/Planetary.

Upland *Center* ASTARA, 800 W. Arrow Hwy., P.O. Box 5003, 91786, (714) 981-4941.

Valyermo *Monastery* PRIORY OF ST ANDREW THE APOSTLE, 93563, (805) 944-2178. Located near Los Angeles, this Benedictine retreat has 18 monks.

Valley Center *Center* ACTUALISM, 29928 Lilac Rd., 92082, (714) 714-1325.

Valley Ford *Center* MEDICINE WAYS, P.O. Box 443, CA 94972, (707) 795-4789.

Venice **Center** THE TEMPLE OF MAN, Revs. Robert and Anita Alexander, Co-Pastors, 1439 Cabrillo Ave., 90291, (213) 399-9747, 396-6438.

Vina **Monastery** ABBEY OF OUR LADY OF NEW CLAIRVAUX, 96092, (916) 839-2161. Near Red Bluff on the Sacramento River, the abbey was founded from Gethsemani. Guests may come in choir and sing with the monks. There are 28 monks who grow walnuts, plums and barley.

Walnut Creek **Center** SUFISM REORIENTED, 1300 Boulevard Way, 94595, (415) 938-4820.

UNITY CENTER, 1871 Geary Rd., 94596, (415) 937-2191 and Dial-a-thought: (415) 937-0777.

Watsonville **Center** MOUNT MADONNA CENTER, P.O. Box 51-BB, 95077, (408) 847-0406.

Yuba City **Center** MATRI SATSANG (SRI ANANDAMAYI MA), 2103 Holcomb Rd., 95991.

Yucca Valley **Center** INSTITUTE OF MENTALPHYSICS, P.O. Box 640, 92284, (714) 366-2241, 366-8471. Haven is at 59700 Twenty-nine Palms Hwy., Star Route 2, P.O. Box 435.

___Colorado___

Aspen **Foodstore** PITKIN COUNTY GRAINERY, 716 East Hyman Ave., 81611, (303) 925-6629.

Aurora **Bookstore** THE METAPHYSICAL BOOKSTORE, 9511 E. Colfax, 80010, (303) 341-7562.

Boulder **Center** 3HO -- GRD, 3460 Berkeley, 80303, (303) 494-4643.

TAOIST MOUNTAIN RETREAT, P.O. Box 234, 80466, (303) 258-7846. Ongoing classes and summer intensives in all aspects of Taoist Temple healing and martial arts.

INFORMED HOMEBIRTH, P.O. Box 788-S, 80306, (303) 449-4181.

ROCKY MOUNTAIN HEALING ARTS INSTITUTE, P.O. Box 4573, Dept. O, 80306, (303) 443-5131.

SRI AUROBINDO'S ACTION CENTER, P.O. Box 1977, 80306, (303) 499-3313.

TRUTH CONSCIOUSNESS, Gold Hill, Salina Star Route, 80302, (303) 447-1637.

VAJRADHATU, 1345 Spruce St., 80302, (303) 444-0190.

School LE CENTRE DU SILENCE MIME SCHOOL, P.O. Box 1015 (NC), 80306-1015, (303) 494-8729.

Colorado Springs **Center** 3HO GURU RAM DAS ASHRAM, 738 E. Willamette, 80903, (303) 473-4510.

Bookstore CELEBRATION, 2209 W. Colorado Ave., 80904, (303) 634-1855. Natural clothing -- metaphysical books & supplies, New Age music.

Instruction D.O.M.E., THE INNER GUIDE MEDITATION CENTER, P.O. Box 25358, 80936, (303) 594-0088.

Denver **Center** 3HO -- GRD, 1072 N Josephine, 80206, (303) 377-7494.

ANANDA MARGA, 854 Pearl St., 80203, (303) 832-6465, TLX 450404.

BUDDHIST WATS (TEMPLES) OF THAILAND, Wat Buddhawararam, 4801 Julian St., 80221, (303) 433-1826.

SAWAN KIRPAL RUHANI MISSION, 878 S. Dexter St., Apt #303, 80222, (303) 753-9425.

Community DENVER CHRISTIAN COMMUNITY, (Holy Order Of Mans), 1660 Ogden St., 80218, (303) 831-8394.

Collins 3HO -- GRD, 331 Winchester St., 80525, (303) 226-4652.
   Community SUNSET'S GOOD EARTH FARM AND ANANDA CENTER, 230 Worth Sunset, 80521, (303) 484-4538.
Hotchkiss *Community* ISKCON -- NEW BARSANA SPIRITUAL FARM COMMUNITY, P.O. Box 112, 81419, (303) 527-4584.
Nederland *Center* ACADEMY OF TAOIST HEALING ARTS, P.O. Box 234, 80466.
Snowmass *Monastery* ST BENEDICTS MONASTERY, 81654, (303) 927-3311. Founded in 1956 from St Joseph, it is high in the mountains near Aspen. Guests live right with the community. Reservations are important as space is limited.
Telluride *Health* THE AMERICAN HOLISTIC NURSES' ASSOCIATION (AHNA), P.O. Box 116, 81435, (303) 728-4575.

Connecticut

Bristol *Center* ALPHA LOGICS, P.O. Box 920, 229 Cross St., 06010-0920, (203) 589-2533.
Greenwich *Center* EAST/WEST CENTER OF GREENWICH/STAMFORD, 90 Club Rd., Riverside, 06878. (203) 637-9771. Macrobiotic programs.
   Foodstore HEALTH WELL NATURAL FOOD SHOP, 356 Greenwich Ave., 06830, (203) 622-9454. The source of all your natural food needs at low prices.
   Restaurant LOVE AND SERVE NATURAL FOODS RESTAURANT, 35 Amogerone Way, 06830, (203) 661-8893. Incredible food! Off I-95.
Hartford *Center* 3HO -- GURU HARKRISHAN, 127 Tremont St., 06105, (203) 236-1191.

The Whole Life Times is devoted to helping its readers achieve and maintain the highest level of optimal health through the pursuit of better diet, natural healing, exercise, personal growth and social involvement. Our scope is both personal and planetary. Each issue brings its readers how-to-do-it articles for maximizing personal health as well as relevant information on government policies, social systems, and the health of our environment. Our intention is to reflect a positive vision of the world that can inspire and empower our readers to live to their fullest potential.

   We publish local directories for **Boston, New York, Los Angeles, San Francisco,** and **Seattle.** For advertising or subscription information, contact: **Whole Life Times,** 18 Shepard St., Brighton, MA 02135. (617) 783-8030.

Whole Life Times

SAWAN KIRPAL RUHANI MISSION, 40 Frontage Rd., 06076, (203) 684-7908.

Middletown *Bookstore* PRINTER'S DEVIL BOOKSTORE, 20 Riverview Center, 06457, (203) 344-0022. We buy & sell used books and comics ... Andreia Flynn/Proprietor.

New Haven *Center* 3HO -- GRD, 1519 Boulevard St., 06511.

NEW HAVEN ZEN CENTER, 193 Mansfield St., 06511, (203) 787-0912. Residential Zen Center, daily practice, Zen Master Seung Sahn.

Norwalk *Center* CENTER FOR SHAMANIC STUDIES, Executive Director, P.O. Box 673, Belden Station, 06852.

Norwich *Service* BE HEALTHY EDUCATION CO., 4 Lauren Ln., 06360. Sylvia Klein Olkin, Director, (203) 887-4971. Self-help cassette tapes using yogic techniques. Our titles include: Fundamentals of Yoga I & II, Stress Management, Anti-Insomnia Program, Stretching for Runners, Shape-Up!!! and others. Write for free brochure.

Ridgefield *Foodstore* RIDGEFIELD HEALTH FOOD CENTRE, Copps Hill Plaza, 06877, (203) 438-7000. The good food store. Everything for the natural foods kitchen.

Waterbury *Center* MORRIS FOUNDATION, INC., 26 North Elm St., 06702, (203) 755-1143.

Westport *Center* TEMENOS INSTITUTE, INC., 29 East Main St., 06880, (203) 227-4388.

District of Columbia

Washington, D.C. *Center* 3HO, 1704 Q St., N.W., 20009, (703) 435-4411.

DEVADEEP RAJNEESH SANNYAS ASHRAM, 1430 Longfellow St., N.W., 20011.

INTEGRAL YOGA INSTITUTE, P.O. Box 23530, 20024, (703) 931-7333. Founder/director: Sri Swami Satchidananda. The IYI offers ongoing programs and classes in the various aspects of Yoga: Hatha, Raja, Meditation, Karma, Bhakti, and Jnana Yogas -- as well as instruction in Yogic diet, stress management and other related topics. Affiliated with the Integral Yoga Institutes and Satchidananda Ashrams worldwide.

KRIYA YOGA CENTER, 1201 Fern St., N.W., 20012, (202) 723-4077.

NATIONAL SPIRITUAL SCIENCE CENTER, 5605 16th St., 20011, (202) 723-4510.

SCHOOL OF SPIRITUAL SCIENCE, 5605 16th St., 20011, (202) 723-4510.

SIVANANDA YOGA VEDANTA CENTER, 1929 19th St. N.W., 20009, (202) 331-9642.

School THE WASHINGTON BUDDHIST VIHARA, 5017 16th St., 20011, (202) 723-0773.

Bookstore TREE OF LIFE BOOKSTORE, 1705 Desales St. N.W., 20036, (202) 233-1396.

Restaurant YES!, 1035 31st St., N.W., 20007, (202) 338-6969. Natural food and herb shop spiritual bookshop with largest stock in the world. Mail orders. Educational Society. *Pathways,* directory of spiritual, growth & healing activities in Washington/Baltimore area.

Counseling REV. DIANE S. NAGORKA, SPIRITUAL COUNSELOR, 5605 16th St., N.W., 20011, (202) 723-4510. Educator, Lecturer.

Bodywork BOB COLEMAN, 1852 Columbia Rd., N.W. #505, 20009, (202) 234-2941. Massage therapy balances spirit body and mind. Uses catharsis, creative imagery, massage and deep relaxation.

Florida

Altamonte Springs *Center* 3HO -- BABA SIRI CHAND, 400 Center St., 32701, (305) 831-2201.

Aripeka *Health* ARIPEKA HEALTH LODGE, 3139 Gulf Dr., P.O. Box 407, 33502, (813) 862-3152. On the Gulf -- Nutritional meals -- Self-awareness programs. Director Reverend Alice Bartelme.

Boca Raton *Health* CENTER OF HEALTH, 2351 N. Federal Hwy., 33431, (305) 391-8533.

JACULIN LOMBARD, C.T., Colon Therapist, Center of Health, 2351 N. Federal Hwy., 33431, (305) 391-8533.

JACULIN LOMBARD, H.D., Homeopath, Center of Health, 2351 N. Federal Hwy., 33431, (305) 391-8533.

JAMES PINKMAN, C.A., Certified Acupuncturist, Center of Health, 2351 N. Federal Hwy., 33431, (305) 391-8533.

Bodywork PATRICK DORMAN, R.M.T., Deep Muscle Massage Therapist, Center of Health, 2351 N. Federal Hwy., 33431, (305) 391-8533.

Bonita Springs *Center* THE CREATIVE LIVING GUIDANCE CENTER, P.O. Box 25, 33923, (813) 992-0834.

Boynton Beach *Center* INSTITUTE FOR ADVANCED PERCEPTION, 119 S.E. 29th Ave., 33435, (305) 717-6645. Classes.

Cape Canaveral *Bookstore* RAINBOW NEW AGE BOOKS AND GIFTS, 6290 N. Atlantic Ave., 32920, (305) 784-0930.

Foodstore SUNSEED FOOD COOP, 6290 N. Atlantic Ave., 32920, (305) 784-0930.

Coral Gables *Center* CHURCH OF SCIENTOLOGY/DIANETIC CENTER, 120 Giralda, Dept. NCS, 33134, (305) 445-7812.

Health PURIFICATION PROGRAM, The Dianetic Center, 120 Giralda, Dept. NCS, 33134, (305) 445-7812.

Daytona Beach *Center* 3HO -- GRD, 506 S Palmetto Ave., 32014, (904) 252-6448.

Ft. Lauderdale *Center* I AM NATION, Dept. SG, P.O. Box 290368, 33329, (305) 587-5555.

MARK-AGE, Dept. SG, P.O. Box 290368, 33329, (305) 587-5555.

SIVANANDA YOGA VEDANTA CENTER, 739 N.W. 2nd Ave., 33311, (305) 467-7632.

Ft. Pierce *Center* LIFE SCIENCE INSTITUTE, P.O. Box 1057, 33454.

SIVANANDA YOGA ACRES, Route 4, P.O. Box 112, 33450.

Gainesville *Center* FLORIDA INSTITUTE OF NATURAL HEALTH, 1115 North Main St., 32601, (904) 378-7891.

SOMA INSTITUTE, Dept. WCS, P.O. Box 12624, 32604.

Hollywood *Counseling* MARCIA ROSE BECKER, PH.D., P.O. Box 827, 33022, (305) 922-2132. Counseling, astrology, psychic.

Key West *Health* DR. DEBRA FLYNN, KEY WEST CHIROPRACTIC CLINIC, 3401 Flagler Ave., 33040, (305) 296-5626.

RUSSELL HOUSE, 415 William St., 33040, (305) 294-8787. Detoxify, juice fast, lose weight and learn.

Keystone Heights *Center* 3HO -- GRD, 315 Nightingale St., 32656, (904) 473-3760.

Lake Worth *Center* SAWAN KIRPAL RUHANI MISSION, 115 South O St., 33460, (305) 588-1287.

Miami *Center* 3HO -- GRD, 15040 South River Dr., 33167, (305) 685-5515.
INNER DEVELOPMENT CENTER, P.O. Drawer H, 33133, (305) 661-7890.
YOGA RESEARCH FND., 6111 S.W. 74th Ave., (305) 595-5580.
Bookstore THEOSOPHICAL SOCIETY BOOK DEPARTMENT, 119 N.E. 62nd St., 33138, (305) 754-4331.

Miami Beach *Health* SHEILA SHEA, R.M.T., 804 Ocean Dr. #3, 33139, (305) 673-3830. Colonic irrigation. Toxygen machine, gentle water cleansing, thorough abdominal massage, oxygen optional.

North Miami Beach *Center* THE ACUPUNCTURE EDUCATION CENTER, 13757 N.E. Third Court, Suite 210 A, 33161 (November-May), (305) 891-0062, 891-7333.
Foodstore THE UNICORN, INC., 164 N.E. 6th Ave., 33162, (305) 944-5595. Vegetarian cuisine restaurant; full service food and vitamin stores.

Orlando *Center* 3HO -- GRD, 309 E Yale, 32804.
Bookstore SPIRAL CIRCLE, INC., 750 N. Thorton Ave., 32803, (305) 894-9854.
Foodstore HERBAL WORLD, 1419 North Orange Ave., 32804, (305) 896-1017. Herbs, spices, ginseng (imported and domestic), essential oils, extracts, herbal cigarettes, herbal baths, books, teas. Free catalog available.

Pinellas Park *Bodywork* THE HUMANITIES CENTER -- SCHOOL OF THERA-PEUTIC MASSAGE, 3565 Cypress Terrace, 33565, (813) 522-1697. Bodywork and massage.

St. Petersburg *Center* INSTITUTE OF ADVANCED STUDIES, 1025 First Ave., 33705, (813) 894-6564.
SAWAN KIRPAL RUHANI MISSION, (Darshan Science of the Soul), Sunnie Cowen, Southern Representative, 3976 Belle Vista Dr. E., 33706, (813) 360-8046.
Bookstore TEMPLE-OF-THE LIVING GOD BOOK NOOK, 1950 Second Ave., N., 33713, (813) 822-3157.

West Palm Beach *Bookstore* THE RAINBOW BRIDGE NEW AGE STORE, 125 Lakeview Ave., 33401, (305) 655-0136. Books, tapes, cards, fragrances, herbs and good vibes.

Georgia

Atlanta *Center* AMERICAN-INTERNATIONAL REIKI ASSOCIATION, P.O. Box 13778, 30324, (404) 233-5549.
REIKI NATURAL HEALTH CENTER, 545 Pharr Rd., N.E., 30305, (404) 233-5549. Reiki treatments and classes available.
Bookstore OLIVERS UNLIMITED, 220 Sandy Springs Circle, 30328, (404) 252-8558 (books), (404) 252-1177 (food). General books with specialty in metaphysics and astrology. Complete line of natural foods. New age music.
THE SPHINX METAPHYSICAL BOOK CENTER, 1510 Piedmont Ave., 30324, (404) 875-2665.
Foodstore GOLDEN TEMPLE NATURAL FOODSTORE AND RESTAURANT, 1782 Chesire Bridge Rd., N.E., 30324, (404) 875-0769. Featuring all major food

items, vitamins, herbs, bulk foods, books & Shakti shoes. Try our complete vege.
meals.

Health AMERICAN-INTERNATIONAL REIKI ASSOCIATION, P.O. Box 13778,
30324, (404) 233-5549. A membership organization for those who have completed
a Reiki Natural Healing Course.

REIKI SEMINARS, INC., P.O. Box 14305, 30324, (404) 874-9142. Fully certified
Reiki teachers to travel to your area.

Conyers *Monastery* MONASTERY OF THE HOLY GHOST, 30201, (404) 483-8705.
This Trappist retreat was founded from Gethsemani in 1944. It has 60 monks who
built their own church, which is reminiscent of medieval architecture. There is a
large guesthouse, modern, with about 50 rooms. There is also a guesthouse for
women. The retreat master has studied the teachings of Zen, especially Huang Po.
There are two hermits on the property.

Lakemont *Center* CENTER FOR SPIRITUAL AWARENESS -- CSA, P.O. Box 7,
30552, (404) 782-4723.

Roswell *Center* 3HO -- GRD, 112A Millbrook Circle N.W., 30075, (404) 993-6633.

Stone Mountain *Center* JAN'S WORK, The Future/Now Federation, P.O. Box 1365,
30086.

Hawaii

Haiku *Center* DIAMOND SANGHA, Maui Zendo, R.R. 1, P.O. Box 702, 96708,
(808) 572-8163.

T.O.P. TRAINING: THE OMNISION PROGRAM, Call Jiun *Person-to-Person* collect at (808) 572-0666 for local availability across the continent.

Honolulu *Center* DIAMOND SANGHA, 2119 Kaloa Way, 96822, (808) 946-0666.

Kealakekua *Bookstore* OHANA 0 KA AINA, P.O. Box 1662 (Mamalahoa Hwy.),
96750, (808) 323-3600. Natural food coop, vege cafe, herb shop.

Kihei *Counseling* MEREDITH MOON, M.A., P.O. Box 1519, 96753, (808) 879-4895.
Hadiqa: Transpersonal Psychology, Dream work and Psycho, spiritual growth.

Makawao *Center* SUFI ISLAMIA RUHANIAT SOCIETY, Sufis Hawaii, P.O. Box
729, 96768.

Paauilo *Center* SAWAN KIRPAL RUHANI MISSION, P.O. Box 375, 96776, (808)
775-7311.

Pearl City *Center* JAI MA MUSIC, P.O. Box 359, 96782.

Idaho

Coeur d'Alene *Health* AUM CENTER FOR SELF REALIZATION, 1717 Lincoln
Way, 83814, (208) 667-2683.

HOLISTIC NATUROPATHIC CENTER, 1717 Lincoln Way, Coeur d' Alene Professional Arts Bldg., 83814, (208) 667-2683.

Sand Point *Service* THE ROCKY MOUNTAIN CO., 300 N. 1st (P.O. Box 1547),
83864, (208) 263-5201. We seek and research high energy land in North Idaho,
Western Montana, and Eastern Washington for personal use or for retreats, and
communities. Free booklet.

193

Illinois

Alto Pass *Community* MEDICINE WHEEL COMMUNITY, R.R. 1, P.O. Box 70, 62905, (618) 833-8357. Disciples of Paramahansa Yogananda; we welcome all sincere seekers.

Champaign *Community* LIVING TAO FOUNDATION, P.O. Box 5060, Station A, 61820.

Chicago *Center* 3HO -- GRD, 7015 N. Sheridan Rd., 60626, (312) 338-6066, 338-2227.

AQUARIAN FELLOWSHIP, 1328 W. Newport Ave., 60657, (312) 528-7254.

THE FOCUSING INSTITUTE, 5637 S. Kenwood, 60637.

THE HUMAN PROCESS, INC., 6117 North Winthrop, 60660, (312) 743-0798.

INTERNATIONAL ASSOCIATION FOR WORLD PEACE, 3315-23 North Clark St., 60657, (312) 248-7959.

NARAYANANDA UNIVERSAL YOGA (N.U. YOGA), N.U. Yoga Center, 1418 North Kedzie, Ave., 60651, (312) 278-2737.

SAWAN KIRPAL RUHANI MISSION, (Kirpal Science of the Soul), Olga Donenberg, Midwest Representative, 6007 N. Sheridan Rd. #14B, 60660, (312) 784-2977.

SOCIETY FOR THE PROTECTION OF THE UNBORN THROUGH NUTRITION, 17 North Wabash St., Suite 603, 60602, (312) 332-2334.

VIVEKANANDA VEDANTA SOCIETY, 5423 South Hyde Park Blvd., 60615, (312) 363-0027.

Other FIELD MUSEUM OF NATURAL HISTORY, Roosevelt Rd. at Lake Shore Dr., 60605. Approximately 1200 Tibetan personal and household items, 95 musical instruments, 170 masks and costumes, 800 religious articles, 388 paintings, 94 prints.

Deerfield *Center* COPTIC FELLOWSHIP INTERNATIONAL, 1223 Arbor Vitae Rd., 60015, (616) 531-1339.

Oak Park *School* INSTITUTE FOR ADVANCED PERCEPTION, 719 S. Clarence Ave., 60304, (312) 386-1742. Classes in Psychic and Spiritual Development.

Stelle STELLE -- CITY OF TOMORROW, The Stelle Group, P.O. Box 27, 60619, (815) 256-2200.

Villa Park *Center* INSTITUTE FOR ADVANCED PERCEPTION, 45N Ardmope, 60181, (312) 833-3218. Classes.

Wheaton *Bookstore* QUEST BOOKSHOP, 306 E. Geneva, 60187, (312) 665-0123. Home of Quest Books -- located on 40 acre estate of the Theosophical Society in America. Open 7 days per week.

Wilmette *Center* BAHA'I FAITH, 112 Linden St., 60091, (312) 869-9039.

Indiana

Bloomington *Center* THE TIBET SOCIETY, 101 Goodbody Hall, Indiana University, 47405, (812) 335-2233.

Greenfield *Foodstore* THE GOOD THINGS "NATURALLY", 610 W. Main St., 46140, (317) 462-2004. Restaurant, Bakery & Store. "Nutrition and Health Food."

Indianapolis *Community* INDIANAPOLIS CHRISTIAN COMMUNITY, (Holy Order Of Mans), 241 E. 12th St., 46202, (317) 636-1621.

South Bend *Restaurant* CORNUCOPIA, 303 S. Michigan, 46601, (219) 288-1911. Natural foods. The only vegetable restaurant in Michiana area. In its sixth year.

Williams *Community* GOD'S VALLEY, Rachel Summerton, R.R. 1, P.O. Box 478, 47470, (812) 388-5571.

Iowa

Boone *Center* 3HO -- GRD, 1510 Carroll St., 50036, (515) 432-1924.
Dubuque *Monastery* ABBEY OF OUR LADY OF NEW MELLERAY, Dubuque, 52001, (319) 588-2319. Founded from Ireland in 1849, this beautiful place has 100 monks who farm the land. The guest house for retreats is usually full, so it is best to write ahead for reservations.

Kansas

Wichita *Community* WICHITA CHRISTIAN COMMUNITY, (Holy Order Of Mans), 3224 E. Douglas, 67208, (316) 682-8972.
   Bookstore DAWN OF LIGHT, 2717 E. Central, 67214, (316) 684-6951. New Age books and gifts.

Kentucky

Bardstown *Monastery* ABBEY OF GETHSEMANI, Trappist, 40073 (P.O. near Bardstown), (502) 549-3117. Since this is the Motherhouse of other U.S. Trappist abbeys, it is stricter and more contemplative-oriented than others, but within the community itself are Jungian, Zen, yoga and charismatic groups. It is most famous for being the abbey where Thomas Merton lived and was later a hermit. There is a guest house for men, but only by reservation. Anyone can visit the chapel and stay for the Divine Office or Mass.

Louisiana

New Orleans *Center* 3HO GURU RAM DAS ASHRAM, 3027 Monroe, 70118, (504) 482-5225. Sikh Gurudwara -- Kundalini Yoga classes.

Maine

Cape Elizabeth *Health* ALEXANDRA BOTTINELLI, 60 Olde Colony Ln., 04107, (207) 799-8616. Healing thru nature: BACH REMEDIES, aromatherapy, and self expression.
South Berwick 3HO -- GRD, RFD #1, P.O. Box 522, Tatrie Rd., 03908.
Stonington HEALING THROUGH ARTS, INC., P.O. Box 399, 04681, (207) 367-5076. *Center*
Waterville *Instruction* THE OXBOW CENTER/LILLAIN MCMULLIN, 32 Western Ave., 04901, (207) 873-1351. Instruction -- yoga and massage.

Maryland

Baltimore *Center* 3HO -- PUNJ PYARE, 6017 Park Heights Ave., 21215, (301) 358-7106.

JANUS GROWTH CENTER, 21 W. 25th St., 21218, (301) 366-2123.

Restaurant HEALTH CONCERN, 28 W. Susquehanna Ave., 21204, (301) 828-4015.

Instruction INSTITUTE FOR CONSCIOUSNESS & MUSIC TRAINING SEMINARS, 7027 Bellona Ave., 21212, (301) 377-7525. Professional training in guided imagery and music.

Chevy Chase *Center* THE NETWORK OF LIGHT, 4617 Hunt Ave., 20815, (301) 986-1223.

College Park *Foodstore* BEAUTIFUL DAY TRADING CO., 5010 Berwyn Rd., 20740, (301) 345-6655. Organic produce, bulk foods, herbs, cafe, juice bar, books, clothes.

Freeland *Community* HEATHCOTE CENTER, 21300 Heathcote Rd., 21053, (301) 343-1070. Organic gardening apprenticeships.

Potomac *Center* THE COSMIC CIRCLE OF FELLOWSHIP, 7405 Masters Dr., 20854, (301) 299-7158.

Rockville *Therapy* TRANSACTIONAL ANALYSIS COMMUNITY COUNSELING CENTER OF MONTGOMERY COUNTY, 1002 Brice Rd., 20852, (301) 762-9090. Groups; Individual Sessions; Family Therapy; Marriage Counseling; Couple Counseling; Adults, Teens; "Borderline"; RAGE, DEPRESSION, Dependency Addictions; M.D. Licensed and certified psychotherapists.

Silver Springs *Center* MANKIND RESEARCH FOUNDATION, 1110 Fidler Ln., Suite 1215, 20910, (202) 882-4000.

Stevenson *Center* KOINONIA FOUNDATION, 1400 Greenspring Valley Rd., 21153, (301) 486-6262.

Thurmont *Center* UNITY WOODS YOGA CENTER, 11432 Old Frederick Rd., 21788, (301) 898-5909.

Massachusetts

Allston *Community* ALLSTON COMMUNITY: BOSTON CHRISTIAN COMMUNITY, (Holy Order Of Mans), 64 Harvard Ave., 02134, (617) 254-2666.

Amherst *Center* AMERICAN INSTITUTE OF BUDDHIST STUDIES, 86 College St., 01002, (413) 256-0281.

Community SIRIUS, P.O. Box 388-G, 01004, (413) 256-8015.

Bookstore SOPHIA BOOKSHOP, 103 N. Pleasant St., 01002, (413) 253-5574. Mail orders welcome.

Arlington a: SAGITTARIUS RISING ASTROLOGY CENTER AND PUBLISHING COMPANY, P.O. Box 252, 02174, (617) 646-2692. Spiritual/Humanistic Astrology. Counseling, courses, workshops. Books by Tracy Marks.

Counseling TRACY MARKS, M.A., SAGITTARIUS RISING, P.O. Box 252, 02174, (617) 646-2692. Humanistic/spiritual astrologer, author of 7 books. Counseling classes.

Barre *Center* INSIGHT MEDITATION SOCIETY, Pleasant St., 01005, (617) 355-4378.

Boston *Center* HIPPOCRATES HEALTH INSTITUTE, 25 Exeter St., 02116, (617) 267-9525.

MACROBIOTIC COMMUNITY, Boston is the core of macrobiotics in North America; Michio Kushi, *East West Journal,* Erewhon foods, restaurants etc. are all here.

THE ACUPUNCTURE & SHIATSU THERAPY CENTER, 359 Boylston St., 02116, Dennis Willmont, Director.

THE RAMAKRISHNA-VEDANTA SOCIETY OF MASSACHUSETTS, 58 Deerfield St., 02215, (617) 536-5320.

Media WHOLE LIFE TIMES, 18 Shephard St., 02135, (617) 783-8030. Directory of health care, natural foods, spiritual growth, personal development, national and local products and services.

Other MUSEUM OF FINE ARTS, Huntington Ave., 02115. Many Tibetan brass and bronze sculptures, copper ritual objects, and large number of thankas.

Brookline *Therapy* SUSAN ODLAND, M.A., Psychotherapy For Women, 02146, (617) 566-3503.

Cambridge *Center* 3HO -- YOGA CENTER, 1306 Massachusetts Ave. #205, 02138.

HEALING CHURCH OF KARMU, 526 Green St., 02139, (617) 354-6970.

SOMA, 99 Bishop Allen Dr., 02139, (617) 491-8694.

Bookstore SPHINX & SWORD OF LOVE BOOKSTORE, 111 Mt. Auburn St., 02138, (617) 491-8788. Wholistic spiritual bookstore. Books & tapes focusing on personal transformation & Nonviolent social change. Mail order catalog available.

Cohasset *Center* VEDANTA CENTRE -- ANANDA ASHRAMA, 130 Beechwood St., 02025, (617) 383-0940.

Dover *Center* SAWAN KIRPAL RUHANI MISSION, 105 Center St., 02030, (617) 785-0702.

Gill *Community* THE RENAISSANCE COMMUNITY, The 2001 Center, Main Rd., 01376, (413) 863-9711.

Leverett *Center* 3HO -- GRD, 436 Long Plain Rd., 01054, (413) 549-6449.

Millis *Center* 3HO -- GRD, 368 Village St., 02054, (617) 376-2010, 376-4016.

Northampton *Bookstore* BEYOND WORDS BOOKSHOP, 150 Main St., 01060, (413) 586-6304. New Age books, music and gifts.

Pittsfield *Center* BERKSHIRE CENTER FOR BODY/MIND WHOLENESS, 55 Fenn St., P.O. Box 171, 01202, (413) 442-4418.

Rowe ROWE CAMP & CONFERENCE CENTER, Kings Highway Rd., 01367, (413) 339-4216.

Spencer *Monastery* ST. JOSEPH ABBEY, 01562, (617) 885-3901. This is a very artistic Trappist community of 89 monks. It was founded in 1825. A very beautiful monastery. They make jelly of all kinds and market nationwide. The guesthouse

May the longtime sun shine upon you
All love surround you
And the pure light within you
Guide your way on.
 —*Incredible String Band*

NEW AGE MUSIC CATALOG

featuring:
Songs of the Lord's Love
Children's Stories
CASSETTE DUPLICATION SERVICE
New artists and outlets invited
Write for free catalog to:
GRD Music, P.O. Box 13054
Phoenix, AZ 85002

is available only by reservation. Retreat is conducted by monks. Although a Trappist retreat, Zen roshis and yogis have come and taught here.

Vineyard Haven *Foodstore* VINEYARD NATURAL FOODS, Beach Rd., 02568, (617) 693-2460. On Martha's Vineyard. Vitamins, herbs, cosmetics, dairy, bulk, grains and sandwiches.

Wellesley *Health* ARTHRITIS AND HEALTH RESOURCE CENTER, 486 Washington St., 02181, (617) 431-7080. Multidimensional treatment for arthritis, muscular skeletal disorders and stress.

Michigan

Ann Arbor *Center* THE YOGA CENTER OF ANN ARBOR, 207 E. Ann St., 48104.
  Bookstore DE LA FERRIERE BOOKSTORE, 207 E. Ann St., 48104, (313) 769-4321.
  Restaurant SEVA RESTAURANT, 314 East Liberty, 48104, (313) 662-2019. Ann Arbors oldest and finest natural foods restaurant. Open Sundays.

Berkeley *Center* THE MICHIGAN METAPHYSICAL SOCIETY, 3018 W. Twelve Mile Rd., 48072, (313) 399-8299.

Birmingham *Health* KEVIN L. KOPRIVA, D.C., 280 N. Woodward, LL9, 48011, (313) 540-0060. Chiropractic Physician -- Applied Kinesiology. Member -- International College of Applied Kinesiology.

Chelsea *Center* THE SEVA FOUNDATION, 108 Spring Lake Dr., 48118, (313) 475-1351.

Davisburg *Center* BALANCED LIFE CENTER, Happy Hills Farm, 13120 Rattalee Lake Rd., 48019, (313) 634-4571. Yoga, birth, nutrition, healing.

Detroit *Center* EARTH COMMUNITY, 19731 Forrer St., 48235, (313) 494-0543.

East Jordan *Health* PAN'S FOREST HERB COMPANY, Route 1, P.O. Box 211, Pesek Rd., 49727, (616) 536-7445. Tinctures, amulets, gifts, bath herbs, more. Midwife-owned. Catalog $1.

East Lansing *Center* SAWAN-KIRPAL RUHANI MISSION, c/o Mark Bishop, 326 Marshall, 48823, (517) 337-2553. Teachings of Sant Darshan Singh on meditation and true living.

Fennville *Monastery* VIVEKANANDA MONASTERY & RETREATS, Route 2, 122nd Ave., Ganges Township, 49408 (616), 543-4545. Group of male monastic candidates study the Vedantic scriptures, meditate, depend on donations alone for their living, and try to live by the ideals of Sri Ramakrishna and Swami Vivekananda. Retreats can be arranged.

Ferndale *Center* 3HO MICHIGAN, 484 Academy, 48220, (313) 541-4834. Kundalini yoga classes, women's courses, week-end workshops, Tantric yoga.
  Foodstore WHOLE GRAIN FOODS, 23140 Woodward, 48220, (313) 544-3289.

Kalkaska *Center* SHENANDOAH VALLEY HEALTH RANCH, Flowing Well Rd., Route #1, 49646, (616) 258-2750.

Lathrup *Health* KHALSA MEDICAL CLINIC, 27330 Southfield Rd., 48076, (313) 552-8848.

Southfield *School* WALDORF INSTITUTE OF MERCY COLLEGE, 23399 Evergreen, 48075, (313) 823-4630. Waldorf Institute of Mercy College relocates to woodland campus! Anthroposophical Studies, Waldorf (Steiner) Education, Biodynamic Gardening. Accredited. Financial Assistance.

Sterling Heights *Bookstore* MIDDLE EARTH BOOKSHOP, 2791 E. 14 Mile Rd., 48077, (313) 979-7340. Occult book catalog with 5000 titles -- $2. We mail order.

Service BARBARA KRAFT, 33506 Stonewood Dr., 48077, (313) 268-3521, 268-5849. Psychic reader.

Utica *Health* TAWNI HICKS, 17926 Red Oaks Dr., 48087, (313) 286-5552. Doing nutritional/counseling with Iridology.

Wyoming *Center* COPTIC FELLOWSHIP INTERNATIONAL, 1735 Pinnacle, S.W., 49509, (616) 531-1339. New Age Education focusing on world service in the Christ Consciousness. Techniques of planetary transformation through personal transmutation and self mastery. Modern version of the ancient Egyptian Mysteries. Dedicated to the Universal principle of religious philosophies merging into Oneness.

SPIRITUAL UNITY OF NATIONS, 1735 Pinnacle St., 49509.

Minnesota

Minneapolis *Center* 3HO -- GRD, 4350 Garfield Ave., South, 55409, (612) 822-6704.

THE CHURCH OF THE REALIZATION, INC., P.O. Box 261, 55440, (612) 227-3505.

CENTER FOR HIGHER CONSCIOUSNESS, 631 University Ave., N.E., 55413, (612) 379-2386.

MARK-AGE OF MINNEAPOLIS, 4942 Penn Ave. South, 55409, (612) 920-471.

MINNESOTA ZEN MEDITATION CENTER, 3343 East Calhoun Parkway, 55408, (612) 822-5313.

THE TEMPLE OF MAN, Rev. Don Roberts, Pastor, 3921 France Ave., 55416, (612) 929-9049.

Bookstore SUNSIGHT BOOKS & GOOD STUFF, 616 W. Lake St., 55408, (612) 823-1166. New Age books, tapes, cards, gifts, readings and classes.

St. Paul *Community* TURTLE ISLAND HOLISTIC HEALTH COMMUNITY, 569-571 Selby Ave., 55102, (612) 291-7637. Classes and services in natural health care and birthing.

Missouri

Arnold *Community* MORNING GLORY COMMUNITY, 2700 Oaker Dr., 63010, (314) 296-7846.

Ava *Monastery* ABBEY OF OUR LADY OF THE ASSUMPTION, Route 5, 65608, (417) 683-2310. Very remote. Located on 3,500 acres of wilderness land. There is also a guesthouse for women and families. There are several hermits and many hermit cabins.

Kansas City *Center* 3HO -- SAT TIRATH, 3525 Walnut, 64111, (816) 561-5337.

SUFI ISLAMIA RUHANIAT SOCIETY, Shining Heart Community, 4144 Locust, 64110, (816) 753-5094.

St. Louis *Center* 3HO -- GRD, 6036 Marmaduke, 63139, (314) 644-3338.

THE VEDANTA SOCIETY OF ST. LOUIS, 205 South Skinker Blvd., 63105, (314) 721-5118.

UNIVERSAL GREAT BROTHERHOOD, SOLAR LINE (U.G.B.), U.S.A. H.Q., P.O. Box 9154, 63117.

YOGA CENTER OF ST. LOUIS, 6002 Pershing, 63112.

Restaurant GOVINDA'S SUPERNATURAL FOODS, 3926 Lindell Blvd., 63108, (314) 535-8085.

SUNSHINE INN, 8 1/2 S. Euclid, 63108, (314) 367-1413. Lunch, Dinner, Sunday Brunch.

Service BEVERLY C. JAEGERS -- U.S. PSI SQUAD, P.O. Box 24571, 63141, (314) 872-9127. PSYCHIC RESEARCH.

Montana

Bozeman *Center* 3HO -- GRD, 75 Kountz Ct., 59715, (406) 586-7172.
Kalispell *Health* NATUROPATHIC FAMILY HEALTH CLINIC, 11 South Meridian Rd., 59901, (406) 257-4641.

Nevada

Caliente *Monastery* HERMITAGE OF CHRIST IN THE MOUNTAINS, P.O. Box 247, 89008. A blend of Trappist, Carthusian, Camaldolese and the primitive rule make a modern hermitage here. This monastery is 60 miles from the nearest small town. There are about 5 people. They do have guest accommodations, but one should write for directions or for pickup. Sunday Mass is conducted in Caliente.
Carlin *Center* META TANTAY INDIAN FOUNDATION, P.O. Box 707, 89822, (702) 754-9928.
Las Vegas *Center* 3HO -- GRD, 1201 Greenway Dr., 89108, (702) 648-4747.
Pahrump *Instruction* PAUL CROCKETT, P.O. Box 1271, 89041, (702) 727-5901. Paul is best represented by Castaneda's description of a man of knowledge in his labor, his clarity of mind, his unbending intent and his dedication to teaching others the keys to this unceasing process. For more information, please write or call.
Reno *Center* 3HO -- GRD, 1653 Westfield Ave., 89509, (702) 329-8540.
   Center INTERNATIONAL COMMUNITY OF CHRIST, Admissions Department, 643 Ralston St., 89503, (702) 786-7827.

New Hampshire

North Salem Mystery Hill is located just ouside this town. It is a megalithic site dating back to 2000 B.C., with certain astronomical alignments. It has been linked to the celts and is known by some as the American Stonehenge.

New Jersey

Asbury Park *Bookstore* VISIONS II, 532 Cookman Ave., 07712, (201) 988-7335. Bookstore.
Butler *Foodstore* TASTE OF DAWN NATURAL FOODS, 112 Main St., 07405, (201) 838-0287.

Chester *Foodstore* NEW AGE NATURAL FOODS, 87 East Main St., 07930, (201) 879-6210. Bulk organic natural foods and produce, largest macrobiotic selection in state, open 7 days.

Convent Station *Instruction* TEACHINGS OF THE ASCENDED MASTERS, P.O. Box 101C, 07961.

Fairfield *Service* PSYCHIC FAIR NETWORK/SHIRLEY ANN TABATNECK, 215 Little Falls Rd., 07006, (201) 256-5721.

Franklin Lakes *Therapy* MICHAEL WIESE FILM PRODUCTIONS, P.O. Box 315, 07417, (201) 891-8240. Film rental and sale, *Beauty, Extraordinary Powers, I Move.*

Imlaystown *Center* THE EDENITE SOCIETY, 08526.

Malaga *Center* AMERICAN VEGAN SOCIETY -- AHIMSA, 501 Old Harding Hhwy., 08328, (609) 694-2887.

Moorestown *Monastery* CISTERCIAN MONASTERY, P.O. Box 295, Mt. Laurel, Moorestown, 08057.

Mooristown *Center* THE JERSEY SOCIETY OF PARAPSYCHOLOGY, INC. (JSP), P.O. Box 2071, 07960, (201) 386-1504.

Newark *Other* NEWARK MUSEUM, 49 Washington St., 07101. Tibetan paintings, books, ritual objects, musical instruments.

Princeton *Center* 3HO ASHRAM, 12 Piedmont Dr., 08550, (609) 799-8238.

SRI CENTRES INTERNATIONAL, P.O. Box 3016, 08540, (201) 359-7383.

Health HOLISTIC HEALTH ASSOCIATION, 360 Nassau St., 08540, (609) 924-8580.

Ramsey *Center* SEVERAL SOURCES FOUNDATION, 182 Prospect St., 07446.

Red Bank *Center* THE MOVING CENTER, P.O. Box 2034, 07701, (201) 530-0250, (212) 772-0946.

Ridgewood *Center* YOGA AND GROWTH CENTER OF BERGEN COUNTY, 84 East Ridgewood Ave., 07450, (201) 447-2474.

Washington *Center* LABSUM SHEDRUB LING -- LAMAIST BUDDHIST MONASTERY OF AMERICA, P.O. Box 306A, RD 1, 07882, (201) 689-6080.

Westfield *Instruction* YOGA CENTE R OF WESTFIELD -- U.G.B., 122 Eaglecroft Rd., 07090, (201) 233-3697.

New Mexico

Abiquiu *Monastery* MONASTERY OF CHRIST IN THE DESERT, 87510. This is a very isolated and scenic retreat located along a river. It has a blend of contemplative Trappist and primitive rule of the desert fathers.

Albuquerque *Center* 3HO -- GURU NANAK GURDWARA, 219 Amherst S.E., 87106, (505) 266-6374.

GROUP HARMONICS CENTRE, P.O. Box 25643, 87125, (505) 898-8389. Spiritual Retreat and Growth Centre focused towards advanced Education/ Research and Healing with regard to Holistic Principles.

MOTIVATION DEVELOPMENT CENTRE, N. Coors Rd., P.O. Box 25643, 87125, (505) 265-6557. Classes, lectures, workshops, seminars, tape & film presentations. New Age information/resource exchange.

Bookstore BROTHERHOOD OF LIFE, 110 Dartmouth, S.E., 87106, (505) 255-8980. Established 1969, offers Alburquerque and the surrounding areas a complete selection of metaphysical, New Age and Occult books; a fine selection of imported incense and sundry items. Catalog available. Near the University.

UNIVERSAL SUPPLY CENTRE, 3120 Central Ave., S.E., 87106, (505) 265-6557. Books, herbs, natural vitamins, foods, cosmetics, posters, crystals. Mail Order.

Restaurant MOTHER NATURE & SON VEGETARIAN RESTAURANT, 3118 Central S.E., 87106, (505) 255-7640.

Espanola *Center* 3HO FOUNDATION, 3HO Hacienda de Guru Ram Das, Route 1, P.O. Box 132D, 87532, (505) 753-9438. Kundalini Yoga. Try and see the mural at the Ashram.

Four Corners Often called the Four Corners area, the Colorado Plateau, where Arizona, New Mexico, Utah and Colorado meet, is roughly circular and approximately 350 miles wide. It sits within a ring of volcanic mountains which experience a very high concentration of lightning activity. It has high solar activity, underground water & radioactive minerals. The Hopi and other native people claim this region is a spot of power, one of several particularly sacred places on the planet. In recent years different scientific work has confirmed this. There is also a remarkable number of ancient city ruins in the area.

Jemez Springs *Center* JEMEZ BODHI MANDALA, Jemez Bodhi Mandala, P.O. Box 8, 87025, (505) 829-3854.

Los Alamos *Center* NEW AGE AWARENESS CENTER, P.O. Box 969, 87544, (505) 662-4000.

San Cristobal *Center* LAMA FOUNDATION, P.O. Box 444, 87564.

Santa Fe *Center* HANUMAN FOUNDATION, P.O. Box 478, 87501.

THE PSYCHIC STUDIES INSTITUTE, 535 Cordova Rd., Suite 164, 87501, (505) 983-5681.

SUFI ORDER IN THE WEST, 1570 Pacheco St., 87501, (505) 988-4411. Founded by Hazrat Inayat Khan. Present head is Pir Vilayat Inayat Khan.

School THE NEW MEXICO ACADEMY OF ADVANCED HEALING ARTS, 133 Romero St., 87501, (505) 982-6271.

Bookstore SUNFLOWER BOOKSTORE, 105 E. Marcy St., 87501, (505) 988-9272. Send for our book lists: Acupuncture, Iridology, Medical Texts, Herbology, Pregnancy + Childbirth, Astrology, Nutrition, Homeopathy + Radionics.

Taos A very powerful area, by the Sangre de Cristo mountains. Psychoanalyst Carl Gustav Jung, writer D.H. Lawrence and others all sojourned here.

Center SUFI ISLAMIA RUHANIAT SOCIETY, c/o Tui Wilschinsky, P.O. Box 3024, 87571, (505) 758-8793.

Bookstore WILDERNESS BOOKSTORE, Dunn House on Bent St., 87571, (505) 758-4018. Focusing on New Age subjects. Also: solar, Southwest, topographical, maps.

New York

Albany *Center* 3HO, P.O. Box 12541, 12212.

Restaurant RIBBONGRASS NATURAL FOODS RESTAURANT, 33 Central Ave., 12210, (518) 465-0248.

Amityville *Community* YOGA ANAND ASHRAM INC. SELF REALIZATION CENTER, 42 Merrick Rd., 11701, (516) 691-8475.

Brooklyn *Center* 3HO FOUNDATION OF N.Y., 146 Begen St., 11217, (212) 855-4856. We offer kundalini yoga classes as taught by Yogi Bhajan throughout New York City.

LUBAVITCH YOUTH ORGANIZATION, 305 Kingston Ave., 11213, (212) 778-4270.

SAWAN KIRPAL RUHANI MISSION, 388 Ave., S., Apt. 2C, 11223, (212) 375-0752.

SOLAR YOGA AND ARTS CENTER, 373 9th St., 11215.

Bronx *Center* BUDDHIST ASSOCIATION OF THE UNITED STATES, 3070 Albany Crescent, 10463, (212) 884-9111.

Buffalo *Center* 3HO -- GRD, 132 St., James Pl., 14222, (716) 881-4946.

Dix Hills *Center* PARAPSYCHOLOGY SOURCES OF INFORMATION CENTER, 2 Plane Tree Ln., 11746, (516) 271-1243.

Elmira *Monastery* MT SAVIOR MONASTERY, Pine City, Elmira, 14871, (607) 734-1688. This is the most open, liberal monastery of all. In 1972, a conference was held here with Alan Watts, Ram Dass, Satchidananda, Sasaki Roshi and others. A guesthouse is available on reservation.

Ghent *Center* ANTHROPOSOPHICAL SOCIETY IN AMERICA, Rd. 2, 12075, (518) 672-4601.

Greenville *Center* ORGYEN CHO DZONG, Rd. 1, P.O. Box 555, 12083, (518) 926-4228;

Huntington (Long Island) *School* FRIENDS WORLD COLLEGE, P.O. Box P, Plover Ln., 11743, (516) 549-1102. See listing under Education.

Jamaica *Center* THE SRI CHINMOY CENTRE, P.O. Box 32433, 11431.

Lyons *Center* 3HO -- GRD, Route 2, Warneke Rd., 14889, (315) 946-5523, 946-4656.

Manhasset *Center* INSTITUTE FOR SELF DEVELOPMENT, 50 Maple Pl., 11030, (516) 627-0048.

Merrick *Center* SAWAN KIRPAL RUHANI MISSION, Long Island Center, 8 Copper Beech Pl., 11566, (516) 378-6183.

Monroe *Center* I.C.S.A., ANANDA ASHRAM, Route 3, P.O. Box 141, 10950, (914) 782-5575.

Mt. Tremper *Center* MATAGIRI, 12457, (914) 679-8322.

from **Auroville** South India
Embroidered Cotton Clothing,
Quality Handcrafts ~ Tapestries

Celtic Cards   Books, tapes
& Stationery   & records   **Findhorn**
Scotland

Catalog available $1

Specify Wholesale or Retail

Global View ~ Auro International
R.3, Spring Green, WI, 53588.   608-583-5311

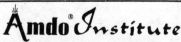
Amdo® Institute
for Human Development Research
Education and Training
emphasizing a wholistic approach to
Personal and Spiritual Growth
**CORRESPONDENCE COURSES
CLASSES * SEMINARS
TAPE RECORDINGS**
Certificate and Degree Programs
send for information
Dr. Fred Stahl   158-160 Boonton Rd.
Stahl Plaza   Wayne, N.J. 07470

**Samuel Weiser
BOOKSTORE**
Largest metaphysical and occult bookstore in the world

740 Broadway • New York, N.Y. 10003
(212) 777-6363

Specializing in:

Acupressure • Acupuncture • Alchemy
Astral Projection • Astrology • Aura &
Color • Buddhism • Chakra Meditation
• Do.In • Egyptology • Edgar Cayce •
Earth Changes • The Goddess • Gurd
jieff • Herbs & Healing • Homeopathy
• Iridology • Jungian Dream Analysis •
Kabbalah • Meditation • Nostradamus
& Prophecy • Numerology • Oriental •
Palmistry • Past Life Therapy • Pendu
lum • Radionics • Rajneesh • Reflexol
ogy • Seth • Shiatsu • Sufism • Tai Chi
Chuan • Tantra • Tarot • Visualization
Yoga • Zen

Send for free catalog of Weiser publications.

New Lebanon *Community* THE ABODE OF THE MESSAGE, P.O. Box 396, 12125, (518) 794-8090. The community of the Sufi Order in the western world, led by Pir Vilayat Inayat Khan.

New Paltz *Foodstore* REAL FOOD STORE, 188 Main St., 12561, (914) 255-8077. Bulk foods. Juice bar. Breakfast, lunch, dinner 7 days.

New York Area (See Listings Under: Amityville, Bronx, Brooklyn, Huntington, Jamaica, Manhasset, Manhattan, Merrick, New York City, Staten Island, Yonkers.)

New York *Center* 3HO -- GRD, 146 Bergen St., 11217, (212) 855-4856.

AFRO-AMERICAN VEGETARIAN SOCIETY, P.O. Box 46, Colonial Park Station, 10039.

AHN TAI CHI STUDIO, INC., 81 Spring St., 10012, (212) 226-6664.

THE AMERICAN BUDDHIST MOVEMENT, 301 West 45th St., 10036, (212) 489-1075.

AMERICAN NICHIREN INSTITUTE, 301 W. 45th St., 10036, (212) 489-1075.

ARICA INSTITUTE, 235 Park Ave. South, 10003, (212) 673-5130.

ASTRO-MUSICAL RESEARCH, P.O. Box 118, 10033, (212) 942-0004.

BHAGAVAN SRI RAMANA MAHARSHI CENTER, 342 E. 6th St., 10003, (212) 477-4060, 854-0322.

BRAHMA KUMARIS RAJA YOGA CENTER, Church Center, 777 United Nations Plaza, (212) 565-5133.

CAFH FOUNDATION, 2061 Broadway St., 10023, (212) 783-4185.

CHOGYE INTERNATIONAL ZEN CENTER, 39 East 31st St., 10016, (212) 683-5049.

DIALOGUE HOUSE, 80 East 11th St., 10003, (212) 673-5880 or toll free (800) 221-5844.

JAIN MEDITATION INTERNATIONAL CENTRE, P.O. Box 730, Radio City Station, 10101, (212) 765-2232.

KARMA THEGSUM CHOLING, 412 West End Ave., Apt. 5n, 10024, (212) 580-9282.

LAWRENCE/HARRISON INSTITUTE, 1990 Broadway St., Suite 1206, 10023, (212) 724-8782.

LUCIS TRUST, 866 United Nations Plaza, Suite 566-7, 10017, (212) 421-1577.

MARTIN STEINBERG CENTER, 15 East 84th St., 10028, (212) 879-4500.

NATIONAL ASTROLOGICAL SOCIETY (NASO), 205 Third Ave., Suite 2A, 10003, (212) 673-1831.

NEW YORK ZEN CENTER, 267 West 81 St., 10024, (212) 724-4172.

PLANETARY CITIZENS, P.O. Box 1715, 10802.

RAMAKRISHNA-VIVEKANANDA CENTER, 17 East 94th St., 10028, (212) 534-9445.

THE SCHOOL OF T'AI CHI CHUAN, 412 Avenue of the Americas, 10011.

SIVANANDA YOGA VEDANTA CENTER, 243 W. 24th St., 10011, (212) 255-4560.

SPIRITUAL SCIENCE CENTER, Pastor/Founder Rev. Stefanie Nagorka, P.O. Box 755, Wall Street Station, 10268, (212) 227-2154.

SRI CENTRES INTERNATIONAL, 45 East 51st St., 10022, (212) 688-6452.

THE TREE OF LIFE, 34 W. 118th St., Rm. 211, 10026, (212) 222-1100.

VEDANTA SOCIETY, 34 W. 71st St., 10023, (212) 877-9197.

WOMEN AND WISDOM, 155 Bank St., 12th Fl., 10014, (212) 807-1222.

YESHE NYING PO, 19 W. 16th St., 10011, (212) 691-8523.

THE ZEN STUDIES SOCIETY, 223 E. 67th St., 10021, (212) 861-3333.

Community SUFI ORDER-NYC KHANAQA AS'SAFIYA, 242 E. 14th. St., 10003, (212) 777-8670.

School THE NATURAL GOURMET COOKERY SCHOOL, 365 West End Ave., Apt. 1E, 10024, (212) 580-7121. Vegetarian cooking classes: Basic (macrobiotic), exotic, gourmet-style and more. Ask for current brochure. Annemarie Colbin, Director.

Bookstore DHARMAWARE, 304 W. 4th St., 10014, (212) 242-2391. Clothing, Gifts, Asian Art.

SAMUEL WEISER INC, 740 Broadway, 10003, (212) 777-6363. Largest metaphysical and occult bookstore in the world.

VAJRADHATU BOOKS, 49 E. 21st St., 10010, (212) 673-7340.

Foodstore INTEGRAL YOGA NATURAL FOODS, 250 W. 14th St., 10011, (212) 243-2642.

Restaurant SPRING STREET NATURAL, RESTAURANT, 149 Spring St., 10012, (212) 966-0290. Everything home-made from all natural ingredients. Plant filled, airy, and turned-on.

Instruction JEFFERY OBOLER, 17 Downing St., 10014, (212) 741-0345 (home), 879-4500 (work). Storyteller, friend, teacher on the Jewish path.

RAVI SINGH KHALSA, 225 E. 5th St. #4-D, 10003, (212) 260-1677.

Bodywork JEFFERY OBOLER, 17 Downing St., 10014, (212) 741-0345. Sharing massage with those on the spiritual path.

Media THE AMERICAN BUDDHIST NEWSLETTER, 301 West 45th St., 10036, (212) 489-1075.

WHOLE LIFE TIMES, 18 Shephard St., 02135, (617) 783-8030. Directory of health care, natural foods, spiritual growth, personal development, national and local products and services.

Other AMERICAN MUSEUM OF NATURAL HISTORY, 79th St., Central Park West, 10024. Tibetan Collection includes paintings, images, ritual objects, masks, costumes and other articles. Just a small part of a fine museum.

THE CLOISTERS, Upper Manhattan. Parts of European monasteries transported, stone by stone, and reassembled. There are cloistered gardens and piped in Gregorian Chants in a park high above the Hudson River. Contains the famous *Unicorn Tapestries*. Go during the week and meditate in the gardens.

JACQUES MARCHAIS CENTER OF TIBETAN ARTS, 338 Lighthouse Ave., Staten Island, 10306. Many fine ritual objects and thankas.

METROPOLITAN MUSEUM OF ART, Fifth Ave. at 82nd St., 10028. One of the world's great art museums has a Tibetan collection with jewelry, musical instruments, paintings, embroidered and applique hangings, costumes.

NICHOLAS ROERICH ART MUSEUM, Agni Yoga Society, 319 W. 107th St., 10029, (212) 864-7752. Wonderful spiritual paintings in incredible colors.

Old Chatham *Other* SHAKER MUSEUM FOUNDATIONS, 95 Shaker Museum Rd., 12136. Shaker museums show the life of one of Americas first spiritual communities.

Parksville *Center* THE ACUPUNCTURE EDUCATION CENTER, Muhlig Rd., 12768 (May-November).

Penfield *Center* 3HO -- GRD, 23 Cove Cir., 14526, (716) 671-3401.

Piffard *Monastery* ABBEY OF OUR LADY GENESSEE, 14533, (716) 243-0660. The chapel here is very beautiful, with a contemplative atmosphere. The abbot has written many articles and a book translating the monastic fathers' prayer texts. The guesthouse is small and reservations are needed. There are several hermits.

Rochester *Center* THE ZEN CENTER OF ROCHESTER, 7 Arnold Park, 14607, (716) 473-9180.

South Fallsburgh *Center* SYDA FOUNDATION, P.O. Box 600, 12779, (914) 434-2000.

MA YOGA SHAKTI INT. MISSION, MYSIM, 114-23 Lefferts Blvd., 11420, (212) 322-5856, 641-0402; (305) 725-4024.

South Ozone Park *Restaurant* ADAMS' PIZZA PARLOR, Main St., 12779, (914) 434-9336. Vegetarian restaurant, wholewheat pizza, wholesome food and surroundings.

Staten Island *Center* ACHARYA SUSHIL JAIN ASHRAM, 722 Tompkins Ave., 10305, (212) 447-4948.

Syracuse *Center* 3HO -- GRD, 190 Parkside Ave., 13207, (315) 471-8847.

Foodstore THE GOOD FOOD STORE & RESTAURANT, 316 Waverly Ave., 13210, (315) 423-3594. Featuring natural, macrobiotic foods, classes each semester.

Health SYRACUSE EAST-WEST CENTER, P.O. Box 6568, 1001 Lancaster Ave., 13217, (315) 475-7230. Natural healing, living, macrobiotics.

Woodbourne *Center* SIVANANDA ASHRAM YOGA RANCH COLONY, Route 1, P.O. Box 228A, 12788, (914) 434-6502.

Woodstock *Service* WHITE BUFFALO MULTIMEDIA, P.O. Box 73, 12498, (914) 9995. Slide, sound, and narration programs oriented to New Age perspectives & cross-cultural issues. Education and entertainment. Mexico, Egypt, Prophecy, Birth. Available for gatherings, events, private/public group showings. Audio tapes for purchase. Free catalog.

Yonkers *Health* TAI CHI CHUAN CENTER OF YONKERS, Central Ave. & Tuckahoe Rd., 10710, (914) 337-9325.

North Carolina

Burnsville *School* ARTHUR MORGAN SCHOOL, Route 5, P.O. Box 335, 28714, (704) 675-4262, 675-4555.

Chapel Hill *Center* LINDENSELF FOUNDATION, P.O. Box 2321, 27514, (919) 364-2723.

Charlotte *Center* SUFI ORDER OF CHARLOTTE, 1137-E Salem Dr., 28209, (704) 372-2280.

THE TWELVE RAYS OF THE GREAT CENTRAL SUN, 3427 Densone Pl., 28213, (704) 598-0692.

Durham *Center* THE PRISON-ASHRAM PROJECT, Bo & Sita Lozoff, Route 1, P.O. Box 201-N, 27705.

Leicester *Center* LONG BRANCH ENVIRONMENTAL EDUCATION CENTER, Route 2, P.O. Box 132, 28748, Big Sandy Mush Creek, (704) 683-3662.

Winston Salem *Bookstore* PHOENIX METAPHYSICAL BOOKS, 1765 Janita Dr., 27107, (919) 784-0562.

Ohio

Bloomingdale *Monastery* HOLY FAMILY HERMITAGE, 43910, (614) 765-4511. This is a small hermitage of the Monte Corona Branch of the Camaldolese hermits. There are stricter, more silent, more cloistered and more eremetical aspects to their life than with other groups. There are about eight people here. They plant trees. They have guest accommodations, but space is limited, so reservations are needed.

Cincinnati **Bookstore** NEW WORLD BOOKSHOP, 336 Ludlow Ave., 45220, (513) 861-6100.

Instruction JILL ROBB MCCONNELL, 575 O North Glen Rd., 45211, (513) 574-2551. Public classes and private consultations available in holistic yoga therapy.

Cleveland **Center** THE LIGHT OF YOGA SOCIETY, 2134 Lee Rd., 44118, (216) 371-0078.

Bookstore COVENTRY BOOKS INC., 1824 Coventry Rd., 44118.

Columbus **Center** 3HO -- GURU RAM DAS ASHRAM OF KUNDALINI YOGA, 92 Northwood Ave., 43201, (614) 299-5687.

Dayton **Bookstore** MOUNTAINTOP BOOKSTORE, 2587 Shiloh Springs Rd., 45426, (513) 854-2855. New Age books, music, jewelry, incense.

Ravenna **Center** ALPHA OMEGA'S ALPHA CENTER, 2633 St., Route 59, 44266, (216) 673-4114, 673-8505. A holistic Center providing various services, counsultations, classwork and seminars.

Yellow Springs **Center** FELLOWSHIP OF RELIGIOUS HUMANISTS, 105 W. North College St., 45387, (513) 767-1324.

Oklahoma

Norman **Foodstore** THE EARTH NATURAL FOOD STORE, 309 S. Flòod, 73069, (405) 364-3551. Finest quality natural foods and herbs in bulk.

Service ASTRA ASTROLOGICAL SERVICES, 7600-11 E. Lindsey, 73071, (405) 364-7211. Professional astrological guidance by Gloria Star-Miller and Govinda Jack Miller with focus upon self-realization and transformation.

Oakahoma **Center** 3HO -- GRD, 3923 N.W. 8th St., 73107, (405) 947-8142.

NEW AGE YOGA INSTITUTE, 4133 N.W. 23rd St., 73107.

Bodywork AQUARIAN AGE MASSAGE, 1401 E. 15th, 74420, (918) 587-5877. Professional masseuses. Steam and sauna baths, hot tub whirlpool, ice plunge, showers. Make appointment for better service.

Oregon

Ashland **Center** SUFI ISLAMIA RUHANIAT SOCIETY, Ikhwan-i-Safa, 645 West Valley View Rd., 97520, (503) 482-3683.

YESHE NYING PO, 36 S. Second St., 96520, (503) 688-2993.

Bookstore GOLDEN MEAN BOOKSTORE, 42 East Main St., 97520, (503) 482-9771. A "door way": Quality new/used books. Service oriented.

Antelope **Center** RAJNEESH FOUNDATION INTERNATIONAL, P.O. Box 12A, 97001, (503) 489-3301.

Beaverton **Center** HUMAN DEVELOPMENT CENTER, 4572 S.W. 103rd Ave., 97123, (503) 643-6036.

PORTLAND VEGETARIAN SOCIETY, P.O. Box 1555, 97075, (503) 635-9421. Hans McCormack, Director Eco-environmental education, healing circles, media projects, public speaking, resource center.

Coos Bay **Center** CLEAR MIND CENTER, 790 Commercial Ave., 97420, (Formerly Cornucopia, St. Mary, Kentucky). We offer 6-day, 12-day, 30-day and apprenticeship trainings in the use of the Living Love Methods outlined in *Handbook To Higher Consciousness* by Ken Keyes.

Eugene **Center** 3HO -- GRD, 830 E 37th Ave., 97405, (503) 686-0432.

RAINBOW TRIBE, P.O. Box 5577, 97405.

SUFI ISLAMIA RUHANIAT SOCIETY, Smiling Forehead Sufi Center, 1991 Garfield, 97405, (503) 342-4695.

THE JESHUA BEN JOSEF SCHOOL OF THE HEART, P.O. Box 2097, 97402, (503) 342-8069.

Bookstore PERALANDRA METAPHYSICAL BOOKS AND RECORDS, 790 E 11th Ave., 97401, (503) 485-4848.

Foodstore SUNDANCE NATURAL FOODS, 748 East 24th Ave., 97405, (503) 343-9142. Large food store, produce shop and restaurant.

Media THE SPROUTLETTER, P.O. Box 10985, 97440, (503) 689-7566.

Grass Pass *Center* ALETHEIA PSYCHO-PHYSICAL FOUNDATION, 515 N.E. 8th St., 97526, (503) 479-4855.

Lafayette *Monastery* ABBEY OF OUR LADY OF GUADALUPE, 97127, (503) 852-7174. The name is taken from the miraculous self-portrait of the Blessed Virgin which appeared on an Indian's poncho around 1500 A.D. and is venerated today at the basilica in Mexico City. The guest master, abbot and community study Zen and meditation.

Mapleton *Restaurant* ALPHA-BIT CAFE & BOOKS, P.O. Box 465, 97453, (503) 268-4311. Also books and crafts.

Mt. Angel *Monastery* MT. ANGEL ABBEY, 97373, (593) 845-3030. 100 Benedictines run a seminary here. It was founded in the 1880's and is a really nice place to visit. There is a gift shop.

Portland *Center* 3HO -- GRD, 2539 S.E. Madison, 97214, (503) 232-0895.

CHRIST TRUTH FOUNDATION, 610 S.W. Broadway St., 97205, (503) 222-2060.

SUFI ISLAMIA RUHANIAT SOCIETY, Ruh Inayat Sufi Center, 9440 S.W. 8th Ave., 97219, (503) 245-0270.

VEDANTA SOCIETY OF PORTLAND, 1157 S.E. 55th Ave., 97215, (503) 235-3919.

Community PORTLAND CHRISTIAN COMMUNITY, (Holy Order Of Mans), 3001 N.E., Ainsworth, 97211, (503) 282-0325.

Bookstore LOOKING GLASS BOOKSTORE, 421 S.W. Taylor, 97204, (503) 227-4760.

Salem *Center* 3HO -- GRD, 3545 Belle Vista CT S, 97302, (503) 364-2380.

Foodstore HELIOTROPE NATURAL FOODS, 2060 Market St., N.E., 97301, (503) 362-5487.

Pennsylvania

Coopersburg *Health* CATHERINE J. FROMPOVICH, D.SC., N.D. (NUTRITIONIST), Rd. 1, Chestnut Rd., 18036, (215) 346-8461. Natural Nutrition Instruction.

Easton *Center* THE SEARCH AT NORTHEON FOREST, P.O. Box 517, Hexenkopf Rd., 18042, (215) 258-9559.

Greenville *Center* 3HO -- GRD, 56 1/2 N High, 16125. (412) 588-1373.

Harrisburg *Health* MINISTRY OF HEALING, SCHOOL OF REFLEXOLOGY, Rev. Hilde Maria Frey, 3828 Kramer St., 17109, (717) 545-7155.

Media *Instruction* REV. LANCE W. DOUGLASS, P.O. Box 974, 19063, (215) 566-7834. Author of the Final Testament of the Holy Bible ($1.95).

New Cumberland *Center* 3HO -- GRD, 1810 Bridge St., 17070, (717) 774-2654.

New Foundland *Restaurant* WHITE CLOUD, Rd. 1, P.O. Box 215, 18445, (717) 676-3162.

New Hope *Bookstore* SAGITTARIUS BOOKS, 87 South Main St., 18938, (215) 862-9430. A New Age bookstore for the body, mind and spirit.

Garland of Letters

Philadelphia's Very Unusual Bookstore...

Astrology	Christianity
Spirituality	Mysticism
Cookbooks	Tao
Nutrition	Travel
Healing	Folklore
Sports	American Indian
Health	Occult
Yoga	Psychology
Meditation	Philosophy
Buddhism	Childbirth
Hinduism	Children's
Judaism	Sufism
Zen	Tarot

Yoga Programs...New Age Classical Music (albums/tapes) ...Custom Jewelry Studio...Gravity Guidance Inversion Systems...Spiritual Art...Incense...Annual Yoga Research Society Conference (October)...and more...

A Very Unusual Book Offering...

PRANAYAMA

by Swami Kuvalayananda

AUTHORITATIVE TEXT ON BREATH REGULATION

Comprehensive and reliable sourcebook for students of Pranayama.

Includes eight techniques advocated by the fathers of Hatha Yoga and outlines four varieties taught by Patanjali.

CLOTHBOUND / 170 PAGES 44 ILLUS. $12.00 PREPAID (PA RESIDENTS + 6%) ADD $2.00 FOR POSTAGE & HANDLING.

Garland of Letters Bookstore
527 South Street, Phila., PA 19147 215-923-5946
Open 7 days/week

Philadelphia *Center* SKY FOUNDATION, 527 South St., 19147, (215) 923-5946.

3HO -- GRD, 2621 Sorento Dr., 19131, (215) 477-1483.

AQUARIAN RESEARCH FOUNDATION, 5620 Morton St., 19144, (215) 849-3237, 849-1259.

B'NAI OR, 6723 Emlen St., 19119, (215) 849-5385.

BAWA MUHAIYADDEEN FELLOWSHIP, 5820 Overbrook Ave., 19131, (215) 879-8631. Public discourses, informal talks, prayer, study, work. All are welcome. Free.

SAWAN KIRPAL RUHANI MISSION, 2111 Latonia St., 19146, (215) 389-5430.

THE STROKING COMMUNITY NETWORK, 1247 Palethorp St., 19122.

YOGA RESEARCH SOCIETY, 527 South St., 19147, (215) 923-5946.

Bookstore GARLAND OF LETTERS BOOKSTORE, 527 South St., 19147, (215) 923-5946. Garland of Letters is a highly specialized bookstore with one of the country's most extensive collections of titles in the fields of Yoga, religion, medicine, science and spirituality. The store also features New Age Classical and meditative music tapes and albums, as well as incense, spiritual art, and other practical aide.

Other PHILADELPHIA MUSEUM OF ART, 25th St. and Ben Franklin Parkway, 19103. Tibetan Collection.

Pittsburgh *Center* 3HO -- GRD, 6500 Jackson St., 15206, (412) 363-5948.

State College *Center* INTERNATIONAL SOCIETY FOR KRISHNA CONSCIOUSNESS, 103 E. Hamilton Ave., 16801, (814) 234-1867. Free feasts Fridays & Sundays.

Stroudsburg *Center* THE HOLY SHANKARACHARYA ORDER, Rd. 3, P.O. Box 3430, 18360, (717) 629-0481.

Summit Station *Center* KRIPALU CENTER FOR HOLISTIC HEALTH, P.O. Box 120, 17979 (717) 754-3051.

Westchester *Center* TERRA, INC., 17 W. Biddle St., 19380, (215) 692-6318.

Wyalusing *Center* THE INTERNATIONAL CHURCH OF AGELESS WISDOM, P.O. Box 101, 18853, (717) 746-1864.

Puerto Rico

Rio Piedra *Center* SUFI ISLAMIA RUHANIAT SOCIETY, c/o Carlos Varona, Aquas Calientes 1675, Venus Gardens, 00926.

Rhode Island

Cumberland *Center* THE PROVIDENCE ZEN CENTER, 528 Pound Rd., 02864, (401) 769-6464.

Providence *Center* THE VEDANTA SOCIETY OF PROVIDENCE, 224 Angell St., 02906, (401) 421-3960.

South Carolina

Columbia *Therapy* 221 PICKENS ST., INC., Co-op, 221 Pickens St., 29205, (803) 771-9353.

Mepkin *Monastery* TRAPPIST ABBEY OF OUR LADY OF MEPKIN, 29461, (803) 899-3428. Founded from Gethsemani in 1949 on land donated by the founder of *Time*, magazine, this retreat has 35 monks. Located near the coast, the retreat has large, old, moss-covered trees, lots of mist and fog, and humid summers. There are several hermits. The guest rule is that one can stay only one night unless he has reservations. (All Trappist monastery guesthouses have a three-day limit unless a visitor wants to join.)

Myrtle Beach *Center* MEHER BABA CENTER, P.O. Box 487, 29577, (803) 272-6213, 272-5295.

South Dakota

Marvin *Monastery* BLUE CLOUD ABBEY, 57251, (605) 432-5528. This monastery of 50 monks is a mission for Indians.

Sioux Falls *Center* POLESTAR INTERNATIONAL, 620 South Minnesota St., Suite 1, 57104, (605) 338-2888.

Tennessee

Cookeville *Foodstore* THE GROCERY NATURAL FOODS, 201 South Willow, 38501, (615) 526-4860.

Farner *Media* PEPPERLAND FARM CAMP, Star Route, 37333, (704) 494-2353. A summer adventure in harmony with nature for children and adults. From you I receive to you I give; together we share, in this we live.

Knoxville *Center* 3HO -- GRD, 2917 Deanvue Dr., 37920, (615) 579-0582.

Summertown *Community* THE FARM, 156-C Drakes Ln., 38483, (615) 964-3574.

Texas

Austin *Center* 3HO, 911 Jewel St., 78704, (512) 442-3158.

   Bookstore FIFTH RAY BOOKSTORE, 1002B W. 34th St., 78756, (512) 453-5026, 452-7240, 452-4552. Nonprofit, tax-exempt; metaphysical/occult books.

   GROK BOOKS, 503 W. 17th St., 78701, (512) 476-0116. Complete New Age bookstore with over 10,000 titles in stock.

   Foodstore GOOD FOOD STORE, 1101 W. 5th St., 78703, (512) 472-1942.

   Health AUSTIN AREA HOLISTIC HEALTH ASSOCIATION, P.O. Box 13281, 78711, (512) 476-8125.

Blanco *Monastery* ECUMENICAL MONKS OF ST. BENEDICT, Christ of The Hills Monastery, P.O. Box 1049, 78606, (512) 833-5363.

Corpus Christi *Center* SUFI ORDER OF CORPUS CHRISTI -- KRISHNA & RADHA WEINER, 5314 Milam Dr., 78415, (512) 853-7242.

Monastery HERMITAGE OF OUR LADY OF SOLITUDE, 713 Yorktown Blvd., 78418, (512) 937-2736.

Dallas *Center* 3HO -- GRD, 5702 Gaston Ave., 75214, (214) 827-2947.

THE CENTRE, 5416 Gaston Ave., 75214, (214) 823-0292, 824-8256.

THE WORD FOUNDATION, INC., P.O. Box 18428-S, 75218, (214) 348-5006.

Bookstore UNICORN BOOKSTORE, 2616 Worthington, 75204, (214) 826-2772. New Age & transformational books, gifts, tapes & cards.

Houston *Center* 3HO -- GRD, 1123 Jackson Blvd., 77006, (713) 526-8663.

THE ESOTERIC PHILOSOPHY CENTER, 517 Lovett Blvd., 77006, (713) 526-5998.

Bookstore AQUARIAN AGE BOOKSHELF, 5603 Chaucer, 77005, (713) 526-7770. Thirteen years serving the metaphysical community. All New Age books: holistic health, color, N.L.P., religions, meditation, yoga, self help, self hypnosis tapes, crystals, astrology books, supplies, classes. DISTRIBUTOR FOR DR-70 Astrological computer, computerized chart service. New Agemusic tapes and records.

Foodstore ABRAZOS/JAN SMITH, 3317 Montrose #1025, 77006, (713) 522-9491. Individual selling discounted health items -- local, national, SAVE!

Laredo *Center* SILVA MIND CONTROL, 1110 Cedar Ave., P.O. Box 2249, 78040, (512) 722-6391.

Palestine *Monastery* THE HERMITAGE, Route 3, P.O. Box 99, 75801. Located here are 5 or 6 real hermits who only come together 2 to 3 times a week for Mass celebration and to talk with and counsel visitors. The only rule to live there is that one must have had 7 years of monastic life to assure the sanity of each entering. Most are ex-abbots who have a community to support their needs.

San Antonio *Center* 3HO FOUNDATION OF SAN ANTONIO, 1534 McKinley Ave., 78210, (512) 532-0422.

RAHMA KUMARIS RAJA YOGA CENTER, 710 Marquis, (512) 344-8343.

Spring *Center* THE ROSELAND FOUNDATION, 9722 Galston Ln., 77379, (713) 376-1892.

Utah

Huntsville *Monastery* ABBEY OF OUR LADY OF THE HOLY TRINITY, 84317, (801) 745-3784. Located high in the mountains, this retreat, founded in 1947 from Gethsemani, has 30 monks. They run a book/gift shop, selling their own honey and bread. Many of the old Trappist traditions, such as hand signs, are re-

THINKING AND DESTINY
by Harold W. Percival
Penetrating insight into the deepest mysteries of Man's existence! Illuminates the path of Self-discovery. Basic and advanced information. A complete and comprehensive system of thought with a practical solution for the art of spiritual living.
Your Book Dealer Or
THE WORD FOUNDATION, INC.
P.O. Box 18235-S, Dallas TX 75218

full color chakras poster

15"x 23"

$3 to: Poster
P.O. Box 504
Larkspur
CA 94939

tained here. A good retreat house is available, and reservations are helpful.

Ogden *Center* 3HO -- GRD, 950 27th St., 84403, (801) 399-3614.

Salt Lake City *Center* 3HO -- GRD, 4790 Cherry St., 84107, (801) 266-1624.

  Community SUNBURST -- THE ANCIENT BUILDERS, 77 E. St., 84103, (801) 363-1222.

  Foodstore WHOLE EARTH NATURAL FOODS, 1026 2nd Ave., 84103, (801) 355-7401.

  Counseling THE COTTAGE PROGRAM INTERNATIONAL, Bernell N. Boswell, 736 South, 500 East St., 84102, (801) 532-6185. Holistic approaches to family functioning.

Vermont

Burlington *School* BURLINGTON COLLEGE, Director of Admissions, 90 Main St., 05401, (802) 862-9616.

  Foodstore ORIGANUM NATURAL FOODS, 247 Main St., 05401, (802) 863-6103.

Rutland *Health* ESSENTIAL ALTERNATIVES, 38 Center St., 05701, (802) 773-8834. Futons, natural fiber home furnishings. Brochure $1.

Webster *Monastery* CONVENTUAL PRIORY OF ST GABRIEL THE ARCHANGEL, 05161, (802) 824-5409. There are guesthouses for men and women.

Wilmington *Foodstore* KLARA SIMPLA, 10 Main St., 05363, (802) 464-5257.

Virginia

Alexandria *Center* SAWAN KIRPAL RUHANI MISSION, T.S. Khanna, General Representative, 8807 Lea Ln., 22309, (703) 360-9112.

  Center STELLAR CRYSTAL COMMUNICATIONS, 431 N. Armistead St., Suite 1, 22312, (703) 941-0965, 941-7799.

Alum Ridge THE WINGED HEART HOMESTEAD, Route 67, P.O. Box 47, 24051, (703) 763-3137.

Annandale *Health* AMERICAN HOLISTIC MEDICAL ASSOCIATION, 6932 Little River Tpke., 22003, (703) 642-5880.

Arlington *Center* LEGACY INTERNATIONAL YOUTH PROGRAMS, 822 South Taylor St., 22204, (703) 920-1650.

Batesville *Center* SUFI ISLAMIA RUHANIAT SOCIETY, c/o Beasley, Boxwood Lane Farm, P.O. Box 43, 22924.

Bedford *Ashram* INSTITUTE FOR PRACTICAL IDEALISM & WORLD COMMUNITY/BEDFORD, Route 4, P.O. Box 265, 24523, (703) 297-5982. An environment for guided personal growth. Evolutionary Education, combining the mystical with the practical, seeing daily life as the vehicle for conscious living. Step by step procedure for becoming acquainted with the community and work of the Institute through correspondence, study, and visits over a period of time.

Berryville *Monastery* ABBEY OF OUR LADY OF THE HOLY CROSS, 22611, (703) 955-1425. Founded from St Joseph in 1950 in the Shenandoah Valley, this retreat is 50 miles from Washington, D.C. The Guesthouse is small and quiet. The 38 monks here bake bread for a living.

Bowling Green *Center* SAWAN KIRPAL MEDITATION CENTER: SAWAN KIRPAL RUHANI MISSION, Route 1, P.O. Box 24, 22427, (804) 633-9987.

Buckingham *Center* INTEGRAL YOGA INSTITUTE (IYI), Satchidananda Ashram -- Yogaville, Route 1, P.O. Box 172, 23921.

Charlottesville *Center* 3HO -- GRD, 108A Longwood Dr., 22903, (804) 971-2055.

Hampton *Center* MAHAYANA YOGA ASHRAM, 117 Algonquin Rd., 23661, (804) 722-3487.

Herndon *Center* 3HO FOUNDATION 3HO East Regional H.Q., Guru Ram Das Ashram, 1740 Whitewood Ln., 22070, (703) 435-4411.

McLean COMMUNITY CENTER FOR WHOLISTIC LIVING, 1477 Chain Bridge Rd. #201, 22101, (703) 556-0650.

Newport News *Center* 3HO -- GURURAM KAUR KHALSA, 625 73rd St., 23605, (804) 380-8772.

Rockbridge Baths *Community* STONEYFOOT FARM, INC., R.R. 1, P.O. Box 118, 24473, (703) 348-5036.

Shipman *Center* DHARMA SELF-HELP & ANALYTICAL CENTER, Route 1, P.O. Box 283, 22971, (804) 263-5279.

Virginia Beach *Center* ASSOCIATION FOR RESEARCH AND ENLIGHTEN-MENT, INC. (A.R.E.), P.O. Box 595, 23451, (804) 428-3588.
THE FELLOWSHIP OF THE INNER LIGHT, 620 14th St., 23451, (804) 422-0635.
Bookstore THE HERITAGE STORE, 317 Laskin Rd., P.O. Box 444-G, 23458, (804) 428-0100. Open Monday-Saturday. Edgar Cayce cosmetics, gems, formulas. Metaphysical books. Free pricelist.

Warrenton *Center* KESHAVASHRAM INT'L CENTER, P.O. Box 260, 22186, (703) 347-9009. Center for spiritual pursuits and counseling with emphasis on meditation technique used in ancient Vedic India. Research library.

——Washington——

Ashford *Center* THE NEW AGE FOUNDATION, Cedar Park, 98304.

Bellingham *Bookstore* AKASHA METAPHYSICAL CENTER, 1300 Bay St., 98225, (206) 671-6153. Books, classes, and records.

Deming *Center* RAJ-YOGA MATH AND RETREAT, P.O. Box 547, 98244.

Edmonds *Center* PSYCHOSYNTHESIS CENTER HIGH POINT NORTHWEST, 23700 Edmonds Way, 98020, (206) 775-1090. Training and programs based on psychosynthesis for professional and non-professionals.

Seattle *Center* 3HO -- GRD, 10319 42nd Ave., N.E., 98125, (206) 524-5101.
3HO -- GRD, 5556 31st Ave., N.E., 98105, (206) 522-7723.
3HO -- GRD, 5837 Oberlin Ave., N.E., 98105, (206) 524-3686.
SAKYA TEGCHEN CHOLING CENTER, 5042 18th, 98105, (206) 522-6967.
SUFI ISLAMIA RUHANIAT SOCIETY, Ruh Allah Sufi Center, 6330 5th, N.E., 98115, (206) 524-9137.
VEDANTA SOCIETY OF WESTERN WASHINGTON, 2716 Broadway East, 98102, (206) 323-1228.
VIETNAMESE BUDDHIST TEMPLE AND FOREST RETREAT CENTER, 1651 S. King St., 98144, (206) 323-2669.
Community SEATTLE CHRISTIAN COMMUNITY, (Holy Order Of Mans), 700 E. Pike St., 98122, (206) 329-9411.
Bookstore QUEST BOOKSHOP OF SEATTLE, 717 Broadway E., 98102, (206) 323-4281. LP's and tapes, books on theosophy, healing, psychology and metaphysics. Seattle's finest metaphysical & occult bookshop: Theosophy, religions, astrology, healing, etc.

Health KHALSA HEALTH CENTER, 1305 N.E. 45th St., Suite 205, 98105, (206) 634-3204. Holistic health. Kinesionics.
Media WHOLE LIFE TIMES, 18 Shephard St., 02135, (617) 783-8030. Directory of health care, natural foods, spiritual growth, personal development, national and local products and services.
Spokane *Center* SUFI ISLAMIA RUHANIAT SOCIETY, Garden of Noor, W. 2117 Broadway, 99201, (509) 325-5017.
THE BEAR TRIBE, P.O. Box 9167, 99209.
Vashon *Center* WASHINGTON PSYCHIC INSTITUTE, 10924 S.W. 168th, Route 5, P.O. Box 479, 98070, (206) 463-9671.

West Virginia

Moundsville *Community* THE NEW VRINDABAN COMMUNITY -- ISKCON, Rd. 1, P.O. Box 319, 26041, (304) 843-1600.
Pullman *Health* EMILY ZUCKETT, P.O. Box S, 26421, (304) 659-2301.

Wisconsin

Madison *Center* 3HO -- GRD, Route 5, 3284 #1, Hwy. 88, 53704, (608) 221-4522.
CIRCLE, P.O. Box 9013-N, 53715-0013, (608) 767-2345.
Bookstore SHAKTI BOOKSHOP, 320 State St., 53703, (608) 255-5007. Metaphysical books, futons, records, crystals, and cards.
Spring Green *Center* WILLOW GOLD, Route 3, 53588, (608) 583-5311.
Wilmot *Center* WILMOT CENTER, 30626 112th St., 53192, (414) 862-6968.
Bookstore LOTUS LIGHT BOOKS & INCENSE, 30626 112th St., 53192, (414) 862-6968.
Winter *Center* NARAYANANDA UNIVERSAL YOGA (N.U. YOGA), Route 2, P.O. Box 24, 54896, (715) 266-4963.

Wyoming

Wilson *Foodstore* HERE AND NOW NATURAL FOODS, 1/2 Mile North on Teton Village Rd., 83014, (307) 733-2742. Serving Jackson Hole since 1970.

Canada

Alberta

Calgary *Center* 3HO -- GRD, P.O. Box 5422, Station A, (403) 290-0387.
Edmonton *Center* BESHARA, 11506-87th St., T5B 3M3, (403) 474-9819.

British Columbia

100 Mile House *Center* INTEGRITY INTERNATIONAL, P.O. Box 9, VOK 2EO.
Fernie *Center* STILL MOUNTAIN SOCIETY, R.R. 1, VOB 1MO, (604) 423-6406.
Kootenay Bay *Center* YASODHARA ASHRAM, P.O. Box 9, VOB 1XO, (604) 227-9224.
Nelson *Instruction* KOOTENAY TAI CHI CENTER, 609 Baker St., V1L 4J3, (604) 352-3714.
Vancouver *Center* 3HO -- GRD, 3204 W. 13th Ave., (604) 733-5072.
BRAHMA KUMARIS RAJA YOGA CENTER, 535 50th Ave.
SAWAN KIRPAL SATSANG, 3-1815 W. 4th Ave., V6J 1M4, (604) 731-4777.
Bookstore BANYEN BOOKS, 2685 West Broadway, V6K 2G2, (604) 732-7912. Thoroughest Canadian transformative booksource. Over 7,000 titles. Also New Age records, tapes, cards, prints, illuminations. Open 9-9 daily, 1-9 Sundays.
PHOENIX METAPHYSICAL BOOKS, 10202 152nd St., Surrey, V3R 6N7, (604) 584-7684. Mail order catalog available.
Foodstore LIFESTREAM NATURAL FOODSTORE, 1813 West 4th Ave. Canada's original natural foodstore & restaurant. Complete natural foods selection -- fresh, dried & bulk. Vegetarian.
WOODLANDS NATURAL RESTAURANT & GENESIS FOODSTORE, 2582 West Broadway, V6K 2E9, (604) 733-5411, 734-1822.
Restaurant LIFESTREAM NATURAL FOODSTORE & MOTHER NATURES INN, 1813 West 4th Ave.
WOODLANDS NATURAL RESTAURANT & FOODSTORE, 2582 W. Broadway, Y6K 2E9, (604) 733-5411, 734-1822. Gourmet vegetarian restaurant; seats 85. Canada's largest natural foodstore. Live mellow music on weekends. Reasonable prices.
Victoria *Bookstore* SRI ATMAN BOOKSTORE, 1308 Government St., V8W IYS, (604) 383-3032. Metaphysical and New Age books; mail orders welcome.

Manitoba

Winnipeg *Center* CHAUTAUQUA LEARNING COMMUNITY, 869 Westminister Ave., R3G 1B3. An evolving information exchange.
Bookstore PRAIRIE SKY BOOKS, 871 Westminister Ave., R3G 1B3.

Nova Scotia

Halifax *Foodstore* THE BEAN SPROUT TRADITIONAL FOODS, LTD., 1588 Barrinton St., B3J 126, (902) 423-8630.
Kemptville *Monastery* NOVA NADA CONTEMPLATIVE CENTER, Yarmouth County. This is a Carmelite hermitage in the wilderness. It receives many guests up to six months or a year. See Sedona, Arizona.

Ontario

Ottowa *Center* 3HO -- GRD, 1103 Bank St.
Perth *Center* LANARK HILLS FOUNDATION, R.R. 4, K7H 3C6, (613) 267-4819.
Toronto *Center* 3HO FOUNDATION -- YOGI BHAJAN, 3HO Canada, Guru Ram
   Das Ashram, 346 Palmerston, M6G 2N6, (416) 964-0612.
   BAWA MUHAIYADDEEN FELLOWSHIP, 70 Forest Hill Rd., (416) 961-9906.
   BRAHMA KUMARIS RAJA YOGA CENTER, 19 Lakeview Ave., M6J 3B2,
   (416) 537-3034.
   Bookstore THE FIFTH KINGDOM BOOKSHOP, 77 Harbord St., M5S 1G4,
   (416) 929-5649.
   Restaurant ANNAPURNA VEGETARIAN, 138 Pears Ave., M5R IT2, (416)
   923-6343. Run by members of Sri Chinmoy Centre. Devoted to serve the public.

Quebec

Montreal *Center* SIVANANDA YOGA VEDANTA CENTER, 5178 St. Lawrence
   Blvd., H2T 1R8, (514) 279-3545.
   School LIBRAIRIE L'ESOTERIQUE, 1707 St-Denis, H2X 3K4, 844-1719.
Quebec City *Center* SIVANANDA YOGA VEDANTA CENTER, 270 Chemin Ste.
   Foy., (418) 843-5563, 623-2062.
   3HO -- GRD, 370 Roslyn, Ave., (514) 932-9635.
   INTEGRAL YOGA INSTITUTE, 5425 Park Ave., H2V 4G9, (514) 279-8931. We
   offer French and English courses in the various branches of yoga and vegetarian
   diet.
   SAWAN KIRPAL RUHANI MISSION, 290 Lawrence St., Apt. 239, J4V 2Z4,
   (514) 672-6184.
Val Morin *Center* SIVANANDA ASHRAM YOGA CAMP, H.Q., 8th Ave., JOT
   2RP, (819) 322-3226. Yoga, skiing, meditation, sauna, swimming, guest accomodations, teachers training courses.

Bahamas

Nassau *Center* SIVANANDA ASHRAM YOGA RETREAT, P.O. Box N7550,
Paradise Island, (809) 325-5902. Yoga, quiet beach, meditation, open all year,
teachers training courses.

Mexico

Cuernevaca *Center* SAWAN KIRPAL RUHANI MISSION, Arteaga 10-12, 2-09-30.
Mexico City *Center* UNIVERSAL GREAT BROTHERHOOD, SOLAR LINE
(U.G.B.), International H.Q. Avenida Insurgentes Sur 226, Mexico 7, D.F.

South America

ARGENTINA
Buenos Aires *Center* RAMAKRISHNA ASHRAMA, Gaspar Campos, 1149 Bella Vista, 666-0098.

PERU
Cusco *Community* INTI AYLLU - SOLAR ASHRAM, Ollantaytambo, 4180 (Hotel in Cusco).

Europe

ENGLAND
London *Center* BRAHMA KUMARIS RAJA YOGA CENTER, 96/98 Tennyson Rd., N.W. 6, (328) 2478/4273.
RAMAKRISHNA VEDANTA CENTRE, Unity House, Blind Ln., Bourne End, Bucks, SL8-5LG, 26464.

FRANCE
Gretz *Center* CENTRE VEDANTIQUE RAMAKRICHNA, 1 Boulevard Romain Rolland, 77220 Gretz, 407-03-11.

HOLLAND
Amsterdam *Center* 3HO FOUNDATION -- YOGI BHAJAN, 3HO European Regional H.Q., Guru Ram Das Ashram, Den Texstraat 46, 1017zc, telephone: 24-19-77. *Bookstore* AU BOUT DU MONDE B.V., Singel 313 1012 WJ, (020) 251397. New Age books & records.

SCOTLAND
Findhorn *Center* FINDHORN, The Park, Findhorn, Forres, Morayshire, IV 36 OTZ, telephone: 030932582.

SWEDEN
Hamneda *Center* SCANDINAVIAN YOGA AND MEDITATION SCHOOL, 340 13, (0372) 550 63.

SWITZERLAND
Geneva *Center* CENTRE VEDANTIQUE, 20 Avenue Peschier, 1200 Geneva.

Asia

INDIA
New Delhi *Center* SAWAN KIRPAL RUHANI MISSION, International Headquarters, Living Master Sant Darshan Singh, Kirpal Ashram, 2 Canal Rd., Vijay Nagar, 110009, 718707.

Classified Listings

MAGICIAN

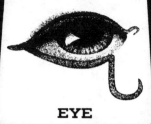
EYE

TUNNEL

WHAT IS
star+gate®?

A game of personal
insights. A tool for self-transformation. A
window on the secret garden. A symbolic system.
A storyteller. A guide. STAR+GATE is all these things. It's
a process for exploring questions, problems and feelings in a
highly visual manner. Ninety-six symbolic cards come with the game, each
beautifully crafted and rich with meaning. Lay out your cards in order on the
Sky Spread Sheet, and see your topic come to life before your eyes. Suddenly
ideas and associations spring to mind, and what has been obscure brightens and becomes clear. STAR+GATE is an exhilarating experience to have by yourself, or with friends.

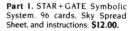

Part 1. STAR+GATE Symbolic System. 96 cards, Sky Spread Sheet, and instructions: **$12.00.**

Part 2. Circle Pattern. 15" × 15" full color map of consciousness, for deeper interpretation of the cards: **$6.00.**

Part 3. Diary of Discovery. 84 page softcover journal of the STAR+GATE experience: **$6.00.**

Order together or separately. Send check or money order payable to: Cloud Enterprises,
P.O. Box 1006C, Orinda, CA 94563. Add 10% for shipping and handling.

BARKSDALE FOUNDATION FOR FURTHERANCE OF HUMAN UNDER-STANDING, P.O. Box 187-NCS, Idyllwild, CA 92349, (714) 659-4676. Self-esteem and stress control books, tapes and workshop seminar kits for individuals or groups. Free catalog.

BOOK LIST, SUN PUBLISHING COMPANY, P.O. Box 4383 (SCG), Albu-querque, NM 87196-4383. Write for our free list of Metaphysical and New Age books.

THE BUILDERS PUBLISHING CO., 77 E. St., Salt Lake City, UT 84103. *Return of the Ancient Builders,* by Norman Paulsen.

CHRISTWAY RESEARCH PUBLICATIONS, Casa de la Luce, P.O. Box 9, Rock-ville, UT 84763. Publishers of books on Gnostic Intuition (See display ad.).

COMMUNITY SERVICE, INC., P.O. Box 243, Yellow Springs, OH 45387. Publi-cations related to building community where you are. Send $1 for sample bi-monthly *Newsletter* and booklist.

FREESTONE PUBLISHING, 10001 E. Zayante Rd., Felton, CA 95018. A small publishing collective presenting *Hygieia, A Woman's Herbal* and *Prenatal Yoga & Natural Birth.* Both successful publications provide information to assist people in utilizing their personal healing process. Other works include *Consciousception* and *Body As Metaphor.* Write for further information.

IDHHB PUBLISHING, P.O. Box 370, Dept. S, Nevada City, CA 95959, (916) 878-8505. Paperback books on Sufism, death and dying, and Angelic invocation: *New American Book of the Dead;* $7.95. *The Gabriel Papers;* $7.95. *Secret Talks with Mr. G.;* $5.95. *Joy of Sacrifice: Secrets of the Sufi Way;* $5.95. *The Angels' Song-book;* $9.95. Plus a series of limited editions -- write for brochure.

JOURNEY PUBLICATIONS, P.O. Box 423, Woodstock, NY 12498. Publishes the complete works of Dr. R.P. Kaushik, who was a philosopher in the original sense of the word -- one who loves truth and enquires into truth. Catalog of books and tapes on the life of self inquiry is available upon request.

KUNDALINI RESEARCH INSTITUTE, 800 N. Park Ave. #5, Pomona, CA 91768. Books on Kundalini Yoga, meditation, conscious cookery, teachings of Yogi Bhajan. Send for free catalog.

LLEWELLYN PUBLICATIONS, P.O. Box 43383, Dept. SC, St. Paul, MN 55102, (612) 291-1970. The major astrological and occult publisher in the U.S.A. Busi-ness offices located above Gnostica Bookstore, the Twin Cities center for New Age activities. We have grown into a total experience of Esoteric Thought at its very best. Visit or write for our free book catalog.

LORIAN PRESS, Books by David Spangler, Dorothy Maclean. P.O. Box 147, Mid-dleton, WI 53562, (608) 833-0455. Music on record and cassette by the New Troubadours and Kathi & Milenko. Lecture tapes, booklets, and more. Write for free catalog or call.

MANDALA PUBLICATIONS, The Journal of Holistic Health, seven volumes. Read articles by leaders in the field who have been successful in using the new modalities of healing. The Holistic Education Series, two volumes: Contains tech-niques used by individuals who are changing the face of education. For brochures: Mandala, P.O. Box 1233, Del Mar, CA 92014, (714) 481-7751.

NATUREGRAPH PUBLISHERS, INC., P.O. Box 1075S, Happy Camp, CA 96039, (916) 493-5353. Books on natural history, American Indian culture, living on the land, crafts, natural foods, and new age thought. Free catalog.

NEW WORLD FRESNO, A quarterly community resources newspaper/directory dis-tributed freely to the greater San Joaquin Valley's new-age, holistic community.

For ad rates, contact: New World Publishing, 20511 S. Blythe Ave., Riverdale, CA 93656.

SAWAN KIRPAL PUBLICATIONS, A division of Sawan Kirpal Ruhani Mission, publishes books and literature by and about the Masters of Surat Shabd Yoga: the living Master Sant Darshan Singh, Sant Kirpal Singh, Hazur Baba Sawan Singh, and other Masters who came in the past. For free catalog and literature, write: Sawan Kirpal Publications, Dept. S, Route 1, P.O. Box 24, Bowling Green, VA 22427.

TIMELESS BOOKS, P.O. Box 60, Porthill, ID 83853. *Kundalini Yoga for the West* by Swami Sivananda Radha. A classic spiritual "road-map" now in paperback ($9.95). *Radha: Diary of a Woman's Search.* A remarkable journal from an extraordinary woman ($6.95). *Mantras: Words of Power* by Swami Sivananda Radha. The complete handbook on the meaning, purpose and practice of Mantra ($5.95). *Gods Who Walk the Rainbow.* Swami Radha's meetings with other spiritual teachers. Entertaining and inspiring. $6.95. To order: please include $0.75 for the first book & $0.30 each additional title. Send for free catalog listing other books and cassette tapes.

WHATEVER PUBLISHING & RISING SUN RECORDS, 158 E. Blithedale, Ste. 4 & 5, Mill Valley, CA 94941, (415) 388-2100. Exquisite books and music for a New Age. Free catalog.

YOGA RESEARCH FOUNDATION, 6111 S.W. 74th Ave., Dept. SC, Miami, FL 33143, (305) 595-5580. Unfold your latent resources. Send for your *free* informative booklet on Integral Yoga and complete list of over 30 fine books covering all aspects of Yoga written by renowned Swami Jyotir Maya Nanada.

Magazines & Periodicals

AGADA, 2020 Essex St., Berkeley, CA 94703, (415) 848-0965. New Jewish literary magazine, invites subscriptions and contributions. Tri-annual publication: $11/yr., $4/single issue. First two issues available now for $7.50.

THE ARIZONA NETWORKING NEWS, P.O. Box 15103, Phoenix, AZ 85060, (602) 957-3322. The Arizona Networking News (formerly known as the Holistic Networking News) wishes to link with its friends and supporters through its resource directory connecting people ideas in Arizona and beyond. Our directory exists to connect Arizona to its resources, the world community to Arizona, and its readership to the practical tools for harmonious living. Our directory will be published four times a year in March, June, September, and December. The Arizona Networking News will not only be a useful resource tool but will contain educational literary contributions for reader interest: People and Events Around the World, In and About Arizona, Accent on Health, Profiles of Networkers, Recipes, Gardening, Book and Tape Reviews, and Addresses of other Networking magazines ... Arizona Networking News is a publication of the International Holistic Center, Inc., a non-profit educational and service organization that believes that the primary obligation of all individuals is to integrate and develop to the fullest degree their physical, mental, emotional, and spiritual potential. Send for detailed information on how to list or subscribe to the Arizona Networking News. Please consider this publication as a way to reach the Arizona Community and beyond. We are part of the world network, and our publication is distributed internationally.

CIRCLE NETWORK NEWS, P.O. Box 9013-N, Madison, WI 53715. Shamanic-Magickal quarterly newspaper. $7/yr.; $2/sample. Free brochure.

COMMON GROUND, 9 Mono Ave., Fairfax, CA 94930, (415) 459-4900. A quarterly directory of resources for personal transformation. Yoga to art schools. $1.50/copy; $4/yr.

FAITHIST JOURNAL, Spiritual bi-monthly magazine $7.50; 2324 Suffolk Ave., Kingman, AZ 86401. Books. Tapes.

FELLOWSHIP IN PRAYER, 20 Nassau St., Suite 250E, Princeton, NJ 08540. A monthly chronicle of individual practices and beliefs by people of all faiths. $12/12 issues.

FIFTH RAY NEWS, 4414 Barrow St., Austin, TX 78751, (512) 452-4552, 452-7240. New Age magazine; Holistic Health journal.

THE FLORIDA PAGES, P.O. Box 330027, Coconut Grove, FL 33133, (305) 756-2003. At last! A New Age Travelers Guide to Florida. Send $1.50 for latest issue.

FRY'S MODERN HUMANS, 22511 Markham, Perris, CA 92370. Mind awareness-expansion courses (California Nursing Board approved) world's most unusual mind power & suppressed invention reports & publications. Send stamp and give interest.

GNOSTICA, P.O. Box 43383, St. Paul, MN 55164, (612) 291-1970. A bi-monthly, 100 page journal of Esoteric Knowledge for the new age. A practical guide to self-development through self-awareness. We explore the tools and the path, a journal that is a journey. Astrology, Tantra, Magic, Mysticism, Parapsychology and more. Write: Llewellyn Publications, Gnostica, P.O. Box 43383, Dept. SG, St Paul, MN 55164. $10/yr.; $2/copy.

HEATHCOTE CENTER, 21300 Heathcote Rd., Freeland, MD 21053, (301) 343-1070. "Ecological Use of the Land".

New in '82

PSYCHIC WHEELBARROW

"The Voice of
All kinds of Everything"

The Inner Barrow:
Quantized Parascience
Trancendental Ontology
Relativity Travellers
Psycho-Etherical Manifestations
Cosmic Consciousness
A Paradigm of Virtue
The Serendipity Network
No Space-Time like the Present
A totally Exclusive Case of Inexplicable
*Aerial Phenomena to the Sublime Nth
degree*
Psionic Devices (Issue II)
    Transducers Reflectors Accumulators
1000 Book Bibliography of Psi
Media List
Star Chart

Available only from:
**Eagle Eye Publications, P.O. Box 97
Reading, RG1 7JD England**

£3.50 $7.00 inc postage and packaging

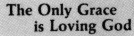

**The Only Grace
is Loving God**

A Statement About the Sacred Message
and Ultimate Teaching Work of
Lee Lozowick

Unique perspectives on Love and enlightenment. A key to transcendence, and a secret passage to the very heart of God

Hohm Press, Box 5839
Prescott Valley, AZ 86312
$5.95 ppd.

INNER QUEST is a free publication; forum and calendar of events for the spiritual community. Within its pages you will discover country-side retreats, wholistic health centers, new age bookstores, businesses, trainings and seminars to unify body, mind and heart. Schools of yoga, martial arts, dance, healing in the arts, therapy and counseling that respect the spiritual dimensions of a person. Advertizing in *Inner Quest* is an excellent way to let people know what you have to share. For information, contact Inner Quest, 3514 Burch Ave., Cincinnati, OH 45208, (513) 244-9066, 871-4950.

THE INNER WAY, P.O. Box 5000, Homeland, CA 92348. A monthly journal promoting Christian meditation. Write for free information.

THE LA LIGHT DIRECTORY, 4026 Beverly Blvd., Los Angeles, CA 90004, (213) 739-0190. A Southern California resource directory for healing, growth and transformation. Over 250 listings in 15 categories including the Arts, Healing & Bodywork, Growth & Psychology, events, Schools, Spiritual Practices, etc. Our Forum Section also carries articles and poetry related to health, personal growth, community service, and planetary transformation. 40,000 copies are distributed quarterly through over 300 outlets including health food stores, bookstores, libraries, and natural food restaurants, etc. Mail subscriptions are available for $1.50/copy, $5/yr. or $9/2 yrs.

LEADING EDGE BULLETIN, Frontiers of Social Transformation, P.O. Box 42247, Los Angeles, CA 90042. $15/yr. ($19 1st class mail). $24/yr. elsewhere (air mail) subscription, only $7!

THE MESSAGE, P.O. Box 396, New Lebanon, NY 12125, (518) 794-8080. Monthly journal of the Sufi Order.

NEW AGE ADVERTIZERS, Reach greater San Joaquin Valley's holistic community through *New World Fresno*, a quarterly newspaper/directory. Contact: New World Publishing, 20511 S. Blythe Ave., Riverdale, CA 93656.

THE NEW ATLANTEAN JOURNAL, 5963 32nd Ave., North, St. Petersburg, FL 33710. The nation's most unique quarterly magazine of the *unknown,* the *unexplained,* and the *unexplored!*

NEW IN '82 -- THE PSYCHIC WHEELBARROW, Left handed material intended to balance right-handedness and lead to the harmony of the Middle Way (Direct Knowledge of the Divine Order). Michael H. MacAireachtaigh, 52 Bedford Rd., Reading, England, RG1 7HS.

OMEGA NEW AGE DIRECTORY, 6418 S. 39th Ave., Phoenix, AZ 85041, (602) 237-3213. Monthly metaphysical newspaper serving Arizona with directory and calendar.

OPEN EDUCATION EXCHANGE, is the largest circulation, free newspaper of events, classes and conferences distributed throughout the San Francisco Bay Area. A positive force for creativity and cultural diversity! For information about listing or advertising, write P.O. Box 5461, Berkeley, CA 94705. Please send $1 to receive a copy by mail.

PORTLAND REFLECTION, P.O. Box 12290, Portland, OR 97212. Annual local directory of personalized services, mostly in holistic health, published each March. $2/copy.

PSYCHIC OBSERVER, P.O. Box 8606, Washington, D.C. 20011, (202) 723-4578. Bi-monthly journal, established 1938. Parapsychology, spiritual development, frontiers of science. Subscription $9.50 (sample issue $1).

REINCARNATION REPORT, P.O. Box R, Dept. SC, Malibu, CA 90265. Full size, major magazine devoted exclusively to reincarnation. Sample issue ($2).

THE RISING SUN, "Insights for Positive Living", 5911-A Winsome Ln., Houston, TX 77057, (713) 780-3631. Monthly tabloid including human potential, health and related subjects. Distribution: Houston and Dallas. Subscription: $10/yr. Rate sheet available on request.

SAT SANDESH: THE MESSAGE OF THE MASTERS, Monthly magazine on all aspects of the spiritual life. Featured are discourses by the world's foremost exponent of Surat Shabd Yoga, Sant Darshan Singh. Also: articles by Sant Kirpal Singh and Baba Sawan Singh, poetry, photos, illustrated story for children ($14/yr.). Sample on request. Write: Dept. S, Rt. 1, P.O. Box 24, Bowling Green, VA 22427.

SERIATIM: THE JOURNAL OF ECOTOPIA, 122 Carmel, El Cerrito, CA 94530, (415) 843-5167. Pacific Northwest stable-state economy; regional self-reliance; new lifestyles; possible futures.

THE SUN, 412 West Rosemary St., Chapel Hill, NC 27514, (919) 942-5282. The Sun is a Magazine of Ideas published in Chapel Hill, North Carolina. It prints a variety of essays, articles, fiction, poetry. Contributors have included Ram Dass, Robert Bly, Patricia Sun, Thaddeus Golas, Hugh Prather. *CoEvolution Quarterly* says, "The Sun tries to print the truth. Not the news or the latest, but *the* truth, Mr. Truth, the Queens of All Our Dreams. And it does." Subscriptions are $15/yr. (12 issues).

TRANSFORMATION TIMES, P.O. Box 12290, Portland, OR 97212. Monthly calendar/news magazine for Portland's personal growth/holistic health/new age community. $9/yr. subscription; $0.75/copy by mail.

WHOLE LIFE TIMES, 18 Shephard St., Brighton, MA 02135, (617) 783-8030. Directory of health care, natural foods, spiritual growth, personal development, national and local products and services.

WOMEN AND WISDOM SPIRIT GUIDE, A quarterly devoted to a new manifestation of spirituality for our time, and to the role of women healers, teachers, channels and spiritual leaders in the new age. $10/yr. 155 Bank St., 12th Fl., New York, NY 10014, (212) 807-1222.

Books

100 WAYS TO DEFEAT SATAN, by Vernon Howard ($2). Newlife, P.O. Box 684-QP, Boulder City, NV 89005.

1983 MOON SIGN BOOK, As the tides ebb and flow under the ever watchful gaze of the moon so does our earth and our individual lives. *The Moon Sign Book* is a 500 page annual of guidance based on this ancient truth. Not only for the farmer but everyone sensitive to their environment and interested in the creation of balance and self-improvement. Moon Sign Book, P.O. Box 43383, Dept. SC, St. Paul, MN 55164. $2.50/copy.

AMERICAN BUDDHIST DIRECTORY, Listing Buddhist groups and temples throughout North America. $12. American Buddhist Movement, 301 W. 45th St., New York, NY 10036.

AN INTRODUCTION TO MASTERY by Michael Childs. Unlocks secrets to wisdom. Source Unlimited, 7 Oak Ave., Kentfield, CA 94904, (415) 459-5996.

AURA BOOKS, 7911 Willoughby Ave., Los Angeles, CA 90046, (213) 656-9373. *The Jesus Mystery of Lost Years and Unknown Travels* by Janet Bock. $6.95 plus $1 postage.

BEYOND THE MIND: TOWARDS THE UNKNOWN, Books by renowned spiritual teacher DADA. Explores man's psychological predicament, the mechanism of mind, and the breakthrough for new-dimensional consciousness. Write to Dada Center Publications, 2319 West Dry Creek, Healdsburg, CA 95448.

BOOK OF CHILES, Forthcoming, P.O. Box 1067, Berkeley, CA 94701. Everything you've wanted to know about peppers and more.

CONVERSATIONS WITH JOHN ed. by David Spangler. A spiritual perspective on the 80's, communicating hope for the future, the drawbacks of predictions and the *real* dangers of the 80's. Highly recommended. 32 pages. $3 postpaid, Lorian, P.O. Box 147S, Middleton, WI 53562 (write for free catalog).

CORE OF CREATIONS, Syzygy, P.O. Box 18-D, Rush, NY 14543. Profound scientific model generates evolution, quantum physics, light, time, consciousness, more. $7.50 guaranteed.

CREATIVE POWER by Rhea Zuessmann Bernstein. Understanding this book guarantees an increase in your creative ability. Man's true purpose in the cosmic plan revealed. New theory of discipleship motivation. The source of a spiritual master's power to inspire his followers. Reveals the intuitional process that may have led the Master Jesus to his revolutionary concept of sacrifice and divine sonship. $5. Meditation Research Press, P.O. Box 517c, Yardley, PA 19067.

D.E. WHELAN-SAMADHI, P.O. Box 729, Newberry, FL 32669, (904) 472-3451. Metaphysical books, used, rare. Occult, astrology, herbology, homeopathy. Search service.

FASTING, LONGEVITY, AND IMMORTALITY, Charles Johnson, 213 pages. Fasting: Spiritual Discipline, Survival Skill, Health Regimen, Therapeutic Technique. Extensive personal experiences, research. Literature survey. Speculations about Immortality. More. $3. Survival-S, Turkey Hills, Haddam, CT 06438.

THE GROWTH OF A PSYCHIC, A diary about what happens when psychic development occurs. 12 Spring St., Eureka Springs, ARK 72632. $9.95.

HOW TO DEFEND YOURSELF WITHOUT EVEN TRYING by Dr. Terry Chitwood (holistic psychologist/martial arts expert). Chapters on telepathy, devotion, quality thought, inner energy (ki), nonviolence, and more. Ten day money back guarantee. $6.95 postpaid. Polestar Publications, 620 South Minnesota, Suite 1, Sioux Falls, SD 57104.

HOW TO USE YOUR POWER OF VISUALIZATION by Emily Lyons ($9.95). Lyons Visualization Series, 22175 Shoreline, Marshall, CA 94940. A workbook designed to help you find the silence and untapped creative resources within yourself.

INTERNATIONAL YOGA GUIDE, Yoga Research Fnd., 6111 S. W. 74th Ave., Dept. SC, Miami, FL 33143, (305) 595-5580. Discover the harmony of Integral Yoga with this monthly magazine of the practical essays and high spiritual teachings of renowned Swami Jyotir Maya Nanada. Send for your *free* informative booklet.

JUNGIAN-SENOI DREAMWORK MANUAL, 1525 J Shattuck Ave., Berkeley, CA 94709, (415) 848-0311. State-of-the-Art 35 techniques, 302 pages, $15.85.

KAREZZA, A reproduction of the Original Copyrighted 1903. Harmony Horizons, Inc., P.O. Box 663, Franklin, MI 48025.

KUNDALINI YOGA, Lotuslight, P.O. Box 2, Wilmot, WI 53192. $3.75 postpaid.

LEAD ON! THE COMPLETE HANDBOOK FOR GROUP LEADERS, Easy to use guide answers every leader's questions. $5.95. Free catalog of human growth books: Impact, P.O. Box 1094, San Luis Obispo, CA 93406.

LEARN TO HELP YOURSELF and others to become healthier and happier. Read *Dianetics: The Modern Science of Mental Health* by L. Ron Hubbard. Send $3.95 to Dianetic Center, 120 Giralda, Dept. NCS, Coral Gables, FL 33134.

LEGENDS OF ANELLEH by Roberta Herzog, P.O. Box 808, Wyalusing, PA 18853. Mystical allegories of 200 year old woman Initiate as she is taught by The Great White Brotherhood. $7.95 postpaid.

LEONARD ORR, P.O. Box 234, Sierraville, CA 96126, (916) 994-8484, 994-3677. Author of *Rebirthing* ($7) and *Physical Immortality* ($10) and money books and tapes.

THE NEW AGE BROWN RICE COOKBOOK, The array of meat-less recipes from

The Lion Roars

"This is one idea you
will find in Vedanta
bursting like a bombshell
upon ignorance:
Be fearless."

*Books that stress the underlying
unity of all religions.*

•

Write or call for
a free catalog.

Vedanta Press *and Bookshop*
1946 Vedanta Place, Dept. C
Hollywood, California 90068
213/465-7114

Self-esteem & Stress Control
Programs

Barksdale

THE BARKSDALE FOUNDATION
Post Office Box 187NCS
Idyllwild, CA 92349
Phone: (714) 659-4676

**ATTN: Retailers, Co-Ops
& Other Volume Book Users**
Nutri-Books is the **ONE** source
for over 2,000 health-related
books you can sell. Magazines,
charts & tape cassettes are also
available. All current, popular.
*Write us on your business
letterhead for FREE catalog.*
NUTRI-BOOKS
World's Largest Supplier of Health-Related Books
BOX 5793 • Denver, CO 80217

PEACE LAGOON

**SACRED SONGS
OF THE SIKHS**
compiled by
Sardarni Premka Kaur
Intro. by Yogi Bhajan
The wisdom of Guru Nanak
and others in beautiful verse.
Equivalent to Bhagavad Gita
and Tao Te Ching.
$6.00 + $1.50 post.
Spiritual Community Publ.
Box 1067 NC
Berkeley, CA 94701

THE BOOK OF CHILES
Coming
soon

History-recipes
herbal anecdotes
of Capsicum:
cayenne, chile,
jalapenos, paprika.

for info send SAE
**CHILES
Box 1067 NC
Berkeley, CA
94701**

breakfast to dessert is such that one will never again be able to think of rice as a mere addition to a meal. Send $7.95 plus $1.50 postage to Sea Wind Press, Dept. R-31, P.O. Box 222964, Carmel, CA 93922.

NO MORE SECRETS: PROTECTING YOUR CHILD FROM SEXUAL ASSAULT, Sensitive, warm and honest guide for parents. $3.95. Free catalog of human growth books: Impact, P.O. Box 1094, San Luis Obispo, CA 93406.

PORTRAIT OF PERFECTION, A Pictorial Biography of Kirpal Singh. A remarkable record of the life and impact of Kirpal Singh -- sponsor organizer of the first World conference on the Unity of Man, and great Master of Sant Mat. 313 pages, 390 photographs, 9 x 12 inch hardbound. $19.95 plus $2 postage. Sawan Kirpal Publications, Dept. S, Rt. 1, P.O. Box 24, Bowling Green, VA 22427.

REBUILDING: WHEN YOUR RELATIONSHIP ENDS, Love lost? Here are 15 "rebuilding blocks" for putting your life back together. Free catalog of human growth books: Impact, P.O. Box 1094, San Luis Obispo, CA 93406.

THE REST OF MY LIFE, Extraordinary, upbeat journal of life inside a nursing home by Laura Hunter. Send $7.97 for gift-quality larger print paperback to Growing Pains Press, 22 Fifth St., 204-NCS, Stamford, CT 06905.

SHIVAMBU KALPA, 144 pages. Taken from the holy Sanskrit of Damar Tantra. Medicine to heal ones self with. Send $6. There is Light, P.O. Box 15041, Pittsburgh, PA 15237.

SIDEREAL BOOKS, 24 Colorado, Highland Park, MI 48203, (313) 883-1012. Solunar Research Publications and more. Contact John Van Zandt, 24 Colorado, Highland Park, MI 48203.

SIVA'S COSMIC DANCE, For a free copy of this introductory booklet on the world's most ancient religion, Saivite Hinduism, write to: Himalayan Academy, P.O. Box 11011, Dept. SCG, San Francisco, CA 94101.

SPIRITUAL AWAKENING by Darshan Singh. This is a direct, powerful and moving collection of talks which heralds the Coming Golden Age, and presents a practical pathway to spiritual fulfillment. 300 pages. $4.95 plus $0.75 postage to: Sawan Kirpal Publications, Dept. S, Rt. 1, P.O. Box 24, Bowling Green, VA 22427.

SRI AUROBINDO'S WORKS, Books on Yoga, philosophy, physical transformation, health, education by Sri Aurobindo, Mother and others. Free catalog and sample copy of quarterly: Matagiri, Mt. Tremper, NY 12457.

STRESS MAP: LOCATING YOUR PRESSURE POINTS, Find and relieve stress in six key areas of your life. $5.95. Free catalog of human growth books: Impact, P.O. Box 1094, San Luis Obispo, CA 93406.

SUN MAN MOON INC, P.O. Box 5084, 9191 Regatta Dr., Huntington Beach, CA 92646, (714) 962-8945. Dream study materials, manual, journal, consultations, lectures, seminars. Free details.

SUNBURST: A PEOPLE, A PATH, A PURPOSE, Weaver Books, Big Springs Ranch, Wells, NV 89835. Dusk & Willow Weaver's award-winning, personal story of *Sunburst,* perhaps the most provocative spiritual community in America today. Includes 30 pages photos and an informative appendix of other longstanding, broadbased communities. Publisher: Avant. Perfectbound 6X9, 192 pages. $9.95. We pay tax and shipping.

TO HEAR THE ANGELS SING by Dorothy Maclean. The success of the Findhorn gardens arose in part from Dorothy's telepathic contact with the overlighting intelligences or "angels" of nature. This is her story and theirs as well. 217 pages. Send $8 postpaid to Lorian, P.O. Box 147S, Middleton, WI 53562 (write for free catalog).

UNDERSTANDING BODY CHEMISTRY AND HAIR MINERAL ANALYSIS, $5.95 postpaid. CJ Frompovich Publications, RD. 1, Chestnut Rd., Coopersburg, PA 18036. The most comprehensive book on minerals, nutrition, hair analysis. 128 pages. ISBN 0-935322-18-3.

YOGA OF KNOWLEDGE, Lotuslight, P.O. Box 2, Wilmot, WI 53192. $6.50 postpaid.

YOGA OF LOVE, Lotuslight, P.O. Box 2, Wilmot, WI 53192. $4.50 postpaid. Retail -- wholesale.

Records & Tapes

ASHRAM BOOKS & CRAFTS, P.O. Box 9, Kootenay Bay, B.C. VOB1XO Canada, (604) 227-9224. Complete line spiritual, self-help and inspirational books. Harmoniums, tapes.

CARMEL SOUNDS, 620 14th St., Virginia Beach, VA 23451, (804) 422-0635. Wide selection (including all books and tapes by Paul Solomon) on spiritual, human potential, holistic health, Qabalah, Bible, etc. Send for catalog.

CASSETTES FOR YOUR BODY, MIND, AND SPIRIT, Free information. Polestar Publications, 620 South Minnesota, Suite 1, Sioux Falls, SD 57104.

CHANGES, P.O. Box 2598, Santa Cruz, CA 95060. Cassettes to get you high, aware, conscious. Send for list.

EMERALD WEB, 29 Canterbury Ln., Unionville, CT 06085. Beautiful, celestial, progressive music. Flutes and synthesizers. Five records or cassettes. $9 each. "A visionary voyage."

GUIDED VISUALIZATIONS, P.O. Box 28504-S, San Jose, CA 95159. Visualization exercises, Healing Imagery, Creative Dreaming and more! Cassette tapes. Free Catalog.

GURU RAM DAS PUBLICATIONS & RECORDINGS, P.O. Box 13054, Phoenix, AZ 85002, (602) 252-0077. Real-Time cassette duplication service. Write for free New Age music catalog.

HANUMAN FOUNDATION TAPE LIBRARY, P.O. Box 61498, Santa Cruz, CA 95061, (408) 476-8692. We offer cassette recordings of Ram Dass and others' talks at the low price of $3/hour. Send postage stamp for free catalog.

HEARTSONG PRODUCTIONS, 1775 Old Country Rd. #9, P.O. Box A, Belmont, CA 94002. Meditative and deeply relaxing chanting tapes sung by Rabbi David Zeller. Send for brochure.

HEAVENSONG RECORDINGS, P.O. Box 605-S, Corte Madera, CA 94925, Songs of infinite love, joy, and oneness by Maitreya Stillwater. Meditation music by Maloah Stillwater. Send for free catalog.

HIS HOLINESS THE DALAI LAMA'S, Lectures at Harvard, 1981. *Emptiness and Great Compassion* twelve 90 minutes cassettes. For information: American Institute of Buddhist Studies, 86 College St., Amherst, MA 01002.

HYPNOSIS, MEDITATION, SLEEP PROGRAMMING TAPES, over 200 titles by metaphysical author Dick Sutphen. Valley of the Sun Publishing, P.O. Box 38, Dept. SC, Malibu, CA 90265.

INTERFAITH, P.O. Box 12212, San Diego, CA 92109, (714) 272-0280. New thought music and cassettes.

JAY STEINBERG TAPES, P.O. Box 2282, Sedona, AZ 86336, (602) 282-2373. High quality, low cost cassette tapes: Medicine Wheel, Ancient Memories, New Age Humor and Integrity.

JOEL ANDREWS, c/o Franklin, 899 Green #502-S, San Francisco, CA 94133, (415) 441-7155. Tapes and records of healing music channeled from higher sources for meditation, massage, chakras, dance, painting, therapy. For free catalog, send stamped, addressed envelope.

COME JOIN US!

Be in the next edition (#6)
of NEW CONSCIOUSNESS
SOURCEBOOK
due March 1984.

Send for listing and
advertising information:
Spiritual Community Publications
PO Box 1067 Berkeley, CA 94701

Music

Music for movement. Transcendental and meditative music for relaxation. Inspirational and celebrative music... and so much more!

We're **FORTUNA Records and Tapes** and we represent an incredible spectrum of over 250 titles created for your inner and outer journey.

Iasos, Deuter, Halpern, Kitaro, Vangelis, and Paul Winter are just a few of the hundreds of artists from around the world. We are proud to offer this music on both domestic and imported recordings.

Our long awaited, music-packed, 8½x11 catalog featuring over 100 photos and a complete description of each recording is available for only $2 postage paid. Your catalog purchase is cheerfully credited toward your first music order.

Expand your music horizons... write for your **FORTUNA Records and Tapes** catalog today!

FORTUNA
Records and Tapes
Box 1116 SB, Novato, CA 94947
(415) 892-3669

Wholesale inquiries invited. We distribute worldwide!

KUNDALINI YOGA, Dynamic 60 minute tapes. Write: Khalsa Cassettes, 225 E. 5th St., New York, NY 10003.

MEDITATION TAPES, Guided meditations and relaxation led by Acharya Sushil Kumarji, Jain Monk and master of Arhum Yoga. Etherial Electronic music, "Chakra Meditation". Wind sounds, "Inward Journey to the 3rd Eye". $9/tape (postage included). 722 Tompkins Ave., Staten Island, NY 10305.

NEW AGE CASSETTES!/LARGE SELECTION, For free catalog, send SASE. Conference recording and specialized services also available. Pathmark Tapes, P.O. Box 7251, Grand Rapids, MI 49510.

NIMBUS MUSIC, P.O. Box 10321, Bainbridge Island, WA 98110. Lute and classical guitar music is beautiful. Send $0.25 for brochure of recordings.

ON WINGS OF SONG, Spring Hill Music, P.O. Box 124, Ashby, MA 01431. This music will live in your heart. Robbie Gass's moving lyrics illumined by 25 voice choir. Free brochure.

PYRAMID DISTRIBUTORS, 527 Hill St., Santa Monica, CA 90405, (213) 399-2222. Music for a New Age. Over 300 records and tapes by various artists for relaxation, meditation or just to create a pleasant space. Send for our complete catalog.

SATSANG TAPES, Dept. S, 115 South O St., Lake Worth, FL 33460. Talks on cassette by Sant Darshan Singh and Sant Kirpal Singh. Free catalog.

SELF-HELP TAPES based on yoga. Titles include: Fundamentals of Yoga I & II, Stress Management, Anti-Insomnia Program; Stretching for Runners or Athletes, Shape-Up!!! and others. Narrated by yoga specialist and author, Sylvia Klein Olkin. Send for free brochure. Be Healthy Education Co., 4 Lauren Ln., Norwich, CT 06360.

SHARED VISIONS, Lectures, workshops, seminars, concerts. Send for calendar of events, tape catalog and radio schedule of Will Noffke's *New Horizons* interviews heard on KPFA-FM 94, Fridays at noon. 2512 San Pablo Ave., Berkeley, CA 94702, (415) 845-2216.

SOUNDINGS OF THE PLANET, P.O. Box 43512SG, Tucson, AZ 85733, (602) 628-9658. Cooperative effort of musicians and media artists, providing an alternative system for producing and distributing peaceful, healing music to people wishing to "Reprogram their Soundspace." The music has been shown to enhance many forms of conscious evolutionary practice, i.e., yoga, meditation, healing, art, dance, birthing, or simply creating peaceful lifestyles. In addition to the instrumental tapes (Desert Dawn Song, Shambala, Celestial Flute and many more), a series of informational tapes is being created to share planetary wisdom. A Network of Consciousness is forming. Please send for our free catalog.

SPIRITUAL AND PERSONAL DEVELOPMENT CASSETTES, Free information. Polestar Publications, 620 South Minnesota, Suite 1, Sioux Falls, SD 57104.

STARSONG HEALTH & RELAXATION RECORDS & TAPES, P.O. Box 827, Kihei, Maui, HI 96753. Music that Heals & Soothes. Largest selections, special discounts. Send $0.75 for 12 page catalog. Wholesale availability.

TAPES OF GUIDED IMAGERY, Creative visualization and cosmic music for relaxation, meditation, massage, art, self-healing, etc. Descriptive catalog is $1. Rockwater Tapes, P.O. Box 5861, Santa Fe, NM 87502, (505) 988-1646.

TIRED OF THE SAME OLD SILENT NIGHT?, Try Festival of Light, an album of fresh, joyous Christmas songs by the New Troubadours, cassette or record $9 postpaid. Write for free catalog: Lorian, P.O. Box 147S, Middleton, WI 53562.

YOGA RESEARCH FOUNDATION, 6111 S.W. 74th Ave., Dept. SC, Miami, FL 33143, (305) 595-5580. Hundreds of tapes on the Integral Yoga teachings of Swami Jyotir Maya Nanda. Practical topics -- Mind control, overcoming depression, unfolding talents, Vedanta scriptures. Send special request. *Free* booklet.

AURA PRODUCTIONS, 7911 Willoughby Ave., Los Angeles, CA 90046, (213) 656-9373. 92 minute color film, *The Lost Years of Jesus.*

AURA PRODUCTIONS, 7911 Willoughby Ave., Los Angeles, CA 90046, (213) 656-9373. New Age Films, 16mm and S-8 for rent and sale: *The Lost Years of Jesus, Sai Baba, Aura of Divinity,* and others. Send for free catalog.

CORNERSTONE FILMS & TAPES OF INSIGHT, Spiritual, Psychic and Psychological Media, 470 Park Ave., South, Dept. LA, New York, NY 10016, (212) 684-5910. Write for free catalog all the teaching of Today-Tomorrow.

EMERALD WEB, 29 Canterbury Lane, Unionville, CT 06085. "Photonos": Beautiful moving mandalas, lasers, ethereal computer images on video tape (3/4, VHS, Beta) accompanying "Emerald Web's" celestial music. "A visionary voyage."

GOLDEN POINT, P.O. Box 784, Point Reyes, CA 94956. Films, Video Tapes, Cosmic Greeting Cards for Planetary Harmony. Send $1 for catalog.

PHOENIX PRODUCTIONS, P.O. Box 303, Glen Ellen, CA 95442, (707) 996-2536. Purpose is to create films and videotapes which instill in the viewer a desire for the fulfillment of her/his greatest potentials, and facilitate one's interrelatedness to the rest of the planet. Phoenix productions features: A Production center for *Kinetic Arts* (film and video) located in the wine country near San Francisco. It features State-of-the-Art Film Editing (8 plate flatbed) and Sound Transfers, plus Cinematography, Videography, and Sound Recording. For information on our Services and Films and Video Works contact Stephen Ashton, P.O. Box 303, Glen Ellen, CA 95442, (707) 996-2536.

QUEST FILMS, The Theosophical Society In America, P.O. Box 270, Wheaton, IL 60187, (312) 668-1571. The purpose of the Quest Film series is to encourage an understanding of man and his place in the universe. Selected 16 mm film titles: *How Many Lifetimes, Universal Flame, Esoteric Nature of Music, Holistic Health, Therapeutic Touch.* Noogenesis is a BA program in Transpersonal Psychology offered through Vermont Institute of Community Involvement, a small alternative college in Burlington, Vermont. We offer a wholistic approach to education with a program structure flexible enough to meet the individual needs of each student's own quest for knowledge and sense of purpose.

SAWAN KIRPAL MOVIES, Dept. S, 3 Floridian Ct., Long Beach, NY 11561. Films of Sant Darshan Singh, Sant Kirpal Singh and Baba Sawan Singh.

SAWAN KIRPAL SLIDE SERVICE, Dept. S, 6303 60th Pl., Riverdale, MD 20840. Slide sets of Sant Darshan Singh and Sant Kirpal Singh. Free catalog.

SAWAN KIRPAL VIDEOTAPES, Dept. S, Rt. 1, P.O. Box 24, Bowling Green, VA 22427. VHS and Beta Mode, videotapes of Sant Darshan Singh and Sant Kirpal Singh.

WHITE BUFFALO MULTIMEDIA, P.O. Box 73, Woodstock, NY 12498, (914) 246-9995. Extensive repertoire of multimedia programs on New Age/cultural themes; educational entertainment. Tape & slide resources for purchase. Free catalog.

WORLD TELEVISION, 1200 South La Cienega Blvd., Los Angeles, CA 90035, (213) 748-3898, 657-6978. New Age communication services via the new home video recorder.

Wherever one feels at home with peace and tranquility, it is there that he finds his homeland. Wherever I go I find my Tibet.— Dalai Lama

ROCKWATER TAPES & BOOKS

SEAPEACE .... Georgia Kelly
SPECTRUM SUITE .. **S. Halpern**
ANCIENT ECHOES ..... G. Kelly
& Steven Halpern
PATHLESS PATH . **Charles Lloyd**
BREATHE .... Allen/Bernoff

All of the above titles on cassette or album.
Rapid mail-order service anywhere! To order,
send $10 for each title (ppd.) to: **ROCK-
WATER TAPES & BOOKS, P.O. Box 5861,
Dept.S, Santa Fe, NM 87502**

Complete descriptive catalog free with order,
25¢ alone. Hundreds of the finest tapes, records, and books, often difficult to find locally.

***ROCKWATER: YOUR NEW AGE
MAIL-ORDER COMPANY***

STEVEN HALPERN.
MUSIC FOR MIND, BODY & SPIRIT.

Steven Halpern has established a
reputation of excellence for his
pioneering work in the soothing,
uplifting, and healthful applications
of sound.
 The recordings in his **"Anti-Frantic
Alternative™ Series"** (available on
cassettes and LPs) feature innovative
combinations of grand piano, flute,
harp, and electric keyboards.
 His music is widely used in ashrams,
yoga classes, and private homes
around the world.
 To find out how HALPERN SOUNDS
can add to your life, send for our free
catalog or ask about our demo tape
today. Write to: HALPERN SOUNDS,
Dept. SC, 1775 Old County Road, #9
Belmont, CA 94002.

LISTEN TO THE SOUNDS OF THE NEW AGE

**600 Cassette Tape Titles
A 72-Page Catalog**

Conversations with
"Leading Edge" thinkers.

*"Thanks to Michael Tom's
warm and engaging interviewing style,
you get the essence of the person, a
rounded view . . . indespensable for
building up a tape library."*
New Age Magazine
July, 1982

 Your name on our mailing list is
free: the 72-page catalog is only $1.
Send to: New Dimensions Radio,
267 States St., San Francisco, CA
94114. Or call (415) 621-1126.

MY MIND IS AN OCEAN

**Poems, Koans and
Prophecies from children
96pp Pbk $2.50 + $1.00 post**

The Sun is a battle ship that has ray
guns. The Moon is a lady that's drawing
in the ocean. The winter is an old man
with a frozen beard. Time is a tree that
ticks and a leaf falls off. My Mind is an
ocean that has all
these things.
Bobby I. (9 yrs)

Spiritual
Community
Publications
Box 1067 NC
Berkeley CA
947701

CHURCH OF THE HEALING WAY, Interfaith, 11050 Lorne St., Sun Valley, CA 91352. Elizabeth Johnston, D. Min Pastor. Inspirational Services with music and singing are held every Sunday evenings at 7:00 pm -- Metaphysics is taught here. God through Jesus has brought miraculous healings in our church in Sun Valley. Prayer line (213) 501-4644, 9-11 am, Monday-Friday.

CI.CA.MO. CENTRE OF EXPANSION OF THE NEW AGE, Via Oxila 2, Novara, Italy 28100, 0321 29354. Also bookstore, foodstore and restaurant.

ECOPEACE MEDIA CENTER, P.O. Box 1555, Beaverton, OR 97075, (503) 635-9421. Accepting donations for vital eco-environmental projects and direct action.

FLORIDA STATE NEW AGE MAGAZINE "CONTINUUM", Deep/Tissue intuitive touch bodywork massage stress management -- integral counseling celebrative -- meditative retreats with wooded pathways and motel accommodations. Rama Bhagwan, Dr. Chitta Ranjan Goswami, Human Potential Centre, 1-904-252-6413.

GFU-UNIVERSAL GREAT BROTHERHOOD-SOLAR LINE, Insurgentes Sur 226, Mexico 7 DF, (5) 254480. HQ. World-wide cultural institution working for human re-education to prepare the initiatic foundations of the new Aquarian Age.

HOLYEARTH FOUNDATION, P.O. Box 873, Monte Rio, CA 95462. Dedicated to furthering the evolution of consciousness through personal and planetary transformation. We work to utilize these times of crisis as a doorway to a new more holistic world for all beings. Write for information about seminars, tapes, publications & audio-visual materials, and about joining the *Earthstewards Network.*

INSTITUTE FOR THE DEVELOPMENT OF THE HARMONIOUS HUMAN BEING, P.O. Box 370 Dept. S, Nevada City, CA 95959. Sufi community and center of Angelic invocation. Workshops, conferences, terminal counseling, affiliated study-circles, publications. Write for brochure.

INSTITUTE OF BEHAVIORAL KINESIOLOGY, P.O. Drawer 37, Valley Cottage, NY 10989, (914) 268-5144. Seminars and publications detailing results of BK research into all aspects of the enhancement of *Life Energy,* including psychobiological aesthetics. Emphasis on music and creative communication.

THE INTERGROUP COMMITTEE, P.O. Box 5105, Beverly Hills, CA 90210, (213) 379-9990, (714) 447-4170, 460-1972. The Space Brothers dissertations on the science of healing, 55 volumes of the Unarius library also on cassette tape that explains the inner nature of spiritual man; the science of energy. Send for literature.

THE JESHUA BEN JOSEF SCHOOL OF THE HEART, P.O. Box 2097, Eugene, OR 97402, (503) 342-8069. Love worketh all things man could wish for or conceive of, and more besides.

JOIN CLUB SPECTRUM, Have Fun. Learn a lot and make money, 959 Desoto Ln., Foster City, CA 94404, (415) 349-6946.

KAGYU DRODEN KUNCHAB, 1892 Fell St., San Francisco, CA 94117, (415) 386-9656. A Kargyupa center founded by the Venerable Kalu Rinpoche for the teaching and practice of Mahayana and Vajrayana Buddhism. Lama Lodru is Rinpoche's representative in San Francisco. Practice includes mantra, visualization, and form and formless meditation. Nyung-Ne is observed each full moon. Advanced students do foundation practices.

MADRE GRANDE MONASTERY, Star Route 118, Dulzura, CA 92017, (714) 468-3810. Ecology-oriented, land-based community, living in harmony with Nature, is seeking new residents with practical skills, financial integrity, existing businesses, creativity and Love. For information please write or send resume.

MORNING GLORY COMMUNITY, 2700 Oaker, Arnold, MO 63010, (314) 296-7846. Classes in Polarity & Esalen massage.

NEW THOUGHT CHURCH OF HAWAII, Religious Science and Unity publications. P.O. Box AQ, Kailua-Kona, HI 96740.

SPIRITUAL HIERARCHY INFORMATION CENTER, INC., Free primer on spiritual hierarchy-blue print for New Age. Write for free information, chart of the hierarchy. 2220 N. 42nd Ave., Hollywood, FL 33021, (305) 962-1200.

THE TWELVE RAYS OF THE GREAT CENTRAL SUN, 3427 Densone Pl., Charlotte, NC 28215. Sanat Kumara: Administrator, Christ Jesus: World Teacher. Training Center to prepare leaders to operate their own light center and train to be a channel for ascended masters through studies of Laws, weekly Etheric Operations (dissolution of karma) Akashic Readings, university of the Twelve Rays of the Great Central Sun. Learn how to hear still small voice. Books and Booklets. Write for free information.

WOMEN AND WISDOM, A network of women seeking a new age manifestation of spirituality. Workshops, classes, a center and a country retreat house. 155 Bank St., 12th Fl., New York, NY 10014, (212) 807-1222.

Schools

AMDO INSTITUTE, Center of New Age Living, 158 Boonton Rd., Wayne, NJ 07470. Correspondence and residence, certificate and degree programs.

CLAREGATE COLLEGE OF ENGLAND, Great North Rd., Potters Bar, Herts., England EN6 1JL, (44) 707-42341. Located in a northern suburb of London, Claregate College is a center for teaching and research, under the direction of

Invitation To:

UNIVERSITY OF LIFE

A New Age Open School Teaching Spiritual Mastership On Earth

SELF-STUDY COURSES & TEXTS	FREE CATALOG!
FOR INDIVIDUALS & GROUPS	_write:_
• 12 SCHOOLS •	UNIVERSITY OF LIFE c/o Mark-Age, Inc. Dept. SG P.O Box 290368
• SELF-PACED •	Ft. Lauderdale, FL 33329, USA

Douglas M. Baker, well-known lecturer and author of over 40 books on esoteric subjects. Subjects of special focus are Esoteric astrology, Biomagnetism, and Esoteric psychology. Correspondence courses are available to students who are unable to attend classes at the college. Brochures regarding the correspondence course, cassette tapes, and publications are available on request.

COLUMBIA PACIFIC UNIVERSITY, 150 Shoreline Hwy., Suite 15NC, Mill Valley, CA 94941, (415) 332-7832. It is the largest non-resident graduate university in the United States with over 2,000 students and 250 faculty. All work is done by correspondence. Students pursue individualized independent study leading to Bachelors, Masters and Doctoral degrees in a variety of fields such as Psychology, Counseling, Business Administration, Wholistic Health Services, etc. Credit is awarded for prior traditional and non-traditional academic work, and for relevant life and work experience. Degree programs cost $2,000 to $3,000 and can be completed in 6 months to 3 years depending on student qualifications and initiative.

ESOTERIC SEMINARY & COLLEGE, P.O. Box 101, Wyalusing, PA 18853. Beautiful, meaningful courses in applied Metaphysics, comparative religions, Ancient Wisdoms. Culminates with Bachelor of Esoteric Sciences Degree. Complete Introduction $5.

GREAT OAKS SCHOOL OF HEALTH & TEXTILE STUDIO, 82644 N. Howe LM, Creswell, OR 97426, (503) 895-4967, 895-2440. Holistic health services, weaving program. Consulting & residential. Brochure.

KHALSA CHILDREN'S CENTER, 2669 Le Conte, Berkeley, CA 94709, (415) 843-9106. A New Age spiritual school designed to nourish body, mind and spirit. Montessori based pre-school and elementary. El Cerrito-Richmond area.

THE NATURAL GOURMET COOKERY SCHOOL, 365 West End Ave., New York, NY 10024, (212) 580-7121. Cooking classes: basic vegetarian, exotic vegetarian, salt- & fat-free, sugarless baking, healing. Brochure available.

NOOGENESIS, 90 Main St., Burlington, VT 05401, (802) 862-9616. Noogenesis is a B.A. program in Transpersonal Psychology offered through Vermont Institute of Community Involvement, a small alternative college in Burlington, Vermont. We offer a wholistic approach to education with a program structure flexible enough to meet the individual needs of each student's own quest for knowledge and sense of purpose.

PROGRAM IN THE STUDY OF CONSCIOUSNESS, John F. Kennedy University, 12 Altarinda Rd., Orinda, CA 94563, (415) 254-0200. Fully Accredited B.A. and M.A. programs in Comparitive Mysticism, Parapsychology, Transpersonal Counseling, Consciousness and the Arts. Send for program brochure.

UNIVERSITY OF THE TWELVE RAYS OF THE GREAT CENTRAL SUN, 3427 Densone Pl., Charlotte, NC 28215. Administrator: Sanat Kumara, World Teacher: Christ Jesus, four year course, weekly tapes and booklets. Learn to become a

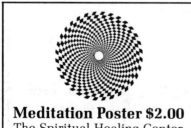

Meditation Poster $2.00
The Spiritual Healing Center
1739 Anza St., San Francisco
CA 94118 🌿 (415) 221-4058

OPEN EDUCATION EXCHANGE
P.O. BOX 5461, BERKELEY 94705.
San Francisco Bay Area's largest circulation newspaper of events, consultations and classes!
☐ Here's one dollar for one issue!
Name _____
Address _____
City and Zip _____

teacher, writer, counselor, speaker, leader and train to become a channel for the Ascended Masters (Administrators within the University). Upon graduation Ordination Certificates awarded enabling each to perform wedding and transitional services.

WALDORF INSTITUTE OF MERCY COLLEGE, 23399 Evergreen, Southfield, MI 48075, (313) 823-4630. Waldorf Institute of Mercy College relocates to woodland campus! Anthroposophical Studies, Waldorf (Steiner) Education, Biodynamic Gardening. Accredited. Financial Assistance.

Workshops & Seminars

BABARA BARTOLE, Full listing, Community Directory section under LaHabra, California.
CRYSTAL CONNECTION, Mechail or Andronica, P.O. Box 969, Los Alamos, NM 87544, (505) 662-4000. "Quartz crystals, therapy, newsletter, booklet, workshops."
DICK SUTPHEN SEMINARS, P.O. Box 38 Dept. SC, Malibu, CA 90265. Reincarnation and human potential. 20,000 have attended.
EXECUTIVE EFFECTIVENESS TRAINING, Source Unlimited, 7 Oak Ave., Kentfield, CA 94904, (415) 459-5996.
PAN-ANGELIC CONFERENCE, P.O. Box 370, Dept. S, Nevada City, CA 95959. Annual retreat and conference for pupils of Fourth Way and Sufi teachings, Voluntary Evolution, Angelic invocation, and Terminal Midwifery.
RE*SOURCE NETWORK, INC., 620 14th St., Virginia Beach, VA 23451. Organizes conferences, classes and seminars around the world offering in particular the Inner Light Consciousness Techniques for holistic growth as channeled by Paul Solomon. We also market tapes of these seminars through *Carmel Sounds.*
TETOTALERS ONLY, P.O. Box 5722, Berkeley, CA 94705. Considers long range spiritual consequences of cultures who use alcohol.
WOMEN AND WISDOM, A network of women seeking a new definition of spirituality for our time, offering workshops, classes, country retreats. 155 Bank St., 12th Fl., New York, NY 10014, (212) 807-1222.

Instruction

COLLEGIANS INTERNATIONAL, P.O. Box 270, Santa Barbara, CA 93102. Cosmology, Reincarnation, and Past Life Recall.
MASSAGE THERAPY LICENSE, Our licensed, accredited school offers residential training or correspondence (home study) course in massage and related therapies. Our 1250 hours state certified training, plus Arkansas license, qualifies you for licensing in your own state. Send $1 (redeemable) for brochures. Ozark Life Center, Rt. 4, P.O. Box 540-S, Springdale, ARK 72764, (501) 361-2155.
PEOPLE NEEDED TO TRAIN as Counselors to help others in distress or with problems. New technique results in a well and happy person. All welcome to apply. Contact The Dianetic Center, 120 Giralda, Coral Gables, FL 33134, (305) 445-7812.
RESIDENTIAL INTENSIVES, Self-Mastery, yoga, meditation, postural restructuring, inner breathing, aikido, weight loss, and vegetarian nutrition. Free information. Polestar International, 620 South Minnesota, Suite 1, Sioux Falls, SD 57104.

TLC - TRINITY LOVE CENTER, 678 Indian Hill, Claremont, CA 91711, (714) 626-4206. The function of TLC is to holistically guide each person to the realization of God's purpose in his/her life.

VOICETAPES, P.O. Box 10689-CG, Chicago, IL 60610. Warming-Up Vocally Cassette Tape. Exercises and improvisation ($12.50). Other quality tapes for speakers and singers available.

Health & Healing

AMERICAN HEALING ASSN., 6311 Yucca St., Los Angeles, CA 90028, (213) 320-2907. Non-profit Association Spiritual/Psychic Healers. Send for free catalog-health aids.

AMERICAN-INTERNATIONAL REIKI ASSOCIATION, is a not for profit membership organization for those who have taken a Reiki Natural Healing Course. P.O. Box 13778, Atlanta, GA 30324, (404) 233-5549.

DISCOVERING BODY TRANSFORMATION, Pioneering research in a readable well written doctoral manuscript. Write to the Transformations Institute, 70 Hilarita Ave., Mill Valley, CA 94941.

ENERGY BALANCING MASSAGE, Shiatsu, Polarity, Swedish, Intuitive Counseling. Call Cynthia at (415) 626-9621.

EXPERIENCES IN AWARENESS, P.O. Box 296, Palm Springs, CA 92263, (714) 320-1517, 323-3033. Classes/seminars, Kundalini Yoga per Yogi Bhajan, Yoga -- all ages, Meditation, Food Vibrations. Private polarity sessions. Holistic Products. Marcia AKAL KAUR Weiting.

F. DAVID ALEXANDER, M.H., Naturalife director, independent distributor & Ortho-Bionomy therapy. 544 Thompson Run Rd., Pittsburgh, PA 15237.

FELDENKRAIS METHOD, Functional integration and awareness through movement (individual and group lessons). Norma Leistiko, 2575 Washington #1, San Francisco, CA 94115, (415) 922-8809.

THE HANDBOOK OF ALTERNATIVES TO CHEMICAL MEDICINE, P.O. Box 12353, Oakland, CA 94604. The Handbook of Alternatives to Chemical Medicine ($5.95). Mental Birth Control ($3) by Mildred Jackson and Terri Teague, Naturopaths. Add $1/book for shipping.

HEARTWOOD: CALIFORNIA COLLEGE OF THE NATURAL HEALING ARTS: RIGHT LIVELIHOOD, Send $2 for catalog. Heartwood, 220 Harmony, Garberville, CA 95440.

HERBAL TRACERS, P.O. Box 343s, Woodmere, NY 11598, (516) 599-2393. Good news for herb users! Take the guesswork out of herbs with our simple saliva test. Gives you the herbs you really require. $25/kit. Herbs discounted 40%. Healthcare practitioners given special offer.

HYGIEIA COLLEGE, P.O. Box 398, Monroe, UT 84754, (801) 527-3738. Healing women-lay Midwifery correspondence course by Jeannine Parvati.

IDA ROLF'S ORIGINAL EXERCISES -- STRUCTURAL AWARENESS, Rachel Harris, Ph.D., 1550 S. Dixie Hwy., Suite 214S, Coral Gables, FL 33146. Comprehensive set of 3 - 60 minute tapes and 3 illustrated booklets designed to improve postural alignment. $39.95. Free brochure.

INDIVIDUALIZED HEALTH CARE, Fasting, yoga, swimming, located in beautiful Northern Michigan. Write Shenandoah Valley, Flowing Well Rd., Route #1, Kalkaska, MI 49646, (616) 258-2750.

INFORMED HOMEBIRTH, P.O. Box 788, Boulder, CO 80306, (303) 449-4181.

THROW YOUR GLASSES AWAY!
& LEARN TO <u>SEE</u> with Jiun

This is the outstanding *T.O.P. Training: The Omnision Program,*® by Jiun . . . for the transformation of Vision. In its Functional aspect, it is the ONLY training which SHOWS you, *on yourself,* HOW your eyes are mis-coordinating and HOW to coordinate them for correct focus. Whatever your focusing problem—near-sighted, farsighted, astigmatism, a wandering eye—it is simply a matter of wrong focusing ADAPTATIONS or HABITS! All habits (or maladaptations) can be unlearned. In its Psychological aspect, we uproot the predispositions to creating and holding visual limitations.

COMPLETE TRAINING IN A SINGLE WORKSHOP

Experience a whole new pattern in HOW TO USE YOUR EYES CORRECTLY, with self-evident demonstrations. Not eyeball exercises or the Bates Method, but introducing a whole new scope in vision capacity. And a whole new emotional liberation from binding conditions limiting one's vision. It does not matter what your age, how long you have worn corrective lenses, or degree of severity of impairment. But speed of results varies individually by degree of application and emotional receptivity.

IMMEDIATE IMPROVEMENT IS USUALLY NOTED

PROVEN, ACCLAIMED

Called "outstanding" and "fantastic" in published reviews and by alternative health and growth organizations, and proven by independent surveys conducted by research organizations, the breakthrough Program is taught by *Jiun,* who himself wore glasses for 18 years. He attained perfect vision in just 3 days, retained for 19 years now!

GUARANTEED

Your satisfaction is guaranteed, or your money will be refunded.

IMMEDIATE OPPORTUNITY IN YOUR LOCALITY IF YOU ACT NOW

Call or write for comprehensive brochure. *See for Yourself!*

T.O.P. *Training:* from FLOWSHIP, Inc., 355-7-A Baldwin Avenue, Makawao, Maui, Hawaii 96768

FOR INFORMATION ON THE PROGRAM IN YOUR LOCALITY
CALL JIUN PERSON TO PERSON COLLECT: (808) 572-0666.

(be sure the call is person-to-person; ideally call after 11:00 A.M. your time)
(or just drop us a postcard saying "Send T.O.P. to: [print mailing address]")

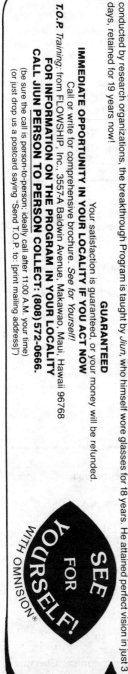

SEE FOR YOURSELF!
WITH OMNISION®

239

MIDWIFERY AND TEACHER TRAINING WORKSHOPS, referrals. Informed Homebirth, P.O. Box 788-S, Boulder, CO 80306.

MOHAVE SUN LODGE - TISHA, P.O. Box 12, Julian, CA 92036. (714) 765-1926. Polargenics, a self-healing process. Limited retreat accomodations.

REIKI NATURAL HEALTH CENTER, 545 Pharr Road, N.E., Atlanta, GA 30305, (404) 233-5549 offers the highly effective natural healing technique called Reiki as a therapy to the public. On-going Reiki classes available.

REIKI SEMINARS, INC., offers Reiki Masters (Teachers), fully certified by the American-International Reiki Association, to teach the highly effective Reiki natural healing technique in your area during the period of a few days. P.O. Box 14305, Atlanta, GA 30324, (404) 874-9142.

Vegetarianism

FIND OUT MORE, About the Vegetarian Way of Life, including our organization, publications & conferences. Send a self-addressed, stamped envelope to Vegetarian Association of America, P.O. Box 547, South Orange, NJ 07079.

NEW AGE WORLD SERVICES & BOOKS, 8416 State St., South Gate, CA 90280, (213) 588-4323. Rev. Dr. Victoria E. Vandertuin, Author's Representative & Literary Service. Free information, State Interest.

PROFESSIONAL VEGETARIAN JOB EXCHANGE, for Classifieds and Personals covering three continents. Send $1 & SASE with your listing to Monthly Vegetarian Management Newsletter, P.O. Box 668, Mendocino, CA 95460, (707) 937-5551.

VITAL HEALTH PRODUCTS INTERNATIONAL, P.O. 4689, Anaheim, CA 92803, (714) 533-4950. Natural supplements from the sea -- completely vegetarian. Dr. Watchers' famous sea blend. Distributorships available worldwide.

Mail Order Book Sellers

BABARA BARTOLE, Full listing, Community Directory section under LaHabra, California.

ANANDA BOOKSTORE, 3663 Canyon Crest Dr. #E, Riverside, CA 92507, (714) 686-3471.

AUROMERE, Sri Aurobindo Books & Indian Spiritual Texts, 1291 Weber St., Pomona, CA 91768, (714) 629-8255. Wholesale, retail, mail order. Over 1000 titles. Catalogs free.

BOOKS OF RUDOLF STEINER and spiritual science. Free catalog. Anthroposophic Press, 258 Hungry Hollow Rd., Spring Valley, NY 10977.

BROTHERHOOD OF LIFE, 110 Darthmouth, S.E., Albuquerque, NM 87106. Metaphysical Book Catalog Available.

CHIP'N BOOKS, 14181 Newport Ave., Tustin, CA 92680, (714) 838-6008. Metaphysical books and supplies, computerized charts, numerology, etc ...

CLAREGATE BOOK DISTRIBUTORS, P.O. Box 170, Westerville, OH 43081. Books, tapes, correspondence course and other information regarding Claregate College of England are available at this office, which serves as a branch of Claregate College in North America.

D.E. WHELAN-SAMADHI, P.O. Box 729, Newberry, FL 32669, (904) 472-3451. Metaphysical books, used, rare. Occult, astrology, herbology, homeopathy. Search service.

THE JUDAIC BOOK SERVICE, 3825 Baldwin Dr., Dept. A, Santa Clara, CA 95051. Kabbalah, Hassidism, Mysticism, Meditation, and Traditional texts. Send $1 for catalog.

THE MAGICK BOOKSTORE, 2304 Highland Ave. #SG82, National City, CA 92050. Occult books and supplies. Alchemy, magic, kaballah, tarot, wicca. $1 catalog.

MIDDLE EARTH BOOKSHOP, 2791 E. 14 Mile Rd., Sterling Heights, MI 48077, (313) 979-7340. Mail order. Catalog available ($5).

NOAH'S ARK BOOKS, P.O. Box 463, S. Sutton, NH 03273, (603) 927-4237. Over 400 titles: Birth, Parenting, Cooking, Gardening, Health, Herbs, Energy, Homesteading, Shelter, etc. Free catalog.

ORIENT BOOK DISTRIBUTORS, P.O. Box 100, Livingston, NJ 07039, (201) 992-6992. Books: Indology, philosophy, Indian religion, yoga and meditation from India.

ROCKWATER ENTERPRISES, P.O. Box 5861, Santa Fe, NM 87502, (505) 988-1646. Motivational, inspirational cassette tapes/books, including Sondra Ray's *I Deserve Love*, all rebirthing materials, *A Course in Miracles*. Catalog, $0.25.

SPHINX & SWORD OF LOVE BOOKSTORE, 111 Mt. Auburn St., Cambridge, MA 02138, (617) 491-8788. Wholistic spiritual bookstore: Unique selection of books & tapes on self-transformation and nonviolent social change. Please write for free catalog.

SUNFLOWER BOOKSTORE, 105 E. Marcy St, Santa Fe, NM 87501, (505) 988-

---

 **HEALING HAVEN**

Research & application of the best techniques for healing the whole (holy) person: mind, body & soul.

ROBERT H. KNAPP, MD, Director of Healing Haven division of Mark-Age, Inc., presents:

● **TWELVE SPIRITUAL SYSTEMS** ●
Healing Mind, Body, Soul

Learn how mind, body & soul interact for healing, through 12 spiritual characteristics of I Am Self.

SELF-ANALYZING QUESTIONS ● MEDICAL DRAWINGS ● $7 pb

Texts & cassettes available. Send for Free Catalog!

HEALING HAVEN, c/o Mark-Age, Inc., Dept. SG,
P.O Box 290368, Ft. Lauderdale, FL 33329, USA

9272. Send for our book lists: Acupuncture, Iridology, Medical Texts, Herbology, Pregnancy + Childbirth, Astrology, Nutrition, Homeopathy + Radionics.
ZEN CENTER OF LOS ANGELES BOOKSTORE, 905 So. Normandie Ave., Los Angeles, CA 90006. Write for free catalog including recommended titles for meditators.

Book & Magazine Distributors

NEW LEAF DISTRIBUTING CO., 1081 Memorial Dr., S.E., Atlanta, GA 30316, (404) 876-6018. Books, magazines, sidelines for Holistic Age. Free catalog. Wholesale only.
NUTRI-BOOKS CORP., P.O. Box 5793, Denver, CO 80217, (303) 778-8383. All health-related books, magazines, etc., from one source. See Ad, p. 227

Music & Musical Instruments

ALI AKBAR COLLEGE OF MUSIC, 215 West End Ave., San Rafael, CA 94901, (415) 454-6264. Music of India for world instruments, taught by masters.
CELESTIAL ZITHERS, Maloah Stillwater, Sales Representative, P.O. Box 605, Corte Madera, CA 94925. Beautifully hand-crafted, easy to play. Soothing, healing music.
DO'A-KEN LA ROCHA/RANDY ARMSTRONG, P.O. Box 128, Dover, NH 03820, (603) 749-3433. Music of the Whole Earth Internationally Acclaimed concerts, workshops, recordings, filmscores.
EAST INDIAN INSTRUMENTS, Harmoniums, tablas, tanpuras, flutes, sitars, etc. Write Encinitas Imports, P.O. Box 419-A, Encinitas, CA 92024.
JOEL ANDREWS, Harp music for healing, meditation, and background. Selection of over 24 cassettes and 3 LP's (including lectures) are available. Joel is also available worldwide for concerts and group healing seminars. For information write c/o Franklin, 899 Green #502-S, San Francisco, CA 94133, (415) 441-7155.
MUSIC BASED ON PLANETARY POSITIONS, Individual Astro-charts in music based on your time and place of birth available on cassette. For information contact: Astro-Musical Research, P.O. Box 118, New York, NY 10033.
ORIGINAL PIANO MUSIC, Caring, nurturing background for massage practitioners, therapists, meditation, movement and sleep. Devadeep I/II. $12.50 each or Double tape, $20. Voicetapes, P.O. Box 10689-CG, Chicago, IL 60610.
RAVI SHANKAR MUSIC CIRCLE, 7911 Willoughby Ave., Los Angeles, CA 90046, (213) 656-9373. Send for mail order catalog of new exclusive Indian music stereo cassette tapes and LP's.
WINDHARPS in windows bring Nature's music indoors. W'harpsong, P.O. Box 112, Dept. -S, Asheville, NC 28802.

Services

3HO DRUG AND ALCOHOL PROGRAM, 1050 North Cherry Ave., Tucson, AZ 85719, (602)327-1734. Natural holistic approach -- Yoga, Meditation, Nutrition, Massage, Positive Family environment.

LOVE THE GREAT OUTDOORS
Meditate in Comfort

Protects from overhead sun.

No more flying & crawling insects.

Full Top & Side Zipper.

34" Wide.

48" Tall.

Finest quality packcloth & net.

Frame not shown

SIT IN A HANUMAN TENT patent applied for

- Light Internal Frame
- Collapses for Back-Pack
- Free Standing, 360° View

HANUMAN ENTERPRISES
5231 60th St. Sacramento, CA 95820

PSYCHIC
Handwriting Analysis

Psychic Graphologist
Indepth, Insightful Reading by Nations Leading Perceptionist of Past, Present & Future thru

HANDWRITING
Learn of self or secrets of others Receive Indepth Reading on Cassette Tape Send Handwriting Sample and $15. per Reading to:

GRAPHOPSYCHE
P.O. Box 20005 N
FERNDALE, MICH. 48220

YOUR GOOD HEALTH DEPENDS ON YOU!

It's your every day health habits that help or hinder your overall well-being. What you eat, how often you exercise, how you feel about yourself—are the important ingredients.

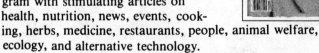

VEGETARIAN TIMES provides you with the information, incentive, and source for self-improvement. Every issue complements your personal fitness program with stimulating articles on health, nutrition, news, events, cooking, herbs, medicine, restaurants, people, animal welfare, ecology, and alternative technology.

All that in VEGETARIAN TIMES—the trailblazer magazine of the 80s—it doesn't ruin the scenery!

Vegetarian Times Dept. SCP   41 E. 42 St. Suite 921, NY, NY 10017

__ Check   __ MasterCard   __ VISA

AC #_____ Exp. Dt._____

Name _____

Address _____

City_____ State_____ Zip _____

Rates	Domestic	Foreign
☐1 yr.-12 issues	$19.95	$25.00
☐2 yr.-24 issues	$36.00	$46.00
☐3 yr.-36 Issues	$49.95	$65.00

A TEMPS + ON TIME, ($2) Journal of applied metaphysics in cooperation; research, counseling, products: Solunar Calendar of Peace ($2.95), (spirally shaped). Write: Un Village Planetaire, P.O. Box 128 "C", Montreal, Qc H2L 4J7, Canada.

ACCOUNTING, RICHARD WELLS, C.P.A., 6101 Chelton Dr., Oakland, CA 94611, (415) 933-6152. Accounting and tax services from the heart.

ALPHA DISTRIBUTORS, P.O. Box 487G, Cotati, CA 94928, (707) 585-3458. Fill your mailbox with friendly helpful mail. New Age groups and businesses, $3.50 for 6 months ($5/yr.) or free info SASE.

BABARA BARTOLE, Full listing, Community Directory section under LaHabra, California.

COLLEGE OF CLINICAL HYPNOSIS AND HOLISTIC HEALTH, P.O. Box 3829, Honolulu, HI 96812, (808) 947-3369. Become a new age professional hypnotherapist. Send $2 for exciting details.

DECLARE YOURSELF A PLANETARY CITIZEN, Write for free bumper sticker and information on the major global issues. Planetary Citizens, 777 United Nations Plaza, New York, NY 10017.

DIVINE CONNECTIONS, P.O. Box 705, Larkspur, CA 94939, (415) 927-0910. A matchmaking and relationship readiness service for those on a spiritual/personal growth path.

ESPRESS, INC., P.O. Box 8606, Washington, D.C. 20011, (202) 723-4578. Since 1969, serving the New-Age author. Publishing, promotion, merchandising. For brochure: P.O. Box 8606, Washington, D.C.

FREE booklet explaining herbal capsules. Catalog of natural living products. Send 3 stamps. Lotus Shoppe, P.O. Box 5, Pullman, WV 26421.

FREE HOLISTIC HYPNOSIS, 717 Hyde St. #6, San Francisco, CA 94109, (415) 885-4752. Consultation/Brochure. Certified.

HIGH ROCK GRAPHICS, 38 Sunrise Ave., Katonah, NY 10536, (914) 232-7577, 232-8042. Affordable, computerized, phototypesetting. Specializing in Newsletters, Flyers, and Brochures for New Age Groups and Holistic Health Centers.

HYPNOTHERAPY, Elizabeth Eilerman, Ph.D., C.M.H., 1041 Second St., Santa Rosa, CA 95405, (707) 523-3011 Stress Reduction, self image, age regression, maternal/infant bonding, hypnomeditation, spiritual hypnosis.

INTERNATIONAL SOCIETY OF TERMINAL MIDWIVES, P.O. Box 370, Dept. S, Nevada City, CA 95959. Counseling for terminal patients based on the *New American Book of the Dead* and related techniques and exercises, and training and certification programs for Terminal Midwives.

LEONARDO LITERARY SERVICES specializing in books and booklets for the New Age. I.B.M. Electronic Composer. Editing, typesetting, proofreading, paste-up-making camera-ready. Years of experience as writer, publisher, editor, former teacher of English. Distance no problem -- I work for authors nationwide and in other countries. Tender, loving care; reasonable rates; free self-publishing counseling with job. Free introductory packet. Blanche Leonardo, Ph.D., P.O. Box 5688, Santa Monica, CA 90405, (213) 396-5164.

NAM MAILING LISTS, P.O. Box 1067, Berkeley, CA 94701, (415) 644-3229. Please see our full page ad in this book.

NEW AGE HEALTH SERVICES, 1. Mailing list rental of over twenty thousand health conscious people. Targeted for workshops, seminars or mailorder. Mailing services also available. 2. Holistic Health Discount Club -- savings on all products -- mail order. P.O. Box 84562, San Diego, CA 92138, (714) 275-5075.

NEW AGE MAILING LISTS, P.O. Box 487G, Cotati, CA 94928, (707) 585-3458. Compiled from individual requests for mail from groups and businesses. List is quranteed current. Information from Alpha Distributors, P.O. Box 487G, Cotati, CA 94928, (707) 585-3458.

NEW AGE MATING, P.O. Box 5562, San Francisco, CA 94101, (415) 647-9665. Compatibility mating services. Send SASE, self and desired mate descriptions.

NEW WORLD PUBLISHING CO., Typesetting, paste-up and layout services. Contact: New World Publishing, 20511 S. Blythe Ave., Riverdale, CA 93656.

NEW-AGE SPEAKER'S BUREAU, for organizations and speakers. If you are an organization seeking speakers, or a speaker interested in providing programs to organizations, contact: Yvonne J. Johnson, Pres., Stellar Crystal Communications, 431 N. Armistead St., Suite 101, Alexandria, VA 22312, (703) 941-0965, 941-7799.

OMNIC DIRECTIONARY AE5, P.O. Box 206, Station A, Vancouver, B.C., V6C 2M3. Unique application of Biorhythm and Numerology.

PLACE, Architecture, Planning, and Design. 1137-E Salem Dr., Charlotte, NC 28209, (704) 372-2280.

POWERFULLY TRANSFORMING GUIDANCE, for personal/spiritual growth and healing of negative life patterns, lovingly channeled on tape for you by deeply psychic, highly skilled and very compassionate spiritually-orientated psychotherapist-M.D. Open to deeper truth about yourself, your relationships and the direction and purpose of your life, in the quiet of your own home. For further information: Mark Kramer, M.D., P.O. Box 8323, Santa Cruz, CA 95061 or call (408) 475-3140.

PROFESSIONAL INVESTMENT ADVICE, as a seasoned Wall St. broker, recently drawn to the environs of Virginia Beach, I offer my clients thoughtful investment selections, aided by an experienced eye for "the market". Minimum account: $20,000, contact: John H. Cammack, Dean Witter Reynolds, 4460 Corporation Ln., Virginia Beach, VA 23462, 1-800-368-3108.

PSYCHIC INTERIORS, Andronica or Mechail, P.O. Box 969, Los Alamos, NM 87544, (505) 662-4000. "Raising consciousness thru Environmental Harmonizing."

RAINBOW BRIDGE CONSTRUCTION COMPANY, P.O. Box 9626, San Diego, CA 92109. Far touch through chakra bridging. 8 volume *RB Guide Series*, $8.

THE ROCKY MOUNTAIN CO, 300 N. 1st (P.O. Box 1547), Sand Point, ID 83864, (208) 263-5201. We seek and research high energy land in North Idaho, Western Montana, and Eastern Washington for personal use or for retreats, and communities. Free booklet.

SEX-PROBLEM COUNSELING, SASE: Church New World Religion, P.O. Box 5562, San Francisco, CA 94101, (415) 431-8790.

WHOLE LIFE SUPPORT SYSTEMS, 6311 Yucca St., Los Angeles, CA 90028, (213) 320-2907. Free brochure, creating your own perfect environment through technological breakthroughs.

WRITERS OF THE AQUARIAN AGE, P.O. Box 772313, Steamboat Springs, CO 80477. Writers come together to share New Age concepts.

YOUNGER/MAN-OLDER/WOMAN INTRODUCTIONS, SASE: May-December, P.O. Box 5562, San Francisco, CA 94101.

_____*Food & Health Products*_____

ABTAZOS, 3317 Montrose #1025, Houston, TX 77006. Discounted juicers, flour mills, distillers, dehydrators, more - postpaid - save!

ALOHA ENERGY & HEALTH PRODUCTS, P.O. Box 595, Makawao, HI 96768. Only the finest products available! *Aqua Purity* sentinel Water purefyers - $99.95. *Saunier Duval* "on demand" tankless gas water heaters $235-$585; *Dynajet* Flow restricting shower heads $11; hand wheatgrass/fruit juicer $59.95; airionizers. Write for price list/specific information.

AYURVEDIC GEMSTONE REMEDIES, P.O. Box 2960, Santa Cruz, Ca 95062. Free Brochure.

AYURVEDIC HERBAL PRODUCTS + INCENSE FROM INDIA, 1291 Weber St., Pomona, CA 91768, (714) 629-8255. Wholesale, retail, mail order. Catalogs & information free. Pure, light, inspiring.

BODYWORK EMPORIUM, 602 Old Coast Hwy. 101, Leucadia, CA 92024, (714) 942-9565. Portable massage tables; 700+ products for health and relaxation; therapy; classes; equipment -- write for catalog.

E&K ENTERPRISES, 3820 Allison, Brentwood, MD 20722. Spaceage gourmet, dried, *delicious* vegetarian food. Compact, stores for years! No fat, low calories. Also, whey beverages (white, chocolate, orange). Wholesale prices.

ENJOY SIGNIFICANT INCOME with SuperNutrition System. Send $6.50 for Handbook to: Dan Kassell, 533 Sutter St., San Francisco, CA 94102, (415) 982-7375.

FAITH PRODUCTS LTD., 52/56 Albion Rd., EH7 5QZ. Edinburgh, Scotland, U.K., biodegradable shampoos, moisturizers, soap and body oil -- wholesale, mail order, bulk.

FOOD LEARNING CENTER, 114 1/2 E. 2nd, Winona, MN 55987. Co-op Food Facts, sheets & signs. Book $17 page catalog.

HERITAGE STORE, 317 Laskin, P.O. Box 444-SC, Virginia Beach, VA 23458, (804) 428-0100. Has hard to find items mentioned in the Edgar Cayce readings.

HOLISTIC HEALTH DISCOUNT CLUB, savings on everything from body care to backswings -- every product fully researched. Free brochure. P.O. Box 84562, San Diego, CA 92138, (714) 275-5075.

LINDEN'S ELFWORKS, Rt.1, P.O. Box 43-D, Rougemont, NC 27572, (919) 364-2723.

NATURAL FOOD BACKPACK DINNERS, P.O. Box 532, Corvalis, OR 97330, (503) 757-1334. Quick cooking, complimentary protein, all vegetarian meals in one pot. No preservatives, additives. Write for free catalog.

NATURAL FORTUNE COOKIES with your own messages for celebration and promotion, or our messages (esoteric/inspirational) and messages for children. Ingredients: whole wheat flour, whole wheat pastry flour, honey, fertile eggs, pure almond extract, natural (no aluminum) baking powder. Write for details. Wei Chi, P.O. Box 718, Fairfax, CA 94930.

PURAN SINGH KHALSA, Distributor Amway Products, 839 Hilldale Ave., Los Angeles, CA 90069, (213) 550-9238, 892-2906.

SUPERNUTRITION, 1442-A Walnut St., P.O. Box 119S, Berkeley, CA 94709. (415) 540-0671. Nutrition program. Easy and complete. Vitamins, minerals, full supplements, counseling, information.

UNDERSTANDING BODY CHEMISTRY AND HAIR MINERAL ANALYSIS, 128 page paperback ($5.95 postpaid). CJ Frompovich Publications, RD. 1, Chestnut Rd., Coopersburg, PA 18036. $19.

U.S.S. GOODSHIP, P.O. Box 12072, Portland, OR 97212. Herbs, Health Products, D-cells. Bach Flower Readings, etc. Free catalog.

VITAL HEALTH PRODUCTS INTERNATIONAL, P.O. Box 4689, Anaheim, CA 92803, (714) 533-4950. Distributors of Wachters' Organic Sea Products* (the famous Wachters' blend of sea vegetation is the finest source available). Complete line of supplements and herbs; health books; negative Ion Generators; juicers and free newsletter and literature. *Distributorships available worldwide.

Fed up with endless ego-mind trips?
Take a fresh look at the Christ-Way!
Read Orphanus Ayudante's:—
LOOK WITHIN (285p $4.50)
BAG OF MAYA (190p $3.50)
VIVEKA (315p $4.00)
INTUITION/INSIGHT (162 p $3.00)
GREAT WORLD TEACHER ($2.50)

($1 postage plus 35¢ each add'l book)
All 5 books only $15 plus $2 postage
CHRIST-WAY
Box 9, Rockville, UT 84763

Authentic Confection, Exquisite Taste!

The Alchemy of Wizard Baldour brings the magic back to confections, long lost since ancient times.

Like the ancient recipes, Wizard Baldour's confections are sweetened with honey and include generous portions of ginseng and golden bee pollen.

Linden's Elf Works

Box 2321, CHAPEL HILL, N.C. 27514

Questions About Your Health?

Discover the answers in the pages of **East West Journal**, with regular columns on nutrition, family, cooking, gardening, natural products, and features on the latest developments in alternative health care and natural living.

Yes, I'd like to subscribe to East West Journal for: ☐ 1 year $18.00;
☐ 2 years $28.00; ☐ 3 years $40.00; Payment must accompany order.

Name_____

Address_____

City/State/Zip _____
7223

Please mail to:
East West Journal
P.O. Box 970
Farmingdale, NY 11737

Herbs & Seeds

HERBAL WORLD, 1419 North Orange Ave., Orlando, FL 32804, (305) 896-1017. Herbs, spices, ginseng (imported and domestic), essential oils, extracts, herbal cigarettes, herbal baths, books, teas. Free catalog available.

WISH GARDEN HERBS, P.O. Box 1304, Boulder, CO 80306, (303) 449-0059. Tinctures, oils and salves. For pregnancy, birthing, newborns. All homemade on new moons. Catalog $0.50.

New Age Products

AQUARIO, "For the Aquarian Age" A game of Astrology outlining the relationship between the Microcosm and the Macrocosm to force centers which may lead the way to building the Rainbow Bridge in Human bodies in the coming age. Reference material free of charge indicating all of the sources from whence came this information for publication. Founded 1969 by Agnes I. Jackson, Student of Paramahansa Yogananda. Write: Harmony Horizons Inc., P.O. Box 663, Franklin, MI 48025.

AUROSHIKHA INCENSE, Lotuslight, P.O. Box 2, Wilmot, WI 53192. Wholesale -- retail.

AVANT-GARDE CREATIONS, P.O. Box 30160, Eugene, OR 97403, (503) 345-3043. Books, workshops, computer software.

BACK TO THE PEOPLE NEW AGE GOODS, 1615 Long Corner Rd., Mt. Airy, MD 21771. Free catalog.

BODY MASSAGE TOOLS, Lotuslight, P.O. Box 2 Wilmot, WI 53192. Wholesale -- retail.

HEALTH HARVEST UNLTD., P.O. Box 427, Fairfax, CA 94930. Anatomy T-shirts, Acupuncture T-shirts, Sole Sox and more. Send $1 for catalog.

THE INCENSE WORKS INC., P.O. Box 742, Mill Valley, CA 94941, (415) 441-3461. Specialists in highest quality Indian, Japanese and resin incenses.

LIGHT ENTERPRISES, P.O. Box 46026, Los Angeles, CA 90046, (213) 656-9373. Call or send for free catalog of gifts from the heart at loving prices.

ORGANIC GARDENING IS A FERTILITY RIGHT, bumper sticker. Green and white. $2 postage paid. Lindenself Foundation, P.O. Box 2321, Chapel Hill, NC 27514.

RAINBOW CATALOGUE, P.O. Box 5813, Berkeley, CA 94705, (415) 845-0112. An uncommon collection of toys for eyes, meditation playthings, inspirational gifts of science and mystery. Multi-level distributorship available. Send $1 for catalog.

TANTRIC LOVE ESSENCES, Six pure oils from India in beautiful silk brocade box from China. Same fragrances mentioned in ancient texts. $32. Unity Products, Dept. D, P.O. Box 1539, Santa Cruz, CA 95061.

Clothing, Clothware & Cushions

BEAUTIFUL NEW AGE T-SHIRTS, Rainbows, childbirth, nutrition, ecology, peace, whimsical designs. For the whole family, 100% cotton. For catalog, send stamp: Fingerprints, 17554 Hatteras, Encino, CA 91316. Distributors invited.

─ *Everything Researched and Guaranteed Safe, Natural, Effective* ─

HOLISTIC HEALTH DISCOUNT CLUB

Savings on:
- Backswings
- Trampolines
- Massage Tables
- Accessories
- Weight Loss
- Body Care
- Baby Care
- Books & Tapes
- and much more

New Age Products

P.O. Box 84562
San Diego, CA 92138
(714) 275-5075

FREE BROCHURE

also
Wholesale to Clinics, Practitioners
and Health-Oriented Businesses

**Call or write
for information**

Healthful Vacationing

FASTING • REDUCING • EXERCISE
ORGANIC GARDENS • PEACEFUL SURROUNDINGS
POOL • BOATS • BEACHES • SOLARIUMS • TENNIS • YOGA

The SHANGRI-LA

Presents

The NATURAL HYGIENE INSTITUTE

"Where Health is Taught"

*A Six Month Cooperative Educational Program
With Potential Employment Upon Graduation*

WRITE FOR FREE LITERATURE

BONITA SPRINGS–SG, FLORIDA 33923 USA

CHINA ROSE, 112-S N.E. 3rd Ave., Gainesville, FL 32601. Unusual handmade clothing for children and adults. Catalog $1 (stamps ok).

COTTON CLASSICS AND DESIGN, 4660 Ponderosa Dr., Santa Rosa, CA 95404. Beautiful Hand-Painted, Individual Designs on All Cotton Clothing. Custom Made.

COTTON DREAMS, 999 Laredo Ln. #SCG, Sebastian, FL 32958. Large selection of quality natural fiber clothing for the whole family at reasonable prices. Free catalog.

FUTONS, YOGA MATS, beautiful, quality products by Pine Valley Futon Co., Rt. 1, P.O. Box 148, Halfway, OR 97834. Send SASE for pricelist.

GOOSE DOWN COMFORTERS, made by a cottage industry in the redwoods. Finest European design at lower prices. Sheetcasing included. Down Home Comforters -- NC, P.O. Box 440, Willits, CA 95490, (707) 459-4241.

HARMONY & LOTUS, elegant and casual natural fiber clothing for women and men ... at simple prices. Six locations in Northern California: San Francisco -- 2286 Union St., (415) 567-2024; Mill Valley -- 34 Sunnyside Ave., (415) 381-2110; Capitola -- 115 San Jose Ave., (Capitola Mercantile) (408) 462-1338; Santa Rosa -- 513 4th St., (707) 523-2137; Warehouse Clearance Outlet -- 4213 Montgomery Dr., Lakeside Shopping Center, Santa Rosa (707) 538-1920; Wholesale Inquiries -- call (707) 539-1659.

NATURAL FIBER DANCEWEAR AND LINGERIE, Visions, P.O. Box 850 (SC), Menlo Park, CA 94025. Send $1 for catalog. Leotards, tights, stockings, socks, etc.

QUIROZ, P.O. Box 163s, Wyalusing, PA 18853. Exceptionally designed and constructed custom caftans. Your choice of style, fabric, color. SASE.

Astrology, Occult & Occult Supplies

ASTRO*CARTO*GRAPHY*, P.O. Box 22293 (K), San Francisco, CA 94122. Are you in the right place? Astro*Carto*Graphy* shows *where* you will find personal evolution, love, prosperity, or any other human potential, by computer-calculating your horoscope geographically. Fully interpreted, your unique map locates planetary energy power points. Send $18, time, date, and place of birth, or request free information. Peace.

ASTROLIFE, 170 Albemarle Dr., Penllyn, PA 19422, (215) 643-4751. Quality Horoscopes. Free Information.

ASTROLOGY CHARTS TRANSLATED INTO MUSIC, Individual charts available on cassette. For information contact: Astro-Musical Research, P.O. Box 118, New York, NY 10033.

ASTROLOGY NOW, The most respected and serious astrological journal in publication. Under the editorship of Noel Tyl we uphold a policy of constant awareness for the profound future of astrology, as a science and an art. Write: Astrology Now, P.O. Box 43383, Dept. SG, St. Paul, MN 55164. $2/copy, $10/year. Bi-monthly.

BENJAMIN MABRY, 6252A Delmar Blvd. #204, St. Louis, MO 63130. Astrology drawing on Alice Bailey's and E. Krishnamacharya's sources.

BROTHER AND SISTER OF EARTH, P.O. Box 5722, Berkeley, CA 94705. Birth mars, birth venus patches.

EXPLORE THE PATTERN OF YOUR LIFE, See Classified under Calendars.

HUMANISTIC ASTROLOGER/NUMEROLOGIST, Practical guidance. Common sense. Mail-order welcome. Updates free with natal interpretation. Write: P.M.H. Atwater, 235F Rockingham Dr., Harrisonburg, VA 22801.

HUMANISTIC/SPIRITUAL, astrology books by Tracy Marks, M.A. Sagittarius Rising, P.O. Box 252, Arlington, MA 02174.

IRENE KLOEPFER-II, 73 Thompson, New York, NY 10012, (212) 925-1248. Astrologer. Compassionate clairvoyant counseling in person or cassette.

THE MAGICK BOOKSTORE, 2304 Highland Ave. #SG82, National City, CA 92050. Beeswax candles, over 300 custom oils, quartz balls. $1 Catalog.

MAGICKAL BOOKS, RECORDINGS, other items. Catalog, $1. Circle, P.O. Box 9013-N, Madison, WI 53715.

MARCIA R STARCK, P.O. Box 893, San Rafael, CA 94915, (415) 457-7837. Medical astrologer using astrology as a diagnostic tool with holistic health. Author of *Astrology Key to Holistic Health* ($9.95).

MARCIA ROSE BECKER, PH.D., P.O. Box 827, Hollywood, FL 33022, (305) 922-2132. Psychological Counseling, Astrology, Psychic.

NEW DAWN ASTROLOGY, 16 Belvedere, San Francisco, CA 94117, (415) 552-3483. Psychic. No-nonsense approach to understanding self creative potential and lessons to be learned. All forms of astrology available, including relationship analysis.

RAPUNZEL, P.O. Box 703N, Woodstock, NY 12498. For beginner or professional, free catalog of books, tools, inexpensive computer horoscopes, carefully selected from many sources for depth and clarity.

SCHNEIDER CORPORATION, 2209-11 S. Calhoun St., Ft. Wayne, IN 46804. Numerology, Books, Tapes, Computer Charts: Details free -- send SASE or $0.25.

SONGE CLAIR, Birthcharts, Chart Mandalas, Tarot Pictorials, Symbol Graphics on Handmade Paper in Hardwood Frames. 1602 Laburnum, Chico, CA 95926, (916) 342-4451.

XULTUN MAYAN TAROT, Arcana, P.O. Box 2, Wilmot, WI 53192. $13.95 postpaid. Retail -- wholesale.

Calendars & Photographs

EXPLORE THE PATTERN OF YOUR LIFE, through the I-Ching, based upon your birth data, a thorough day-by-day, year-by-year analysis includes illustrated I-Ching manual and computer printout. Send for brochure details to Asian Astrology Co., P.O. Box 827, Larkspur, CA 94939.

SAWAN KIRPAL PHOTO SERVICE, Dept. S, 40 Frontage Rd., Stafford Springs, CT 06076. Photographs of recent Masters of Sant Mat: Sant Darshan Singh, Sant Kirpal Singh and Baba Sawan Singh. Free catalog.

Psychics

BABARA BARTOLE, Full listing, Community Directory section under LaHabra, California.

BEVERLY C JAEGERS- U.S. PSI SQUAD, P.O. Box 24571, St Louis, MO 63141, (314) 872-9127. Psychic Research.

BISHOP ROBERTA HERZOG, P.O. Box 808, Wyalusing, PA 18853. Spiritual psychic portraiture of your Teacher/Guide. Professionally and lovingly drawn and matted. Entity's name and message given. Entire donation $60.

MARCIA ROSE BECKER, PH.D, P.O. Box 827, Hollywood, FL 33022, (305) 922-2132. Psychological Counseling, Astrology; Psychic.

POWERFULLY TRANSFORMING GUIDANCE for personal/spiritual growth and healing of negative life patterns, lovingly channeled on tape for you by deeply psychic, highly skilled and very compassionate spiritually-orientated psychotherapist-M.D. Open to deeper truth about yourself, your relationships and the direction and purpose of your life, in the quiet of your own home. For further information: Mark Kramer, M.D., P.O. Box 8323, Santa Cruz, CA 95061 or call (408) 475-3140.

REV. CHRISTA ADOLPH, P.O. Box 755, Wall St. Sta., New York, NY 10268 (212) 227-2154. Consultation by appointment and thru the mail.

REV. STEFANIE NAGORKA, P.O. Box 755, Wall St. Sta., New York,NY 10268, (212) 227-2154. Consultation by appointment in New York, Boston, and Washington D.C., readings through the mail and by telephone by arrangement.

Children

AFTER THE STORK, Box 1832F, Bisbee, AZ 85603. Free catalog offering 100% cottonwear, sleepwear, underwear. Newborn to size 8 yr. Softshoes, ointments, children's records ... more!

BEAUTIFUL NEW AGE T-SHIRTS, Infant to adult sizes -- childbirth, nutrition, Rainbows and other whimsical designs. 100% cotton with non-toxic inks. For catalog, send stamp: Fingerprints, 17554 Hatteras, Encino, CA 91316. Distributors invited.

COTTON DREAMS, 999 Laredo Ln. #SCG, Sebastian, FL 32958. Largest selection of quality hard to find 100% cotton and wool clothing for children and infants at reasonable prices. Free catalog.

GUARANTEE YOUR CHILD'S SUCCESS!, Foster love of learning and self-esteem with proven early learning methods. Parenting For Excellence Newsletter, P.O. Box 19, Stelle, IL 60919. $15 for issues.

HANDCRAFTED WOODEN TOYS, From the "old country"; colorful, educational. Fine old-fashioned woolen shawls in bright floral prints. Free catalog. Babooshka, P.O. Box 1056, Bisbee, AZ 85603.

Travel & Retreats

ARIPEKA HEALTH LODGE, 3139 Gulf Dr., Aripeka, FL 33502, (813) 862-3152. Lodge available to small groups for workshops, seminars, self-awareness health programs.

DESERT DANCE, Expeditions for the Spirit, P.O. Box 77, Terlingua, TX 79852, (915) 371-2211.

MADRE GRANDE MONASTERY, Star Route 118, Dulzura, CA 92017, (714) 468-3810. Enjoy this beautiful secluded mountain valley retreat, 60 minutes from San Diego; 264 acres, peaceful and serene; hiking, camping, day use; workshop and meditation retreat space available, kitchen, showers; ideal for outdoor festivals, music and celebration. Reservations please.

OZ, THE GROWTH CENTER FOR KIDS, FAMILIES, & ADULTS, P.O. Box 147, Point Arena, CA 95468, (707) 882-2449. Treehouses, hot tubs, alternate energy, journals, sci-fi, consciousness raising, fantasy.

A PILGRIM'S GUIDE TO PLANET EARTH, A New Age travel guide and directory. See full page ad in this book. Spiritual Community, P.O. Box 1067, Berkeley, CA 94701.

PRACTICE INTEGRAL DISCIPLINES in solar Ashram, Ollantaytambo, Peru. For information write: Vegetarian Restaurant, Calle Garcilaso 256, Cusco, Peru.

SAWAN KIRPAL MEDITATION CENTER, The central meditation and retreat center in the United States for Sawan Kirpal Ruhani Mission. Guesthouse, Meditation Hall, Satsang Hall, free kitchen (langar). Write for information: Dept. S, Route 1, P.O. Box 24, Bowling Green, VA 22427, (804) 633-9987.

TRAVEL GUIDEBOOKS and information for worldwide travelers without much money. Send twenty cent stamp to Nomadics, P.O. Box 454-K, Athens, GA 30603.

VRINDABAN VILLAGE ESTATES, Time Sharing vacation homes in a spiritual, paradise resort. For color brochure, write: Rd. 1, P.O. Box 296, Moundsville, WV 26041, (304) 843-1600.

Yoga & Meditation

KUNDALINI YOGA, Dynamic 60 minute tapes. Write: Khalsa Cassettes, 225 E. 5th St., New York, NY 10003.

YOGA RESEARCH FOUNDATION, 6111 S.W. 74th Ave., Dept. SC, Miami, FL 33143, (305) 595-5580. Unfold your latent resources. Send for your *free* informative booklet on Integral Yoga and complete list of over 30 fine books covering all aspects of Yoga written by renowned Swami Jyotir Maya Nanada.

NOURISH YOUR WHOLE SELF
Read the YOGA JOURNAL

Yoga has become very popular as a modern selfcare practice for relieving stress, developing strength and flexibility, and attaining body/mind harmony. Yoga Journal is America's yoga magazine. We've been showing people how to apply this ancient, healthful technique to their modern lifestyles for over seven years. Each bimonthly issue of Yoga Journal brings you information on asanas, exercise, nutrition, teaching yoga, stress management, meditation, books, and paths to optimal health. In addition, YJ features interviews and accounts from people who are making yoga and personal growth an important part of their lives and communities.

SPECIAL   OFFER   NO RISK

You can try an introductory subscription to the Yoga Journal for only $10. (a 17% savings off the newstand price.) If you are not completely satisfied with the magazine, you may cancel at anytime and receive a prompt refund for all unmailed copies.

Send check or money order, with your name and address, to: Yoga Journal Dept. NC, 2054 University Ave., Berkeley, CA 94704. Canada and Mexico add $2.00; Foreign add $3.00. U.S. funds only please.

Prison

SENTENCED TO FREEDOM PRISON ASHRAM PROJECT, c/o IDHHB, P.O. Box 370, Dept. S, Nevada City, CA 95959. Information on Voluntary Evolution and prison study-circles.

Young Adults

WIN SYSTEMS, P.O. Box 1234, Sacramento, CA 95806, (916) 922-2202. Win Systems was established to provide young adults with special seminars in which guided imagery, roleplaying, motivational exercises and internal external teachers are used to provide enlightened awareness and increased feelings of high self-esteem. The common goal of inter-connection with each other, the universe and the Life Force is given special emphasis.

Handicrafts

CHINOOK GLASS WORKS, Richard Purcell. "Windows that serve as access to the vision" Unique - Traditional - Symbols - Mandalas - Abstracts, 1602 Laburnum, Chico, CA 95926, (916) 342-4451.

Miscellaneous

HELP BY MAIL/PHONE, Healing, advice, love, instruction, by author of powerful self-help books and tapes. See *NEEV* in Community Directory. Contact Dr. Elan Z. Neev, P.O. Box 6300, Beverly Hills, CA 90212, (213) 933-NEEV.
PINE VALLEY PORTABLE SHELTER, P.O. Box 853, Halfway, OR 97834. Yurts-Wall Tents. 17' yurt $900. Write for further information.
PROMETHUS PROJECT. Alert people to discount health products and make money. No inventory. Free Brochure. P.O. Box 84562, San Diego, CA 92138, (714) 275-5075.

SYMBOL	SIGN	DATE	KEY WORD	RULED BY	ELEMENT	FULL MOON
♈	Aries	March 20	Initiation	Mars	Cardinal Fire	Libra
♉	Taurus	April 20	Substantiation	Venus	Fixed Earth	Scorpio
♊	Gemini	May 20	Distribution	Mercury	Mutable Air	Sagittarius
♋	Cancer	June 21	Nourishment	Moon	Cardinal Water	Capricorn
♌	Leo	July 22	Creation	Sun	Fixed Fire	Aquarius
♍	Virgo	Aug. 22	Service	Mercury	Mutable Earth	Pisces
♎	Libra	Sept. 22	Unification	Venus	Cardinal Air	Aries
♏	Scorpio	Oct. 23	Transformation	Mars, Pluto	Fixed Water	Taurus
♐	Sagittarius	Nov. 22	Ascension	Jupiter	Mutable Fire	Gemini
♑	Capricorn	Dec. 21	Culmination	Saturn	Cardinal Earth	Cancer
♒	Aquarius	Jan. 19	Perfection	Saturn, Uranus	Fixed Air	Leo
♓	Pisces	Feb. 19	Universality	Jupiter, Neptune	Mutable Water	Virgo

Meditation To Do When Nothing Else Works

What It will Do for You. When you're at your wits' end, when you don't know what to do, when nothing else works, this meditation does!
How to do it:

Interlace the fingers as shown with the palms facing up and the thumbs pointing away from the body. Hold this mudra at the level of the solar plexus (center of the chest). Your eyes should be only one-tenth open.

Chant: *Gobinday, Mukunday, Udaaray, Apaaray, Haree-ung, Karee-ung, Nirnaamay, Akaamay.* Chant this mantra in a mono-tone as fast as possible without garbling the words, so that it forms a continuous stream of sounds. Your breath will regulate it-self. Start with 11 minutes at a sitting and work up to 31 minutes.

For a free pamphlet of five meditations for stress and pres-sure of the times write to: K.R.I. Publications, 800 N. Park Ave. #5, Pomona, CA 91768.

WATERFALL MUSIC
PAUL LLOYD WARNER
P I A N O

A waterfall
pours
liquid music
into the hearing
on rhythms
of delicate tone.

LEMURIAN
SUNRISE

WATERFALL
MUSIC

ELIOT
JOSHU

3 CASSETTES
ONLY

SET OF 3 CASSETTES	19.95
POSTAGE	2.00
INDIVIDUAL CASSETTE	7.95
POSTAGE	1.00

CHECKS PAYABLE TO
GLOBAL PACIFIC
BOX 1784
KAMUELA, HI. 96743

NEW AGE MUSIC

meditative
guided
relaxations
eastern
healing
environments

FREE DESCRIPTIVE GUIDE
Vital Body Mktg., Box 703
Dept. Sa , Fresh Meadows, N.Y. 11365
1-800-221-0200 In N.Y.S. 212/969-7911
WHOLESALE INQUIRIES INVITED

The editors of *The New Consciousness Sourcebook* present:

A Pilgrim's Guide to Planet Earth

A Traveler's Handbook & New Age Directory

Introduction by EDGAR D. MITCHELL
—Apollo Astronaut

"*A Pilgrim's Guide to Planet Earth* is for everyone who desires, by firsthand experience, to better understand this small planet and what we are doing here—" *East West Journal*

Contains:
- Sites of natural and man-made splendor
- Addresses of thousands of New Age centers, natural foodstores, vegetarian restaurants, hotels, etc. around the world
- Description of Planetary Power Points

(International Companion to New Consciousness Sourcebook)

320 pp. fully illustrated
$8.95 plus 1.50 postage & handling
CA residents include 6% sales tax
Send to: Spiritual Community
P.O. Box 1067
Berkeley, CA 94701